COMPREHENSIVE BIOCHEMISTRY

SOLE DISTRIBUTORS FOR THE UNITED STATES AND CANADA:

AMERICAN ELSEVIER PUBLISHING COMPANY, INC.

52 Vanderbilt Avenue, New York 17, N.Y.

Library of Congress Catalog Card Number 62-10359

With 43 illustrations and 30 tables

PRINTED IN THE NETHERLANDS BY

DRUKKERIJ MEIJER - WORMERVEER AND AMSTERDAM

COMPREHENSIVE BIOCHEMISTRY

COMPREHENSIVE
BIOCHEMISTRY

COMPREHENSIVE BIOCHEMISTRY

EDITED BY

MARCEL FLORKIN

Professor of Biochemistry, University of Liège (Belgium)

AND

ELMER H. STOTZ

*Professor of Biochemistry, University of Rochester, School of Medicine
and Dentistry, Rochester, N.Y. (U.S.A.)*

VOLUME 5

CARBOHYDRATES

ELSEVIER PUBLISHING COMPANY

AMSTERDAM · LONDON · NEW YORK

1963

CONTRIBUTORS TO THIS VOLUME

Dr. S. J. ANGYAL
Professor of Organic Chemistry, School of Chemistry, University of New South Wales,
Kensington, N.S.W. (Australia)

S. A. BARKER, D.Sc., Ph.D., B.Sc., A.R.I.C.
Chemistry Department, The University of Birmingham, Edgbaston,
Birmingham 15 (Great Britain)

Dr. LUIS F. LELOIR
Instituto de Investigaciones Bioquímicas "Fundación Campomar" and
Facultad de Ciencias Exactas y Natura'es,
Buenos Aires (Argentina)

J. CONCHIE, Ph.D.
Rowett Research Institute, Bucksburn, Aberdeen (Great Britain)

Dr. HEINZ EGGE
Max Planck Institut für Medizinische Forschung, Institut für Chemie,
Jahnstrasse 29, Heidelberg (Deutschland)

YOHICHI HASHIMOTO, Ph.D.
Assistant Professor, New York Medical College, Flower and Fifth Avenue Hospitals,
Department of Biochemistry, 5th Avenue at 106 Street, New York 29, N.Y. (U.S.A.)

D. HORTON, Ph.D.
The Ohio State University, Department of Chemistry, 140 West 18th Avenue,
Columbus 10, Ohio (U.S.A.)

ROGER W. JEANLOZ, Chem. Eng., D.Sc., A.M. (hon.)
Associate Professor of Biological Chemistry, Harvard Medical School, Laboratory for
Carbohydrate Research, Massachusetts General Hospital, Boston 14, Mass. (U.S.A.)

Z. I. KERTESZ, Ph.D.
Professor of Chemistry, New York State Agricultural Experiment Station,
Cornell University, Geneva, N.Y.; *present address*: Nutrition Division,
Food and Agriculture Organization of the United Nations (FAO), Rome (Italy)

Dr. CARLOS E. CARDINI
Instituto de Investigaciones Bioquímicas "Fundación Campomar" and
Facultad de Ciencias Exactas y Naturales,
Buenos Aires (Argentina)

G. A. LEVVY, D.Sc.
Rowett Research Institute, Bucksburn, Aberdeen (Great Britain)

ELIZABETH E. PERCIVAL, Ph.D., D.Sc., F.R.S.E.
Lecturer in Chemistry, Chemistry Department, The University, Kings Buildings,
West Mains Road, Edinburgh 9 (Great Britain)

WARD PIGMAN, Ph.D.
Professor of Biochemistry, New York Medical College,
Flower and Fifth Avenue Hospitals, Department of Biochemistry,
5th Avenue at 106 Street, New York 29, N.Y. (U.S.A.)

SHIGERU TSUIKI, M.D.
Assistant Professor, Tohoku University, Department of Medical Chemistry,
Sendai (Japan)

M. L. WOLFROM, Ph.D.
The Ohio State University, Department of Chemistry, 88 West 18th Avenue,
Columbus 10, Ohio (U.S.A.)

GENERAL PREFACE

The Editors are keenly aware that the literature of Biochemistry is already very large, in fact so widespread that it is increasingly difficult to assemble the most pertinent material in a given area. Beyond the ordinary textbook the subject matter of the rapidly expanding knowledge of biochemistry is spread among innumerable journals, monographs, and series of reviews. The Editors believe that there is a real place for an advanced treatise in biochemistry which assembles the principal areas of the subject in a single set of books.

It would be ideal if an individual or small group of biochemists could produce such an advanced treatise, and within the time to keep reasonably abreast of rapid advances, but this is at least difficult if not impossible. Instead, the Editors with the advice of the Advisory Board, have assembled what they consider the best possible sequence of chapters written by competent authors; they must take the responsibility for inevitable gaps of subject matter and duplication which may result from this procedure.

Most evident to the modern biochemist, apart from the body of knowledge of the chemistry and metabolism of biological substances, is the extent to which he must draw from recent concepts of physical and organic chemistry, and in turn project into the vast field of biology. Thus in the organization of Comprehensive Biochemistry, the middle three sections, Chemistry of Biological Compounds, Biochemical Reaction Mechanisms, and Metabolism may be considered classical biochemistry, while the first and last sections provide selected material on the origins and projections of the subject.

It is hoped that sub-division of the sections into bound volumes will not only be convenient, but will find favour among students concerned with specialized areas, and will permit easier future revisions of the individual volumes. Toward the latter end particularly, the Editors will welcome all comments in their effort to produce a useful and efficient source of biochemical knowledge.

Liège/Rochester
July 1962

M. FLORKIN
E. H. STOTZ

PREFACE TO SECTION II

(VOLUMES 5–11)

Section II on the Chemistry of Biological Compounds deals with the organic and physical chemistry of the major organic constituents of living material. A general understanding of organic and physical chemistry is presumed, but the reader will find the special topics in Section I of value in the fuller understanding of several parts of Section II. The Editors have made special effort to include a sound treatment of the important biological high polymers, including sections on their shape and physical properties. A number of substances peculiar to plants, certain isoprenoids, flavonoids, tannins, lignins, and plant hormones, often omitted from textbooks of biochemistry, are included. Nevertheless, it is inevitable that some omissions, hopefully minor ones, have occurred. The only intentional omission is the chemistry of the coenzymes and certain components of biological oxidation, which will be covered in connection with their function in Section III.

The previous policy of dividing the section into smaller volumes has been continued, resulting in seven volumes for Section II. Two of the volumes each contain a complete area, namely Carbohydrates (Volume 5) and Sterols, Bile Acids and Steroids (Volume 10). Comments from readers will be appreciated by the Editors and be most helpful for possible future revisions.

Liège/Rochester   M. FLORKIN
December 1962   E. H. STOTZ

CONTENTS

VOLUME 5

CARBOHYDRATES

Chapter I. The Monosaccharides

by ELIZABETH PERCIVAL

Chapter II. Aldonic, Uronic, Oxoaldonic and Ascorbic Acids

by Elizabeth Percival

Chapter III. Amino Sugars

by H. Egge

Chapter IV. Sugar Phosphates

by L. F. LELOIR AND C. E. CARDINI

Chapter V. Glycosides

by J. CONCHIE AND G. A. LEVVY

Chapter VI. The Oligosaccharides

by S. Tsuiki, Y. Hashimoto and W. Pigman

Chapter VII. Polysaccharides

Section a. General

by D. Horton and M. L. Wolfrom

Chapter VII. Polysaccharides

Section b. Polysaccharides

(excluding glycuronans, bacterial polysaccharides and mucopolysaccharides)

by D. Horton and M. L. Wolfrom

Chapter VII. Polysaccharides

Section c. Polyuronides

by Z. I. KERTESZ

Chapter VII. Polysaccharides

Section d. Polysaccharides of Bacteria, Moulds, Yeasts and Protozoa

by S. A. BARKER

Chapter VII. Polysaccharides

Section e. Mucopolysaccharides (Acidic Glycosaminoglycans)

by ROGER W. JEANLOZ

Chapter VIII. Cyclitols

by S. J. ANGYAL

Chapter I

The Monosaccharides

ELIZABETH PERCIVAL

Chemistry Department, University of Edinburgh (Great Britain)

1. General structure of monosaccharides [1]

Monosaccharides or simple sugars are aliphatic carbon compounds concerned in many of the metabolic processes of both plants and animals. From them macromolecules, polysaccharides, are built up. They normally consist of chains of carbon atoms of varying length and are classified according to the number of these atoms in the molecule; the simplest, tetroses*, containing four, pentoses five, hexoses six and heptoses seven carbon atoms and at least one octose has been found in Nature. The majority of monosaccharides are unbranched and may be defined as straight-chain polyhydroxy aldehydes (aldoses) or ketones (ketoses); the former having the carbonyl group at carbon atom number one (C-1) (I) and the latter at C-2 (II); the remaining carbon atoms being hydroxylated.

The monosaccharides are water-soluble solids which are not easy to crystallise, and are very liable to form syrupy supersaturated solutions. They possess varying degrees of sweetness to the taste, give optically active

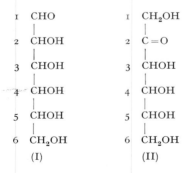

$$
\begin{array}{ll}
1 & \text{CHO} \\
& | \\
2 & \text{CHOH} \\
& | \\
3 & \text{CHOH} \\
& | \\
4 & \text{CHOH} \\
& | \\
5 & \text{CHOH} \\
& | \\
6 & \text{CH}_2\text{OH} \\
& \text{(I)}
\end{array}
\qquad
\begin{array}{ll}
1 & \text{CH}_2\text{OH} \\
& | \\
2 & \text{C}=\text{O} \\
& | \\
3 & \text{CHOH} \\
& | \\
4 & \text{CHOH} \\
& | \\
5 & \text{CHOH} \\
& | \\
6 & \text{CH}_2\text{OH} \\
& \text{(II)}
\end{array}
$$

---

* The systematic nomenclature recommended jointly by American[2] and British[3] authorities will be used throughout this chapter.

solutions and are readily oxidised, especially in alkaline solutions, *e.g.*, the cuprosodium ion in Fehling's solution becomes reduced to cuprous oxide. Although these simple carbohydrates normally exist in six (pyranose) or five (furanose) membered ring forms, many of their properties are consistent with the open-chain structure. In the first instance, the characteristic properties of the two types of functional groups, the carbonyl and the hydroxyl, and the configurations of the different monosaccharides will be described in the acyclic form. Indeed all these facts were established when the monosaccharides were still regarded as being nothing more than open-chain compounds. Furthermore, it is important to remember that a very small proportion of the acyclic form is always present in solution in equilibrium with the various cyclic structures.

(a) Properties of the aldehydic and ketonic groups

A typical aldohexose (the suffix -*ose* denotes all aldose sugars) has the general formula (III). The aldehydic group of the sugar can be oxidised with bromine water or reduced with sodium amalgam and water to yield, respectively, an aldonic acid (IV) or a hexitol (alditol) (V). Careful oxidation of (IV) with, *e.g.*, nitric acid yields a tetrahydroxy dibasic acid (an aldaric or saccharic acid) (VI) (p. 43). Further drastic reduction of the hexitol with hydriodic acid gives 2-iodohexane (VII) clearly showing that no branching occurs in the hexose chain. Additional evidence for this is derived from the formation of *n*-heptylic (*n*-heptanoic) acid (VIII) from a hexose after addition of hydrogen cyanide[4] followed by hydrolysis and reduction (p. 37). The aldonic acids (IV) on storage in aqueous solution form equilibrium mixtures with their 1,5- (δ-) (IX) and 1,4- (γ-) (X) lactones (p. 42). Both types of lactone can be prepared as crystalline compounds. They are readily hydrolysed and can be titrated with alkali; the 1,4-lactones, being the more stable, are cleaved more slowly than the 1,5-lactones.

Ketose sugars, denoted by the suffix-*ulose*, have similar properties to the aldoses, but modified by their being ketonic. Reduction of a hexulose (XI) yields two hexitols (alditols) (XII, XIII). Oxidation of ketoses by nitric acid yields tartaric acid (XIV), and oxalic acid (XV), and must take place by cleavages of the carbon chain. The formation of tartaric acid is in accordance with a ketone group at C-2. Proof of the straight chain in ketose sugars is derived from the formation of 2-methylcaproic acid (2-methylhexanoic) (XVIII) after combination of a hexulose (XVI) with hydrocyanic acid and hydrolysis of the resulting two cyanhydrins and reduction.

Further evidence of the presence of an aldehydic or ketonic group in monosaccharides is the formation of typical carbonyl derivatives such as oximes (XIX) or phenylhydrazones[6] (XX, XXI) by the action of hydroxylamine

$$
\begin{array}{ccc}
 & \begin{array}{c} CH_2OH \\ | \\ CHOH \\ | \\ CHOH \\ | \\ CHOH \\ | \\ CHOH \\ | \\ CH_2OH \\ (V) \end{array} & \xrightarrow[P]{HI} & \begin{array}{c} CH_3 \\ | \\ CHI \\ | \\ CH_2 \\ | \\ CH_2 \\ | \\ CH_2 \\ | \\ CH_3 \\ (VII) \end{array}
\end{array}
$$

$$
\begin{array}{c} CHO \\ | \\ CHOH \\ | \\ CHOH \\ | \\ CHOH \\ | \\ CHOH \\ | \\ CH_2OH \\ (III) \end{array}
\xrightarrow{Na/Hg}
\qquad
\xrightarrow[H_2O]{Br}
$$

$$
\begin{array}{c} COOH \\ | \\ CHOH \\ | \\ CHOH \\ | \\ CHOH \\ | \\ CHOH \\ | \\ CH_2OH \\ (IV) \end{array}
\xrightarrow{HNO_3}
\begin{array}{c} COOH \\ | \\ CHOH \\ | \\ CHOH \\ | \\ CHOH \\ | \\ CHOH \\ | \\ COOH \\ (VI) \end{array}
$$

$$
\begin{array}{c} CHO \\ | \\ (CHOH)_4 \\ | \\ CH_2OH \end{array}
\xrightarrow{HCN}
\begin{array}{c} CN \\ | \\ C-HOH \\ | \\ (CHOH)_4 \\ | \\ CH_2OH \end{array}
\xrightarrow{H^+}
\begin{array}{c} COOH \\ | \\ (CHOH)_5 \\ | \\ CH_2OH \end{array}
\xrightarrow{HI}
\begin{array}{c} COOH \\ | \\ (CH_2)_5 \\ | \\ CH_3 \\ (VIII) \end{array}
$$

$$
\begin{array}{c} C{\nwarrow^O} \\ | \\ CHOH \\ | \\ CHOH \quad O \\ | \\ CHOH \\ | \\ CH \\ | \\ CH_2OH \\ (IX) \end{array}
\rightleftharpoons
\begin{array}{c} COOH \\ | \\ CHOH \\ | \\ CHOH \\ | \\ CHOH \\ | \\ CHOH \\ | \\ CH_2OH \\ (IV) \end{array}
\rightleftharpoons
\begin{array}{c} C{\nwarrow^O} \\ | \\ CHOH \\ | \\ CHOH \quad O \\ | \\ CH \\ | \\ CHOH \\ | \\ CH_2OH \\ (X) \end{array}
$$

and phenylhydrazine respectively. Diazonium compounds in pyridine or alkaline ethanolic solution couple with acyclic aldose hydrazones derived from phenylhydrazine itself to yield bright red crystalline formazans (XXII).

$$
\begin{array}{c}
\text{COOH} \\
|\\
\text{COOH} \\
\text{(XV)} \\
+ \\
\text{COOH} \\
|\\
\text{CHOH} \\
|\\
\text{CHOH} \\
|\\
\text{COOH} \\
\text{(XIV)}
\end{array}
\qquad
\xleftarrow{\text{HNO}_3}
\qquad
\begin{array}{c}
\text{CH}_2\text{OH} \\
|\\
\text{C}=\text{O} \\
|\\
\text{CHOH} \\
|\\
\text{CHOH} \\
|\\
\text{CHOH} \\
|\\
\text{CH}_2\text{OH} \\
\text{(XI)}
\end{array}
\qquad
\xrightarrow{\text{Na/Hg}}
\qquad
\begin{array}{c}
\text{CH}_2\text{OH} \\
|\\
\text{H—C—OH} \\
|\\
\text{CHOH} \\
|\\
\text{CHOH} \\
|\\
\text{CHOH} \\
|\\
\text{CH}_2\text{OH} \\
\text{(XII)}
\end{array}
\quad + \quad
\begin{array}{c}
\text{CH}_2\text{OH} \\
|\\
\text{HO—C—H} \\
|\\
\text{CHOH} \\
|\\
\text{CHOH} \\
|\\
\text{CHOH} \\
|\\
\text{CH}_2\text{OH} \\
\text{(XIII)}
\end{array}
$$

$$
\begin{array}{c}
\text{CH}_2\text{OH} \\
|\\
\text{C}=\text{O} \\
|\\
\text{(CHOH)}_3 \\
|\\
\text{CH}_2\text{OH} \\
\text{(XVI)}
\end{array}
\xrightarrow{\text{HCN}}
\begin{array}{c}
\text{CH}_2\text{OH} \\
|\quad\diagup\text{OH} \\
\text{C} \\
|\quad\diagdown\text{CN} \\
\text{(CHOH)}_3 \\
|\\
\text{CH}_2\text{OH} \\
\text{(XVII)}
\end{array}
\xrightarrow{\text{H}^+}
\begin{array}{c}
\text{CH}_2\text{OH} \\
|\\
\text{HOOC—C—OH} \\
|\\
\text{(CHOH)}_3 \\
|\\
\text{CH}_2\text{OH}
\end{array}
\;+\;
\begin{array}{c}
\text{CH}_2\text{OH} \\
|\\
\text{HO—C—COOH} \\
|\\
\text{(CHOH)}_3 \\
|\\
\text{CH}_2\text{OH}
\end{array}
\xrightarrow[\text{P}]{\text{HI}}
\begin{array}{c}
\text{CH}_3 \\
|\\
\text{CH·COOH} \\
|\\
\text{(CH}_2)_3 \\
|\\
\text{CH}_3 \\
\text{(XVIII)}
\end{array}
$$

$$
\begin{array}{c}
\text{CH}_2\text{OH} \\
|\\
\text{C}=\text{O} \\
|\\
\text{Ketose}
\end{array}
\longrightarrow
\begin{array}{c}
\text{CH}_2\text{OH} \\
|\\
\text{C}=\text{N·NHPh} \\
|\\
\text{(XXI)}
\end{array}
\qquad
\begin{array}{c}
\text{CH}=\text{NOH} \\
|\\
\text{CHOH} \\
|\\
\text{(XIX)}
\end{array}
\xleftarrow{\text{NH}_2\text{OH}}
\begin{array}{c}
\text{CHO} \\
|\\
\text{CHOH} \\
|\\
\text{Aldose}
\end{array}
\xrightarrow[\text{HOAc}]{\text{PhNHNH}_2}
$$

$$
\begin{array}{c}
\text{CH}=\text{N·NHPh} \\
|\\
\text{CHOH} \\
|\\
\text{(XX)}
\end{array}
\xrightarrow[\text{pyridine}]{\text{PhN}=\text{N}^+}
\begin{array}{c}
\overset{\displaystyle \text{N—N}\diagup^{\text{Ph}}}{\text{C}}\diagdown_{\text{H}} \\
|\quad \text{N}=\text{N}\diagdown_{\text{Ph}} \\
\text{CHOH} \\
|\\
\text{(XXII)}
\end{array}
\underset{\text{[H]}}{\overset{\text{[O]}}{\rightleftharpoons}}
\begin{array}{c}
\overset{\displaystyle \text{N—N}\diagup^{\text{Ph}}}{\text{C}} \\
|\quad \text{N}=\text{N}^{\oplus}\diagdown_{\text{Ph}} \\
\text{CHOH} \\
|\\
\text{(XXIII)}
\end{array}
$$

$$
\begin{array}{l}
\text{CH}=\text{N}\cdot\text{NHPh} \\
| \\
\text{CHOH} \\
|
\end{array}
\qquad
\begin{array}{l}
\text{CH}=\text{N}\cdot\text{NHPh} \\
| \\
\text{C}=\text{N}\cdot\text{NHPh} \\
| \\
+\text{C}_6\text{H}_5\text{NH}_2 \\
+\text{NH}_3 \\
(\text{XXIV})
\end{array}
\xrightarrow[\text{pyridine}]{\text{C}_6\text{H}_5\text{N}=\text{N}^+}
$$

$$
\begin{array}{l}
\text{C} \overset{\text{N---N}}{\underset{\text{N}=\text{N}}{\diagup}} \overset{\text{Ph}}{\underset{\text{Ph}}{\diagdown}} \text{H} \\
| \\
\text{C}=\text{N}\cdot\text{NHPh} \\
| \\
(\text{XXV})
\end{array}
\qquad
\begin{array}{l}
\text{HC}=\text{N---N} \overset{\text{Ph}}{\underset{\text{H}}{\diagdown}} \\
| \\
\text{C}=\text{N---N} \overset{}{\underset{\text{Ph}}{\diagdown}} \\
|
\end{array}
\rightleftharpoons
\begin{array}{l}
\text{HC}=\text{N---N} \overset{\text{Ph}}{\underset{\text{H}}{\diagdown}} \\
| \\
\text{C}=\text{N---N} \overset{}{\underset{\text{Ph}}{\diagdown}} \\
|
\end{array}
$$

$$
\text{(XXVII)}
$$

$$
\xrightarrow{\text{conc. HCl}}
\begin{array}{l}
\text{CHO} \\
| \\
\text{C}=\text{O} \\
| \\
(\text{XXVI})
\end{array}
$$

$$
\begin{array}{l}
\text{CH}_2\text{OH} \\
| \\
\text{C}=\text{N}\cdot\text{NHPh} \\
|
\end{array}
$$

The structure present in (**XX**) is necessary for the reaction; it therefore takes place neither with hydrazones derived from N-substituted phenylhydrazines, for example, methyl phenylhydrazine, nor with any hydrazones derived from ketoses, nor with cyclic aldose phenylhydrazones. The reaction has proved of value in distinguishing these different forms of hydrazone[7]. The reversible oxidation of the coloured formazans into colourless tetrazolium derivatives (**XXIII**) has proved of value as an indicator in biological systems.

Prolonged action by at least three molecules of phenylhydrazine, in the hot, attacks C-2 in the aldose and C-1 in the ketose by an intermolecular oxido-reduction yielding a yellow crystalline osazone or *bis*-hydrazone (**XXIV**). Various ring structures have been advanced for D-glucose phenylosazone but this substance gives a positive formazan reaction (**XXV**) due to the presence of —CH=N—NHPh structure on C-1, and must therefore have the acyclic structure (**XXIV**) which is probably stabilised by a chelate ring structure[8] (**XXVII**). Removal of the phenylhydrazine residues either by hydrolysis with concentrated hydrochloric acid or exchange with a competing aldehyde yields a dicarbonyl compound known as an osone[9] (**XXVI**).

$$
\begin{array}{l}
\text{H}\cdot\text{C}=\text{N}\cdot\text{NHPh} \\
| \\
\text{C}=\text{N}\cdot\text{NHPh} \\
| \\
(\text{XXIV})
\end{array}
\xrightarrow{\text{CuSO}_4}
\begin{array}{l}
\text{H}\cdot\text{C}=\text{N} \\
| \qquad\quad \diagdown \text{NPh} \ + \ \text{PhNH}_2 \\
\text{C}=\text{N} \diagup \\
| \\
(\text{XXVIII})
\end{array}
$$

In the early studies on monosaccharides the osazones proved to be valuable crystalline derivatives in the identification and characterisation of sugars, but the more easily purified osatriazoles (**XXVIII**) prepared by Hudson[10] by oxidation of the osazones (**XXIV**) with copper sulphate are to be preferred since they are very stable, have characteristic melting points, and their optical rotations can easily be measured as they are colourless in solution.

Treatment of an aldo- or keto-pentose or hexose with alcohols such as methanol containing hydrogen chloride instead of yielding a diacetal or diketal typical of an ordinary aldehyde or ketone results in reaction with only one molecule of the alcohol, the elimination of a molecule of water, and the formation of a crystalline hemiacetal or methyl glycoside (XXIX). These derivatives exist as cyclic compounds; the size of the ring will be discussed later (p. 21). In contrast to the free sugars the alkyl glycosides are non-reducing, and stable to alkali, but are readily hydrolysed by dilute

$$
\begin{array}{c}
\text{CHO} \\
| \\
\text{CHOH} \\
| \\
\text{CHOH} \\
|
\end{array}
\quad + \text{CH}_3\text{OH} \;\underset{\text{H}^+}{\rightleftharpoons}\;
\begin{array}{c}
\text{CHOCH}_3 \\
| \\
\text{CHOH} \qquad | \\
\qquad\qquad \text{O} \\
\text{CH}\underline{\qquad} |
\end{array}
$$

(XXIX)

acids to the parent sugar and the alcohol. The carbohydrate moiety of the glycoside is known as the glycosyl residue and the non-carbohydrate portion is generally called the *aglycone*. In the above glycosides, methanol is the aglycone and the glycosyl link is through oxygen. A vast number of natural glycosides derived from phenols and alicyclic alcohols have been isolated from natural environments and studied (p. 28).

Sugars also react readily, under mild conditions, with compounds containing the primary amino group, such as amino acids[11] and with a wide variety of amines[12]. With secondary amines the reaction is less facile, but similar products are derived. A typical reaction is between a hexose and

$$
\begin{array}{c}
\text{CHO} \\
| \\
\text{CHOH} \\
|
\end{array}
\quad + \; \text{C}_6\text{H}_5\text{NH}_2 \;\longrightarrow\;
\begin{array}{c}
\text{CH}\cdot\text{NHC}_6\text{H}_5 \\
| \\
\text{CHOH} \qquad | \\
|
\end{array}
$$

(XXX)

aniline to give *N*-phenylhexopyranosylamine (XXX). These derivatives are crystalline with characteristic melting points, but some may decompose on keeping at room temperature, the stability of *N*-aryl-D-glucosylamines increasing in the order *N*-phenyl, *N*-*p*-tolyl, *N*-*m*-tolyl, *N*-*o*-tolyl. In aqueous and alcoholic solution the majority mutarotate to an equilibrium involving partial conversion into an anomeric form (p. 23) through the intermediate production of the acyclic Schiff's base (XXXI), and in acid solution they rearrange to a more stable ketonic form, the 1-amino-1-deoxy-2-ketose[13] (XXXII).

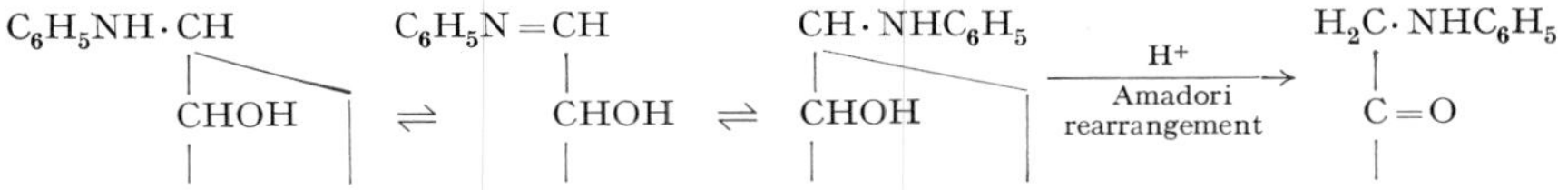

$$
\begin{array}{lcccccc}
C_6H_5NH \cdot CH & & C_6H_5N = CH & & CH \cdot NHC_6H_5 & & H_2C \cdot NHC_6H_5 \\
| & \rightleftharpoons & | & \rightleftharpoons & | & \xrightarrow[\text{rearrangement}]{\substack{H^+ \\ \text{Amadori}}} & | \\
CHOH & & CHOH & & CHOH & & C=O \\
| & & | & & | & & | \\
& & (XXXI) & & & & (XXXII)
\end{array}
$$

The glycosylamines are generally readily soluble in water and are usually recrystallised from methanol and ethanol.

Ketoses also react with both aliphatic and aromatic amines, and the derived ketosylamines (XXXIII) can also rearrange in a reverse of the Amadori rearrangement with the formation of a 2-amino-2-deoxy-aldose (XXXIV).

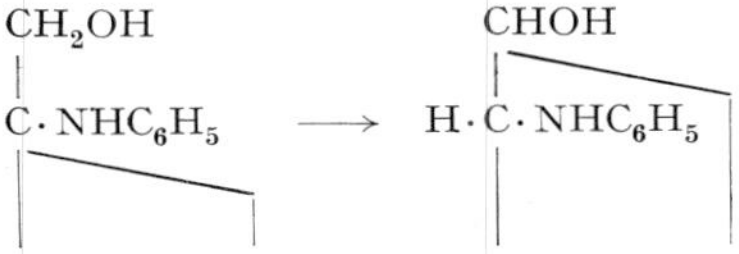

$$
\begin{array}{lcl}
CH_2OH & & CHOH \\
| & & | \\
C \cdot NHC_6H_5 & \longrightarrow & H \cdot C \cdot NHC_6H_5 \\
| & & | \\
(XXXIII) & & (XXXIV)
\end{array}
$$

The N-phenylaldosylamines are often described as nitrogen glycosides since they are essentially similar to the glycosides discussed above except that the union to the aglycone is made through nitrogen instead of oxygen. The universal intracellular macromolecules, the nucleic acids, are chain polymers of nitrogen glycosides in which the aglycones are at least four cyclic nitrogen bases. These aglycones are pyrimidine or purine bases such as cytosine (XXXV) and adenine (XXXVI).

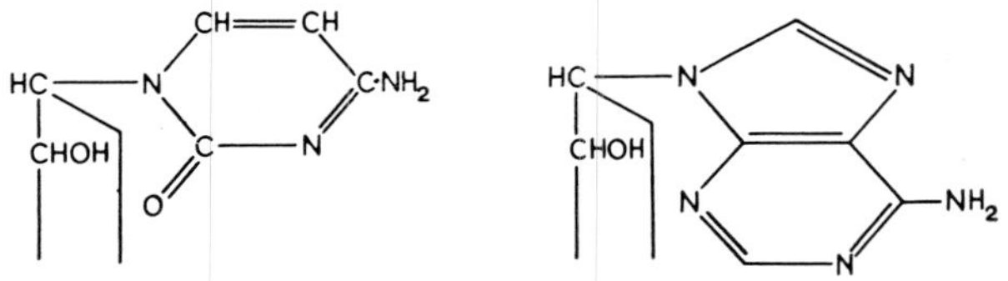

(XXXV)   (XXXVI)

S-Glycosides are also found in natural products[14] such as the mustard oils which contain sinigrin (XXXVII) and sinalbin (XXXVIII) in both of which the glycosidic link is through sulphur.

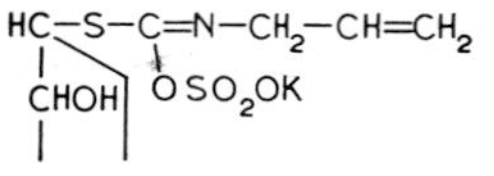

HC—S—C=N—CH$_2$—CH=CH$_2$
| |
CHOH O SO$_2$OK

(XXXVII)

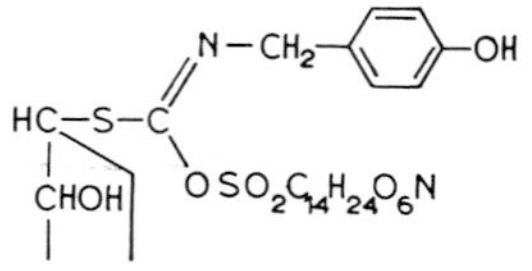

HC—S—C
| | N—CH$_2$—⟨benzene ring⟩—OH
CHOH O SO$_2$C$_{14}$H$_{24}$O$_6$N

(XXXVIII)

(b) Properties of the hydroxyl groups

Evidence that monosaccharides are indeed polyhydroxy compounds is furnished by the action of aqueous periodic acid, or more generally sodium periodate, a reagent diagnostic of the presence of at least two adjacent hydroxyl groups[15]. This oxidising agent quantitatively degrades a free aldose (XXXIX) to formic acid and formaldehyde; the latter is derived from the CH$_2$OH at the highest numbered carbon atom. Lead tetraacetate reacts similarly with sugars, but is less convenient to use since the reactions need to be carried out in glacial acetic acid solution[16].

CHO
|
CHOH
|
CHOH
| + 5 NaIO$_4$ ⟶   5 HCOOH
CHOH   +
|
CHOH
|
CH$_2$OH   HCHO
(XXXIX)

The hydroxyl groups in sugars and their derivatives are readily esterified (p. 45). The most widely used esters in carbohydrate studies are the acetates, benzoates, and toluene p-sulphonates. A free sugar binds in ester linkage one acid radical to each hydroxyl and another one, in glycosidic union to the reducing group; the sugars react in the ring structure. Sugar carbonates in which adjacent hydroxyl groups are esterified may also be prepared, by the action of carbonyl chloride and pyridine on the sugar or its derivative[17]. They are labile to alkali and fairly stable to acid. Phosphate and sulphate esters are of wide biological importance, the former being universally concerned in the metabolic processes of free energy storage and liberation, and in catalysis; the latter are present in many algal polysaccharides and in some animal products associated with several functions such as lubrication of joints, and the formation of specialised structures.

Cyclic acetals may be formed by condensation of the hydroxyl groups of a sugar with other aldehydes and ketones such as acetone, formaldehyde, acetaldehyde and benzaldehyde. The first and last of these have been employed most frequently, in synthetic work, to block temporarily selected hydroxyl groups in the preparation of partially substituted sugar derivatives.

Etherification of sugars may take place internally or externally. In the former case this leads to the production of sugar anhydrides (p. 52). External etherification of carbohydrates has been predominantly the introduction of methoxyl groups (methylation), but benzyl and triphenylmethyl (trityl) (XL) ethers can be made by suitable treatment of the sugar with the respective chloride in the presence of an acceptor of hydrogen chloride, e.g., pyridine. These two groups can be used for temporary blocking of hydroxyl groups (p. 48). Methyl ethers of sugars have played a very large part in the elucidation of the structure of the monosaccharides and of their complex polymeric derivatives. In recent years small amounts of some partially methylated sugars have been isolated from the hydrolysis products of natural complex polymeric carbohydrates, e.g., 2-O-methyl-L-fucose has been separated from the hydrolysates of the polysaccharides from sugar beet, sisal, and Victoria plum leaves, and 6-O-methyl-D-galactose is a constituent of the polysaccharides of the red alga, *Porphyra capensis*.

Methylation is carried out with methyl iodide and silver oxide[18] or with dimethyl sulphate and sodium hydroxide[19] (XLI).

$$
\begin{array}{lll}
\overset{|}{CHOH} & \overset{|}{CHOH} & \overset{|}{CHOCH_3} \\[4pt]
\overset{|}{CHOH} \xrightarrow{(C_6H_5)_3CCl} & \overset{|}{CHOH} \xrightarrow[NaOH]{(CH_3)_2SO_4} & \overset{|}{CHOCH_3} \\[4pt]
\overset{|}{CH_2OH} & \overset{|}{CH_2O-C\langle^{C_6H_5}_{C_6H_5}}_{C_6H_5} & \overset{|}{CH_2O-C\langle^{C_6H_5}_{C_6H_5}}_{C_6H_5}
\end{array}
$$

(XL)   (XLI)
                    Di-O-methyl-mono-O-trityl

With the former, in order to avoid the oxidative effect of the silver oxide it is usually necessary first to block the aldehydic and ketonic group by formation of the glycosides. Other methods of methylation involve successive treatment of the sugar compound with metallic sodium and methyl iodide in liquid ammonia[20], or in ether or benzene[21], or treatment with thallous hydroxide and methyl iodide. Diazomethane has also been utilized for the introduction of methoxyl groups[22]. In all the methods several applications are necessary to ensure complete methylation. Once the methoxyl groups are introduced, except for the glycosidic methyl group, they are very stable and difficult to remove. Hydrobromic acid[23], and boron trichloride[24] have

References p. 63

been utilized successfully for demethylation, under suitable conditions, without destruction of the sugar molecule. Trityl ethers which preferentially replace the primary hydroxyl groups can on the other hand readily be hydrolysed with acid and the hydroxyl groups can be recovered from benzyl ethers by careful hydrogenolysis[25].

(c) Projection formulae

It should be remembered that carbon atoms are linked together at an angle of 109° 28′. Examination of models shows that a chain of carbon atoms by virtue of this angular linkage tends to form a loop and in the planar projection formulae of the sugars introduced by Emil Fischer[26] (in 1891) the loop is theoretically straightened out and the hydrogen atoms and hydroxyl groups are all projecting out from the plane of the paper. The structure may be considered as an arc of a circle viewed from the convex side with the addenda projecting towards the viewer. In the use of these formulae certain conventions must be observed. The aldehydic group is written at the top of the formula and the carbon atoms are numbered from the top downwards (XLII). In the ketoses (XLIII) the carbonyl group is at C-2. It is not permissible to remove a projection formula out of the plane of the paper because

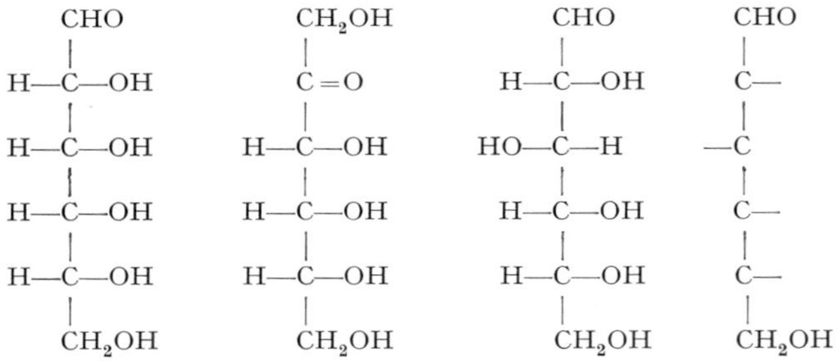

CHO	CH$_2$OH	CHO	CHO
H—C—OH	C=O	H—C—OH	C—
H—C—OH	H—C—OH	HO—C—H	—C
H—C—OH	H—C—OH	H—C—OH	C—
H—C—OH	H—C—OH	H—C—OH	C—
CH$_2$OH	CH$_2$OH	CH$_2$OH	CH$_2$OH
(XLII)	(XLIII)	(XLIV)	(XLV)
Aldohexose	Ketohexose	D-Glucose	
		Fischer formula	Reichstein formula

of the danger of changing it into its enantiomorph (p. 13) but rotation in the plane of the paper is allowed.

A simplified form of the Fischer formula has been introduced by Reichstein[27] in which the hydrogen atoms are omitted and the location of the hydroxyl groups is depicted as shown above (XLV) for D-glucose.

2. The configuration of monosaccharides

Stereochemically all the sugars can be related either to D- or to L-glyceraldehyde, the symbols D- and L- referring to the relative position of the
hydroxyl group attached to the asymmetric second carbon atom in glyceraldehyde. Although this stereochemical arrangement was arbitrarily assigned

```
 1        CHO              1          CHO
          |                           |
 2   H—C—OH              2   HO—C—H
          |                           |
 3       CH₂OH            3          CH₂OH
    D-Glyceraldehyde        L-Glyceraldehyde
```

in the first instance, it has recently been established as correct by Bijvoet
and his co-workers[28] through X-ray studies. In the sugars it is the configuration of the highest-numbered asymmetric carbon atom which defines
the configurational series to which any particular sugar belongs. As in the
case of glyceraldehyde where the hydroxyl group attached to this carbon
atom lies to the right of the carbon chain in the Fischer formula the sugar
is assigned to the D-series, and in the L-sugars this hydroxyl group is situated
on the left of the carbon chain.

(a) Aldoses

(i) Tetroses

The simplest sugars are the tetroses D- and L-erythrose (XLVI, XLVII)
and D- and L-threose (XLVIII, XLIX), formed by the addition of CHOH
between C-1 and C-2 in the two glyceraldehydes.

```
 1      CHO            CHO            CHO            CHO
        |              |              |              |
 2  H—C—OH        HO—C—H        HO—C—H        H—C—OH
        |              |              |              |
 3  H—C—OH        HO—C—H        H—C—OH        HO—C—H
        |              |              |              |
 4     CH₂OH          CH₂OH          CH₂OH          CH₂OH
      (XLVI)         (XLVII)        (XLVIII)        (XLIX)
```

(ii) Pentoses and hexoses

The more common monosaccharides are, however, the pentoses and
hexoses. Each tetrose can give rise to two pentoses, D-erythrose yielding
D-ribose and D-arabinose, and D-threose giving D-xylose and D-lyxose. The
following table of formulae illustrates also how the corresponding hexoses
are derived. By a series of reactions and transformations which will be

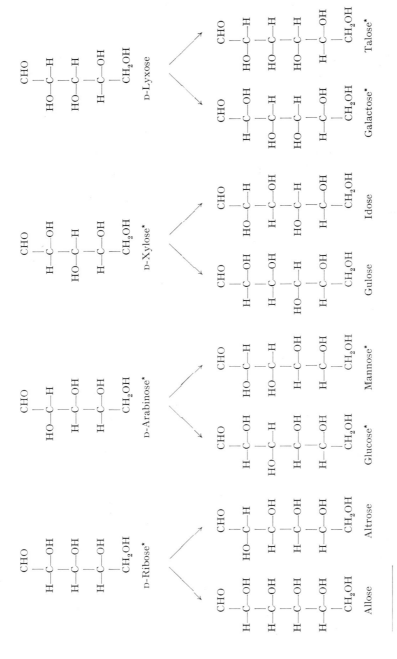

* Denotes those monosaccharides found in natural environments and definitely characterised.

enumerated later the famous chemist Emil Fischer[29] did indeed succeed
in deriving the different hexoses from the tetroses. C-2, C-3, C-4 and C-5 in
glucose are asymmetric and as already stated it is the configuration of the last
of these which determines the configurational series to which the sugar belongs
irrespective of the optical rotation of the sugar (*cf.* D-fructose, $[\alpha]_D$ —92°).
The direction of rotation of a particular sugar is denoted by (+) (*dextro*)
and (—) (*laevo*), *e.g.* D(—)-fructose. Besides the D-forms of each pentose
and hexose there are the corresponding L-forms. In fact the L-forms of
arabinose, rhamnose and fucose are those most commonly found in Nature.
Of the remaining L-pentoses and -hexoses only L-xylulose and L-galactose
have been found in natural environment. The non-superimposable mirror
image of each D-compound forms the corresponding member of the L-series.
Such pairs are termed *enantiomorphs*. They possess identical chemical
properties and differ only in the sign of their rotation and their crystalline
structure. They form theoretically resolvable racemic (DL) mixtures or association compounds. Non-enantiomorphous stereoisomers such as D-glucose and
D-mannose have different energies and are termed *diastereoisomers*. When

CHO	CHO	CHO
HO—C—H	H—C—OH	HO—C—H
H—C—OH	HO—C—H	HO—C—H
HO—C—H	H—C—OH	H—C—OH
HO—C—H	H—C—OH	H—C—OH
CH$_2$OH	CH$_2$OH	CH$_2$OH
L-Glucose	D-Glucose	D-Mannose

they differ only in the configuration of one centre they are known as *epimers*
about that centre. That is, D-mannose and D-glucose are 2-epimers.

(b) Ketoses

In ketose sugars (denoted by the suffix -*ulose*), the CHO group in glyceraldehyde is replaced by

CH$_2$OH
C=O

The resulting tetruloses, D-glycero- (L) and L-glycero-tetrulose (LI) are also
known as D- and L-erythrulose or -threulose, since the asymmetric centre

References p. 63

at C-2 distinguishing erythrose and threose has been converted into $C=O$. Both D-erythrose and D-erythrulose are known as their biologically interchangeable 4-phosphates. Related to the tetruloses there are two D-pentuloses and four D-hexuloses. These are best defined structurally by reference to

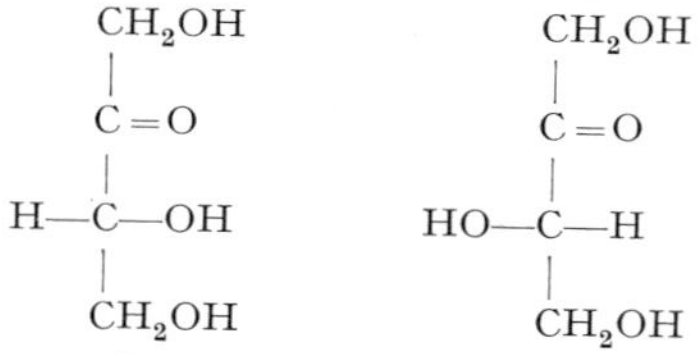

$$
\begin{array}{cc}
CH_2OH & CH_2OH \\
| & | \\
C=O & C=O \\
| & | \\
H-C-OH & HO-C-H \\
| & | \\
CH_2OH & CH_2OH \\
(L) & (LI)
\end{array}
$$

the tetrose and pentose respectively which possess the same asymmetric centres, but the trivial names given to the more common members of this group are in many instances the more familiar names; fructose (laevulose) being more commonly used than 2-deoxy-D-arabinohexulose to describe the ketose sugar formed on hydrolysis of sucrose. Each of the ketoses give osazones identical with those obtained from the two structurally related aldoses and from this their respective configurations can be deduced.

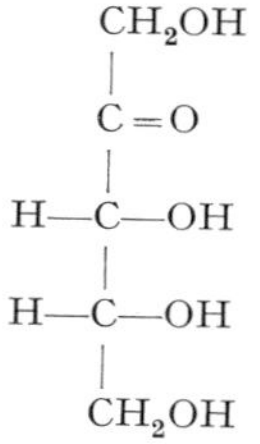

$$
\begin{array}{cc}
CH_2OH & CH_2OH \\
| & | \\
C=O & C=O \\
| & | \\
H-C-OH & HO-C-H \\
| & | \\
H-C-OH & H-C-OH \\
| & | \\
CH_2OH & CH_2OH
\end{array}
$$

D-Erythropentulose*   D-Threopentulose*
D-(Ribulose/Arabinulose) 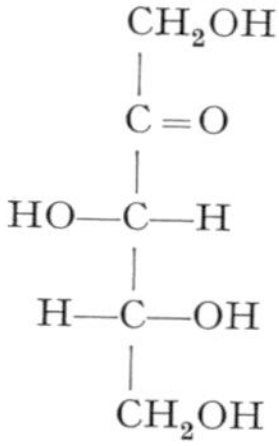   D-(Xylulose/Lyxulose)

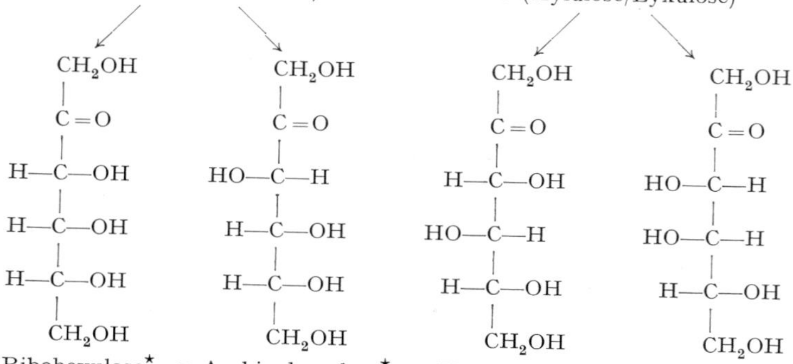

$$
\begin{array}{cccc}
CH_2OH & CH_2OH & CH_2OH & CH_2OH \\
| & | & | & | \\
C=O & C=O & C=O & C=O \\
| & | & | & | \\
H-C-OH & HO-C-H & H-C-OH & HO-C-H \\
| & | & | & | \\
H-C-OH & H-C-OH & HO-C-H & HO-C-H \\
| & | & | & | \\
H-C-OH & H-C-OH & H-C-OH & H-C-OH \\
| & | & | & | \\
CH_2OH & CH_2OH & CH_2OH & CH_2OH
\end{array}
$$

D-Ribohexulose*   D-Arabinohexulose*   D-Xylohexulose   D-Lyxohexulose*
Allulose   Fructose   Sorbose   Tagatose
Psicose

Allulose gives allosazone (altrosazone), fructose gives glucosazone (manno-sazone), sorbose gives idosazone (gulosazone) and tagatose gives galacto-sazone (talosazone).

Similarly D-erythropentulose gives D-ribosazone and D-threopentulose D-xylosazone. As denoted by the asterisks all these ketose sugars except D-sorbose have been found either free in Nature or in compounds from which the free sugar can be derived by hydrolysis.

(c) Heptoses

Heptose sugars are found in the juices of some plants (*Sedum* spp.) where they appear to be the main free sugars. The systematic names of the aldoheptose sugars relates them to hexoses containing a similar stereochemical arrangement on C-2, C-3, C-4 and C-5. The configuration of C-6 (the highest-numbered asymmetric centre) in the aldoheptose is based on D- or L-glyceraldehyde. Aldoheptoses are produced by gram-negative bacteria[30] where they are closely associated with the specific polysaccharides which confer serological specificities on the cells. For example, D-glycero-D-galacto-heptose (LII), is a constituent of the bacterial polysaccharide of certain varieties of *Chromobacterium violaceum*. D-Glycero-L-mannoheptose (LIII)

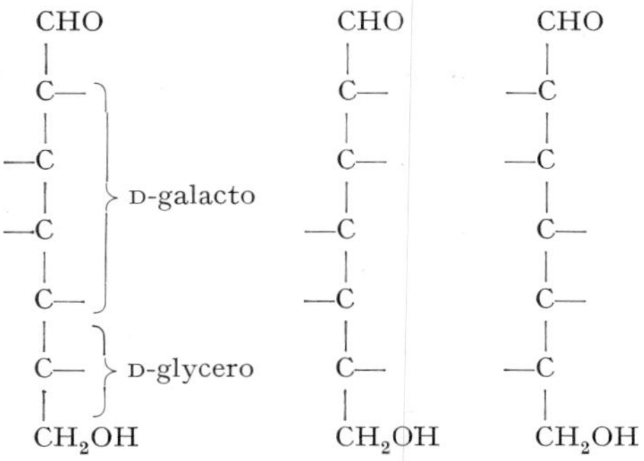

has been isolated from the hydrolysate of the lipopolysaccharide of *Shigella sonnei* and L-glycero-D-mannoheptose (LIV) is a component of the cell walls of *Escherichia coli* B (rough strain). In "smooth" bacteria this sugar appears to be phosphorylated.

(d) Heptuloses

In the heptuloses which carry the carbonyl group on C-2 the configuration of C-3, C-4 and C-5 is related to the hexose with the same stereochemical arrangement on C-2, C-3 and C-4. D-Altroheptulose (sedoheptulose) (LV) may be cited as an example of this type of sugar[31]. It is found free in several species of *Sedum* and is widely distributed in the plants of the *Crassulaceae*. Both it and D-mannoheptulose (LVI) have been known for some years. The latter occurs, in the avocado pear, both free and as its phosphate derivative.

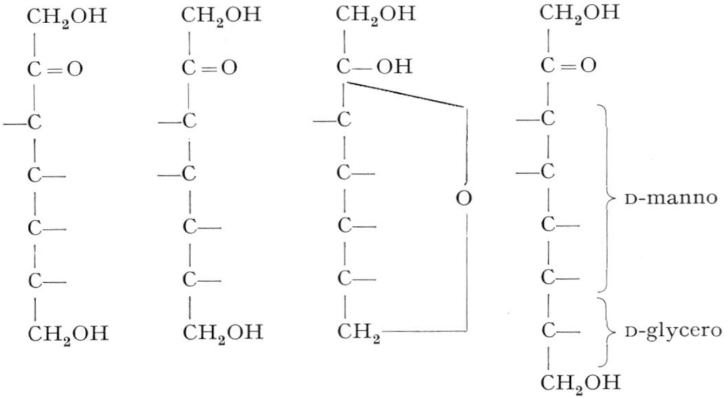

CH$_2$OH   CH$_2$OH   CH$_2$OH   CH$_2$OH

(LV)   (LVI)   (LVII)   (LVIII)

Recent work by Calvin and co-workers and by Horecker *et al.* have demonstrated the importance of sedoheptulose in the photosynthetic cycle of the carbohydrates as being a transitory intermediate in the regeneration of D-erythropentulose, the monosaccharide involved in the fixation of carbon dioxide[32]. This sugar also plays a part in animal carbohydrate metabolism. Its most characteristic chemical property is its ready conversion into sedoheptulosan (2,7-anhydro-β-D-altroheptulopyranose[33] (LVII).

(e) Octose

The only octose, D-glycero-D-mannooctulose (LVIII) so far isolated from natural sources is present in an aqueous extract of the Californian avocado pear, along with D-sedoheptulose.

3. Structurally modified monosaccharides

(a) Branched-chain sugars

In recent years branched-chain sugars[34] of comparatively rare occurrence have been isolated from natural sources; as examples, apiose from the parsley plant and the leaves and fibres of *Posidonia australis* (p. 59), hamamelose from the tannin of witch hazel bark, and deoxy branched sugars such as streptose found in many of the recently discovered antibiotics synthesised by micro-organisms, may be cited.

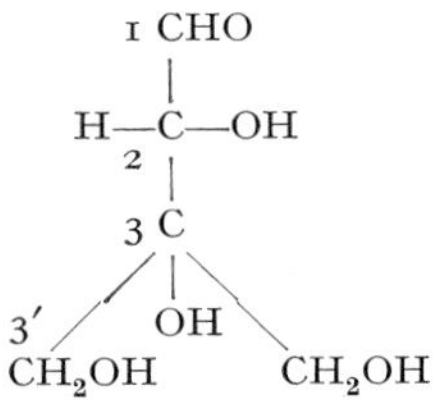

D-Apiose 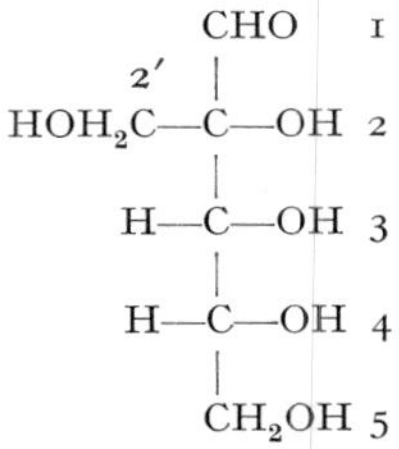   D-Hamamelose
2-D-Hydroxymethyl-
D-ribose

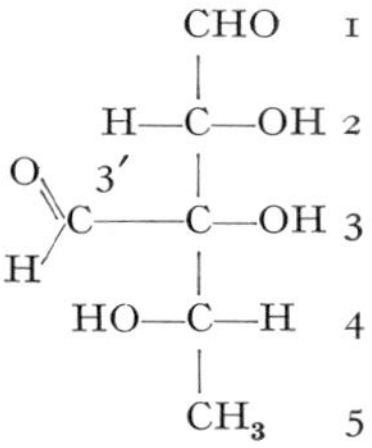

L-Streptose
5-Deoxy-3-C-formyl-
L-lyxose

The general method of numbering these sugars is to give the branch carbon atom the same number, but primed, as the carbon atom to which it is attached. C-2 is the sole asymmetric centre in apiose, and it is this which determines the configurational series to which aldehydo-apiose belongs (see p. 11).

(b) Deoxy-sugars

In a few instances one or more of the hydroxyl groups are replaced by hydrogen atoms and the resulting compound is known as a deoxy-sugar[35] (the number in front of the name denoting the position of the deoxy group in the carbon chain). The most common deoxy-sugars are 2-deoxy-D-ribose (2-deoxy-D-erythropentose) (LIX), the sugar moiety of deoxyribonucleic acid

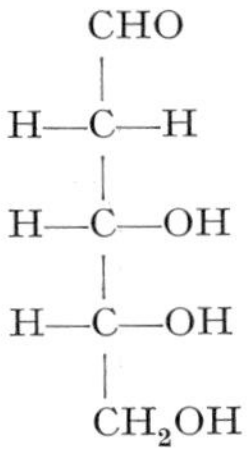

(LIX) 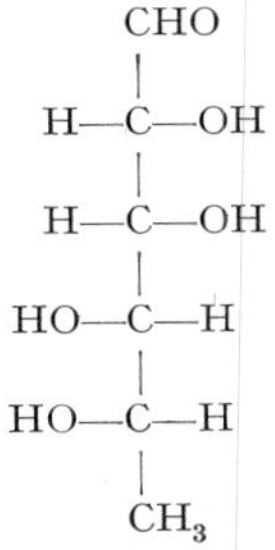   (LX) 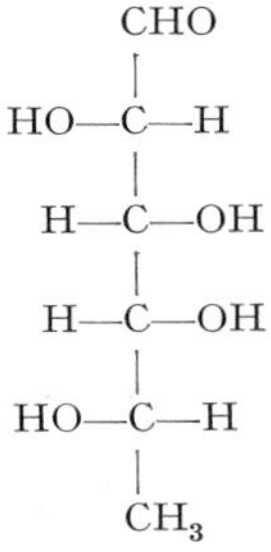   (LXI)

(DNA), L-rhamnose (6-deoxy-L-mannose) (LX), and L-fucose (6-deoxy-L-galactose) (LXI). (LX) is found in plant glycosides and in polysaccharides of gum exudates and of green algae. (LXI) occurs in human milk oligosaccharides, blood group polysaccharides, and numerous glycoproteins; it is the only sugar unit in the brown algal polysaccharide, fucoidin. Other

6-deoxyhexoses and their monomethyl ethers have been found in glycosidic union in Nature but so far no free deoxy-sugar has been found.

Two 2,6-dideoxyhexoses, D-digitoxose (2,6-dideoxy-D-ribohexose) (LXII) and D-boivinose (2,6-dideoxy-D-xylohexose) (LXIII) and four 2,6-dideoxy-2-O-methylhexoses are present as natural glycosides[36]. They are related stereochemically to the pentose which has the corresponding asymmetric centres. A number of 3,6-dideoxysugars have been isolated from bacterial

```
        CHO                      CHO
         |                        |
        CH₂                      CH₂
         |                        |
    H—C—OH                   H—C—OH
         |                        |
    H—C—OH                  HO—C—H
         |                        |
    H—C—OH                   H—C—OH
         |                        |
        CH₃                      CH₃
       (LXII)                   (LXIII)
```

lipopolysaccharides[37] particularly from *Salmonella* spp. and *Pseudotuberculosis* spp. Abequose (LXIV) and colitose (LXV) are respectively 3,6-dideoxy-D- and -L-xylohexose, and tyvelose (LXVI) and ascarylose (LXVII), the corresponding isomers of arabinohexose. The fifth member of this group of hexoses so far isolated from natural sources is paratose (3,6-dideoxy-D-ribohexose) (LXVIII).

```
     CHO           CHO           CHO           CHO           CHO
      |             |             |             |             |
  H—C—OH       HO—C—H       HO—C—H        H—C—OH        H—C—OH
      |             |             |             |             |
     CH₂           CH₂           CH₂           CH₂           CH₂
      |             |             |             |             |
  HO—C—H        H—C—OH        H—C—OH       HO—C—H        H—C—OH
      |             |             |             |             |
  H—C—OH       HO—C—H        H—C—OH       HO—C—H        H—C—OH
      |             |             |             |             |
     CH₃           CH₃           CH₃           CH₃           CH₃
    (LXIV)        (LXV)        (LXVI)       (LXVII)      (LXVIII)
```

Branched-chain deoxy-sugars have been characterised in more recent years as a result of extensive studies on the antibiotics synthesised by micro-organisms. Streptose[38] (p. 25), a constituent of streptomycin, was the first branched-chain sugar synthesised by a micro-organism to be identified. Cordycepose (3-deoxyapiose) (LXIX), mycarose (2,6-dideoxy-3-C-methyl-

hexose) (LXX), and cladinose (2,6-dideoxy-3-C-methyl-3-O-methylhexose)
(LXXI) are other examples of antibiotic deoxyaldose branched-chain sugars
synthesised by micro-organisms. The configuration of the latter two as far

(LXIX)   (LXX)   (LXXI)

as they are known are shown in the formulae. These all occur in some form
of glycosidic combination.

(c) Amino-sugars[39]

Replacement of a hydroxyl group by the amino radical occurs extensively
in the monosaccharides obtained on hydrolysis of animal polysaccharides,
including the blood group substances and glycoproteins. 2-Amino-2-deoxy-
D-glucose (D-glucosamine) (LXXII) is a frequent constituent of such
substances. These amino-sugars, in the natural state, often have the amino
groups substituted by acetyl (LXXIII), sulphate (LXXIV), and it is believed

(LXXII)   (LXXIII)   (LXXIV)

in some instances formyl radicals. In hyaluronic acid, a polymer made up
of alternating D-glucuronic acid and D-glucosamine units, all the amino
groups in the sugar residues carry acetyl residues. In heparin, which is widely
distributed in animal tissues and possesses powerful blood anti-coagulant

properties and is composed of D-glucuronic acid and D-glucosamine, the sugar carries both O- and N-sulphate groups (LXXIV).

(d) Neuraminic acid

This acid which may be regarded as a polyhydroxy 5- (or δ-) amino acid may also be considered as a monosaccharide since it is a derivative of a keto-nonose (nonulose) in which the primary alcoholic group at C-1 has been oxidised to carboxyl and the hydroxyl groups on C-3 and C-5 replaced by hydrogen and an N-acetylamino group respectively (LXXV). The presence of a reducing group (C-2) was shown by hypoiodite titration and by the

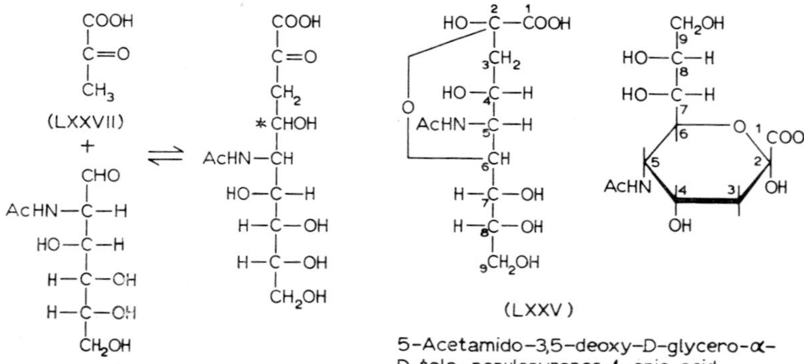

(LXXV)

5-Acetamido-3,5-deoxy-D-glycero-α-
D-talo-nonulopyranos-1-onic acid
α-D-N-Acetylneuraminic acid

consumption of a mole of hydrogen by a mole of sialic acid on reduction with sodium borohydride. The presence of five hydroxyl groups was confirmed by the formation of a pentaacetate, and the reduction of two moles of perio-date by this acid with the release of a mole of formic acid showed that three of the hydroxyl groups are contiguous. The constitution was finally confirmed by the reversible enzymic synthesis from a molecule of N-acetylmannosamine (LXXVI) and pyruvic acid (LXXVII).

N-, O-acetyl and N-glycollyl derivatives of this acid are found in many animal tissues, secretions, excretions and the blood group substances, and are known as nonulosaminic acids (sialic acids)[40]. The N-acetyl derivative (neuraminic, lactominic acid, O-sialic acid) (LXXV) has been found in two trisaccharides separated from human milk[41] and in brain gangliosides, and has also been recognised as an essential component of the carbohydrate portion of some lipopolysaccharides and sialoproteins[42].

---

[*] The stereochemistry of C-4 was determined from the rotation of the 1,4-lactone of the diethylmercaptal derivative.

(e) Uronic acids

Modified aldoses, of wide natural occurrence, are the uronic acids. In these molecules the terminal CH_2OH group of a hexose has been oxidised to carboxyl. Polysaccharides consisting almost entirely of uronic acid units are pectic acid (D-galacturonic acid) (LXXVIII), the main component of pectin found in plant tissues, and alginic acid (D-mannuronic (LXXIX) and L-guluronic acid (LXXX)) synthesised by the brown algae. For a full description of these acids see Chapter II, p. 73.

```
      CHO                CHO                CHO
       |                  |                  |
  H—C—OH            HO—C—H            HO—C—H
       |                  |                  |
 HO—C—H            HO—C—H            HO—C—H
       |                  |                  |
 HO—C—H             H—C—OH            H—C—OH
       |                  |                  |
  H—C—OH             H—C—OH            HO—C—H
       |                  |                  |
     COOH               COOH               COOH
   (LXXVIII)           (LXXIX)            (LXXX)
```

4. The monosaccharides as ring compounds

Although the monosaccharides have so far been considered as open-chain compounds it is doubtful if they ever exist free and unsubstituted in this state except in trace amounts in solution. Infrared and ultraviolet examination indicates the absence of a carbonyl group. The formation of hemiacetals or glycosides (p. 26) from sugars on reaction with alcohols and the formation of di- and higher saccharides are difficult to explain with the open-chain formulae. To account for these facts, for the occurrence of two crystalline interconvertible forms of D-glucose and for the mutarotation of sugars in solution (p. 25), a ring structure was suggested. The formation of ring compounds has already been mentioned in the glycosides and it has previously been pointed out that chains of carbon atoms tend to form a loop or spiral. As a result the hydroxyl group on the fourth and fifth carbon atoms in an aldose (LXXXII, LXXXI) and the fifth and sixth (LXXXIII) atoms in a ketose are in close juxtaposition with the carbonyl group and union through oxygen readily occurs with the formation of five-membered (furanose) or six-membered (pyranose) rings. These are cyclic hemiacetals and each possesses an additional asymmetric carbon atom at C-1 (C-2 in ketoses), and hence is capable of existing in two different forms. The names pyranose and furanose were suggested by Haworth[43] because of their close resemblance

References p. 63

to furane and pyrane. This author also put forward formulae which showed as precisely as possible on a plane surface the stereochemical arrangement of the atoms and groups. In these formulae, *e.g.* (LXXXIV), the ring planes are projecting from the plane of the paper, the edges nearer the viewer being

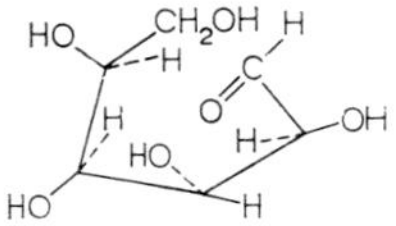

D-Glucose

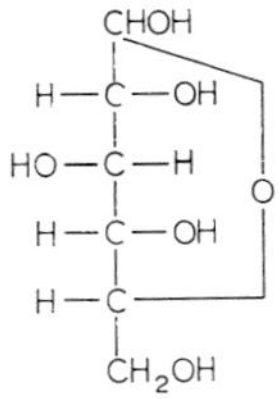

D-Glucopyranose
(LXXXI)

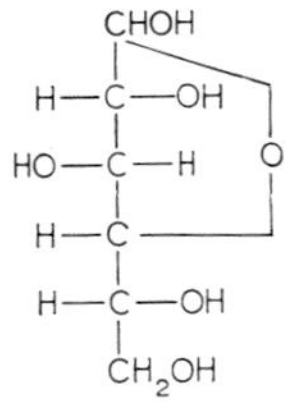

D-Glucofuranose
(LXXXII)

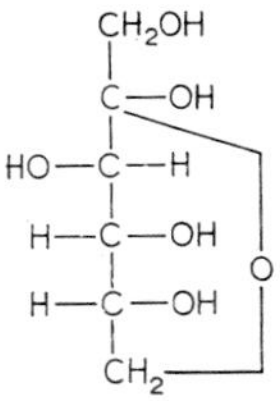

D-Fructopyranose
(LXXXIII)

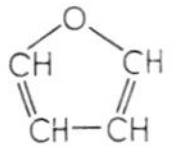

Furane

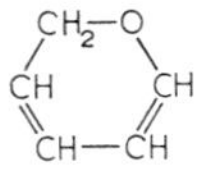

Pyrane

indicated by thickened lines, and the addenda lie above and below the ring planes. It is usual to write these formulae as depicted for β-D-glucose (LXXXIV); it is useful to remember that in this sugar the hydroxyl groups are alternately above and below the plane of the ring. Since the Haworth formulae are not projections of the Fischer type they cannot be rotated in the plane of the paper. Reorientations must take place in space. Thus it is permissible to change from (LXXXIV) to (LXXXV) by turning the plane over while keeping the axis through C-1 and C-4 fixed. The change from acyclic to the Haworth formula is shown in the following formulae (LXXXVI–

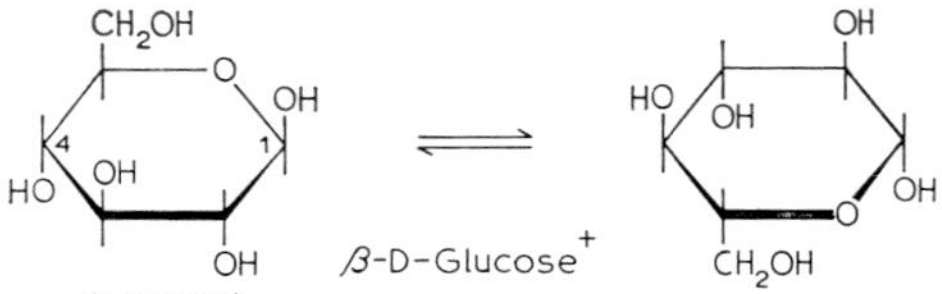

(LXXXIV)   β-D-Glucose   (LXXXV)

LXXXVIII). The movement of the CH_2OH is merely mechanical and due to a torsional effect of the closure of the ring.

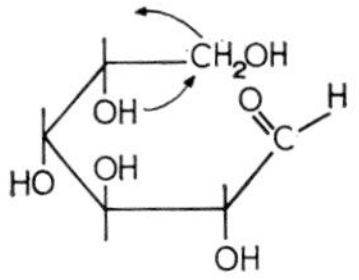

(LXXXVI) 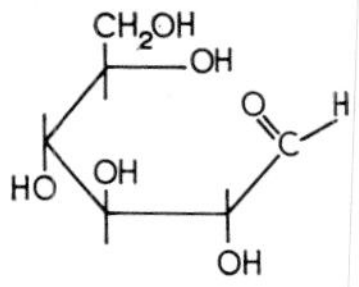   (LXXXVII) 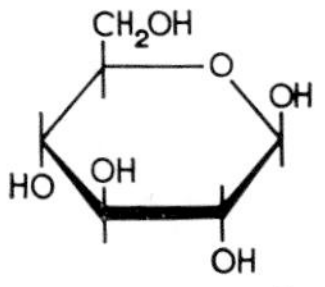   (LXXXVIII) β-Form

Examples of the Fischer and Haworth* ring formulae for different sugars are given below:

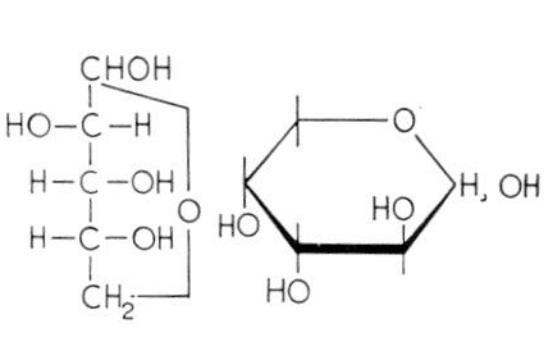

D-Arabopyranose 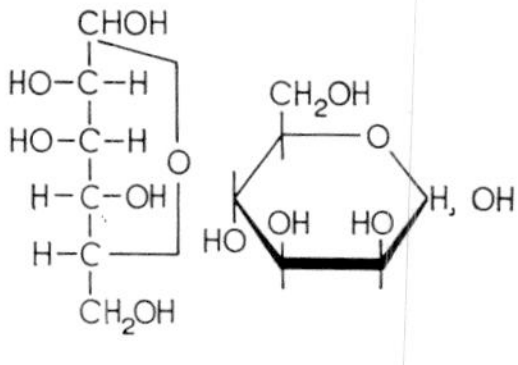   D-Mannopyranose 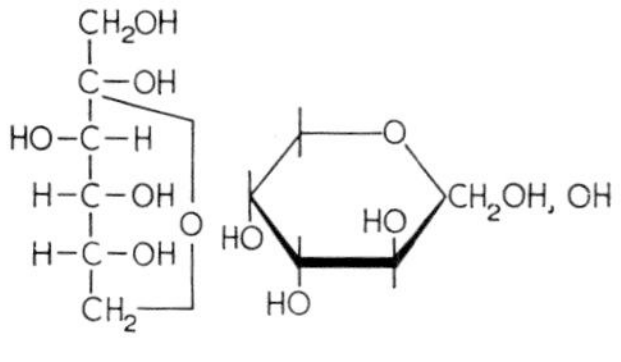   D-Fructopyranose

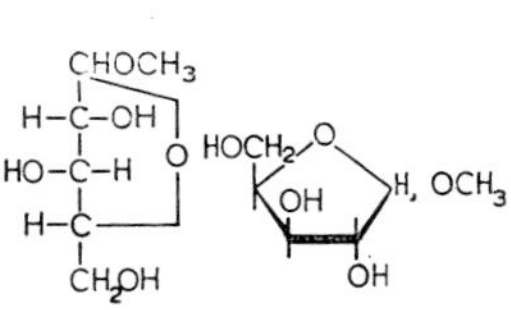

Methyl-D-xylofuranoside 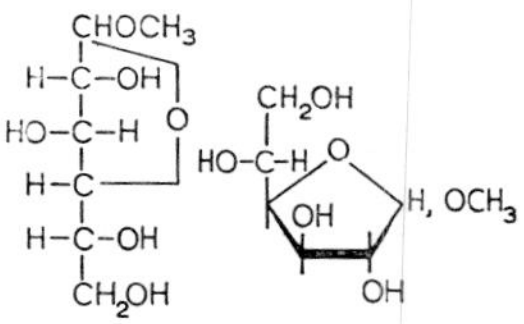   Methyl-D-glucofuranoside 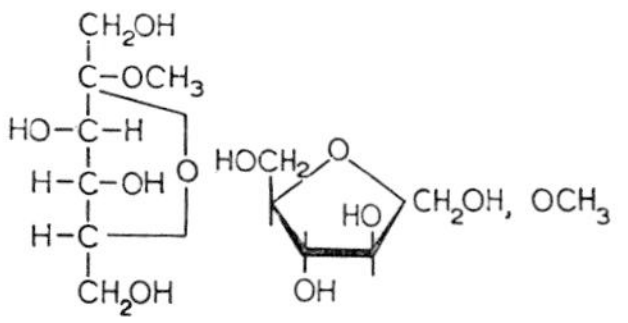   Methyl-D-fructofuranoside

The introduction of an additional asymmetric carbon atom leads to the existence of two isomers, (α and β) of each type of ring, which are described as *anomers*, and C-1 is now referred to as the anomeric carbon atom (C-2 in ketoses). In the D-series of sugars the α-hydroxyl is written on the right of the sugar chain in the cyclic form of the Fischer formulae and *trans* to the CH_2OH in the Haworth formulae. It is necessary to relate the pento-pyranoses to the hexoses to determine whether the anomeric hydroxyl

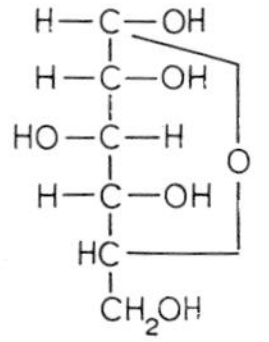

α-D-Glucose α-L-Glucose β-D-Glucose β-L-Glucose

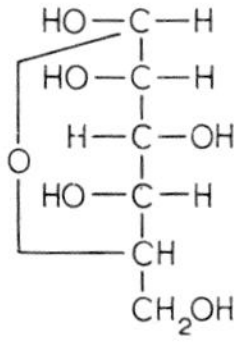

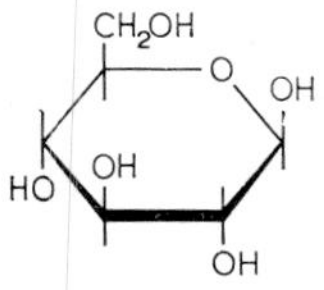

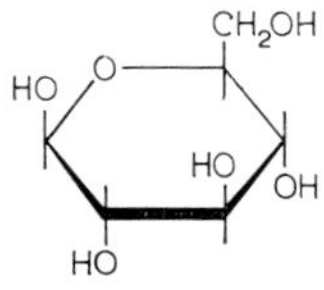

---

* For clarity the hydrogens are omitted in the Haworth formulae.

References p. 63

group should be written above or below the plane of the ring. The L-sugars are the mirror images of the D-sugars. In order to avoid confusion the generally accepted convention, originally proposed by Hudson[44], was to designate the anomer in the D-series with highest positive rotation the

β-D-Xylose   β-L-Xylose   α-D-Xylose   α-L-Xylose

α-form and the isomer of the lowest rotation is called the β-form. The reverse applies in the L-series, α-L-glucose having the lowest positive *i.e.* the highest negative rotation, namely $[\alpha]_D$ —111° and β-L-glucose $[\alpha]_D$ —19°. X-ray and other studies in subsequent years confirmed this ruling. Examination of solid α-sugars by infrared reveals a characteristic peak at 844 ± 8 cm⁻¹ whereas the solid β-sugars display absorption at 891 ± 7 cm⁻¹. It should be noted that anomers are *not* enantiomorphs; except that in solution the groups on C-1 are easily interconverted (whereas the 2-epimers are perfectly stable in absence of alkali), they are as different as say α-D-glucose and α-D-mannose (2-epimers), each pair differing in the stereochemical arrangement of a single carbon atom, C-2 in the example cited.

It should be emphasised that furanose forms of unsubstituted sugars have never been isolated* although in solution they are considered to exist in equilibrium with the open-chain and pyranose ring forms, the amount present depending on the temperature. Furanose derivatives in which the reducing hydroxyl group is involved in linkage to other compounds or in which the hydroxyl group on C-5 in aldoses and C-6 in ketoses is substituted are commonly found in Nature. Indeed, every known natural derivative of D-fructose has the furanose structure. Sucrose consists of a fructofuranosyl moiety linked through C-2 to C-1 of glucose, and it is the furanose form of D-ribose and 2-deoxy-D-ribose which is present in the nucleic acids. Whereas in lactones (intramolecular esters) it is the 1,4- or γ-ring which is stable and the 1,5- or δ-ring which is relatively unstable (p. 2) the opposite is the case among the free sugars and the glycosides.

The branched-chain sugars streptose, apiose and cordycepose (p. 18) which are found only in glycosidic union must, in their natural states, have a hemiacetal ring structure formed in the latter two instances by union of C-1 to either of the CH_2OH groups attached to C-3. This introduces an additional

---

* If solid apiose and codycepose are ring sugars they must be furanose. Also L-xylulose.

centre of asymmetry not only at C-1 but also at C-3 and the possibility of *erythro-* and *threo-*furanose sugars (LXXXIX, XC); C-3 then replaces C-2 as the asymmetric centre which defines whether this sugar is D or L. Since both the *erythro-* and *threo-*sugars could exist in the α- and the β-form four

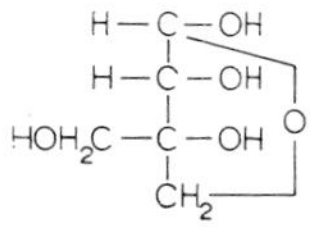

(LXXXIX)

α-D-Apio-D-furanose[45]

3C-(Hydroxy-methyl)-

α-D-erythrofuranose[46]

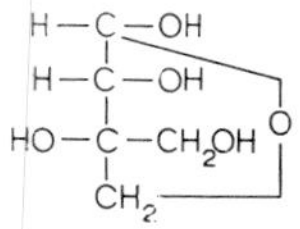

(XC)

α-D-Apio-L-furanose

3C-(Hydroxy-methyl)-

α-L-threofuranose

isomeric furanose ring forms of apiose and cordycepose are possible. The naming of such compounds is difficult and two suggested names for the apiose sugars are given under the respective formulae. There is no means at present of determining the configuration of C-3 in natural apiose, that is of deciding whether it belongs to the D- or to the L-series of sugars. On the other hand streptose (XCI) is definitely a member of the L-series and can form only α- and β-lyxofuranose ring forms, whereas hamamelose (XCII, XCIII), which occurs naturally as an ester, (2,5-digalloyl) can exist as a furanose (XCII) (if C-5 is substituted) or a pyranose sugar (XCIII) in the free state.

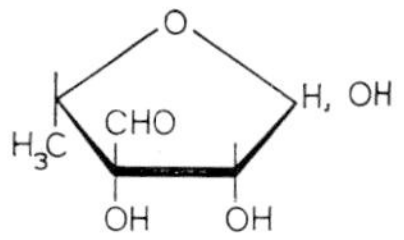

(XCI) 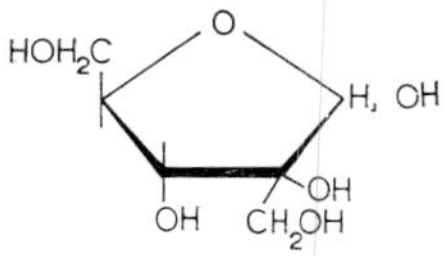   (XCII) 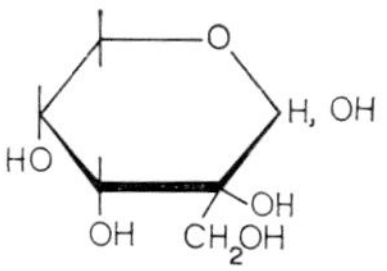   (XCIII)

(a) Mutarotation of the monosaccharides

The anomeric pairs of different sugars have been obtained as stable crystalline compounds but in aqueous solution the optical rotation of the α-D-form (XCIV) decreases and that of the β-D-form (XCVI) increases until they reach the same equilibrium value. In effect one isomeric form is being transformed into the other, most probably through the intermediate production of the aldehydic form (XCV) of which a very small proportion is considered to be present in solution[47]. Cantor and Peniston[48] estimated the amount of the reducible aldehydo form in solution of a number of the common monosaccharides by reduction at the dropping mercury cathode

References p. 63

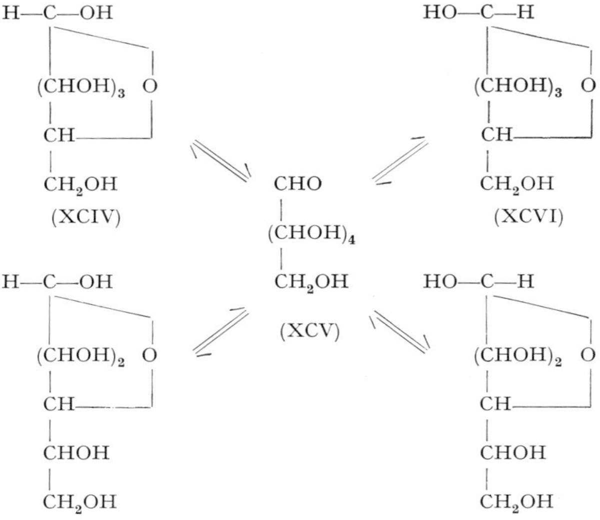

H—C—OH $\qquad$ HO—C—H

$(CHOH)_3$ O $\qquad$ $(CHOH)_3$ O

CH $\qquad$ CH

CH_2OH $\qquad$ CH_2OH

(XCIV) $\qquad$ (XCVI)

CHO

$(CHOH)_4$

H—C—OH $\qquad$ CH_2OH $\qquad$ HO—C—H

$(CHOH)_2$ O $\qquad$ (XCV) $\qquad$ $(CHOH)_2$ O

CH $\qquad$ CH

CHOH $\qquad$ CHOH

CH_2OH $\qquad$ CH_2OH

(XCVII) $\qquad$ (XCVIII)

and showed that it varied with changes in pH, concentration, and temperature. In addition both types of rings (XCIV, XCVIII) are probably present.
The course of the equilibration process, termed mutarotation, is catalysed
by amphoteric solvents. At equilibrium the proportion of α- and β-forms
is not necessarily equal, it varies according to the stereochemistry of the
molecules and their environment such as solvent, temperature etc. In
aqueous solution a relatively high proportion of the aldehydic form of ribose
is present; whereas an appreciable proportion of the furanose form is present
in solutions of D-fructose.

(b) Glycosides

(i) Synthetic glycosides

Brief mention has already been made of glycosides, the non-reducing
hemiacetal derivatives formed by reaction of a monosaccharide with alcohol
in the presence of an acid catalyst. These derivatives are relatively stable
cyclic compounds which do not mutarotate in aqueous solution. They have
in fact lost the properties associated with the carbonyl group and do not
undergo reduction or oxidation at C-1 (or C-2). When formed by reaction
with dry methanolic hydrogen chloride at room temperature the methyl
glycosides have a high proportion of the furanose ring structure (furanoside),
whereas reaction at elevated temperature results mainly in a pyranose ring
(pyranoside). α- and β-derivatives of both ring forms of glycosides (XCIX,

CII) exist. Furanosides, particularly of aldoses, are much more labile to acid than are the corresponding pyranosides; dilute mineral acid (0.01 N) in the cold will hydrolyse furanosides at an appreciable speed. In contrast 0.1 N-acid at 100° for 4 h is normally required completely to recover the free sugar from the aldopyranoside. In contrast, methyl α-D-fructofuranoside is hydrolysed only about three times as fast as the pyranoside. Pentopyrano-

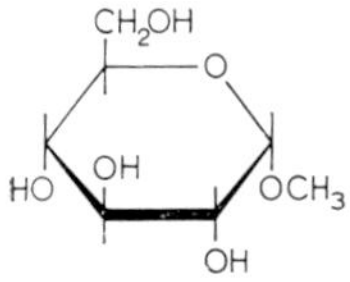

(XCIX)	(C)	(CI)	(CII)
Methyl α-D-gluco-pyranoside	Methyl β-D-gluco-furanoside	Methyl α-D-fructo-pyranoside	Methyl β-D-fructo-furanoside

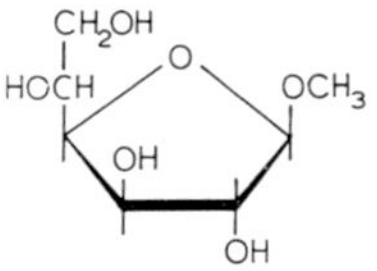

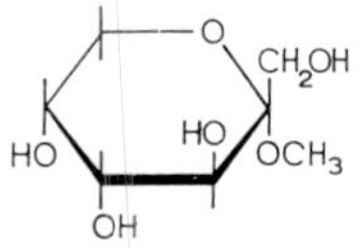

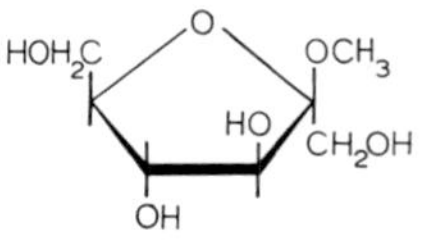

sides and fructosides are more labile to acid than the majority of hexo-pyranosides, but α- and β-D-gulopyranosides are very acid labile glycosides. The relationship of methyl α- and β-glucopyranosides with the corresponding free sugar has been established by the use of specific enzymes. α-D-Gluco-sidases, including maltase, enzymes which cleave α-D-glucosyl links, hydrolyse methyl α-D-glucopyranoside to α-D-glucopyranose and this on addition of alkali mutarotates downwards to the equilibrium mixture. Similarly, treatment of methyl β-D-glucopyranoside with β-D-glucosidases (one is present in emulsin), enzymes which split β-D-glucosidic links, yields β-D-glucopyranose, the rotation of which in the presence of a trace of ammonia rises. The anomeric structure of a particular glycoside can usually be determined from its optical rotation and the application of the "iso-rotation" rules devised by Hudson[49].

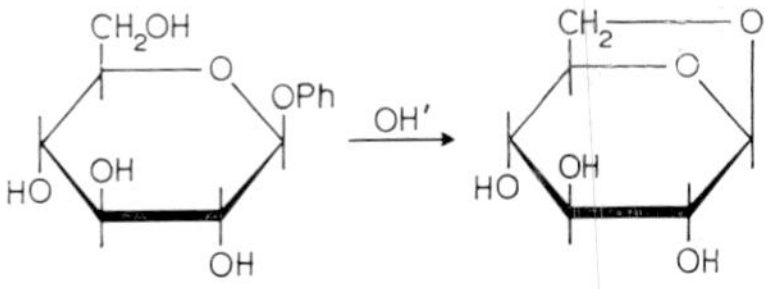

(CIII) (CIV)

The presence of an acetyl residue or halogen atom in place of the hydroxyl group on C-1 (p. 46) makes the potential reducing group more reactive and facilitates the preparation of many aryl and alkyl glycosides[50]. In contrast to alkyl glycosides, phenolic β-glycosides (CIII) are hydrolysed by dilute alkali yielding 1,6-anhydro-sugars (glycosans) (CIV) (p. 54).

(ii) Natural glycosides

Natural glycosides were known long before the preparation of alkyl and aryl glycosides. D-Glucose is the most common monosaccharide residue, but other sugars such as D-galactose, L-rhamnose and D-fucose and some pentoses and even uronic acids are also found in natural glycosides which occur almost invariably in the β-form. Di-, tri- and higher saccharides can form the sugar moieties. The naturally occurring compounds are hydrolysed by acids in the same way as the synthetic alkyl glucosides, and present in the plant, but not in invariably active condition, are the appropriate enzymes capable of hydrolysing the particular glycosides synthesised by that plant. Glycosides in which the aglycone is derived from orthophosphate are of wide occurrence. These so-called aldose 1-phosphates (aldosylphosphates) are quite distinct from phosphate esters, the latter having the properties of reducing sugars. They are of fundamental importance in the metabolic processes of all living organisms, for example, D-ribose- and deoxy-D-ribose 1-phosphates are concerned in the biosynthesis of the nucleosides and nucleotides.

Treatment of tetraacetyl α-glucosyl (CV) and α-galactosyl bromides (p. 46) with silver diphenyl phosphate followed by hydrogenolysis of the phenyl residues and alkaline hydrolysis of the acetyl groups yields α-glucose (CVI)

and α-galactose 1-phosphates respectively. In contrast, phosphorylation of these two acetobromo sugars with silver dibenzyl phosphate and similar subsequent treatment results in the formation of the two β-1-phosphates (CVII). On the other hand the α-1-phosphate is isolated from acetochloro-D-mannose and -D-xylose if either of the above phosphorylating reagents are utilized. Aldose 1-phosphates are much more resistant to alkali than phosphate esters but are relatively sensitive to acid, and like the alkyl glycosides, the β-anomers are usually more acid labile than the α-form.

Disaccharides are glycosides in which the aglycone is a second sugar linked either through its reducing group or any one of its hydroxyl groups. The former type of linkage yields a non-reducing disaccharide, and sucrose (CVIII), which is found in all photosynthetic plants, is an example of this type of disaccharide, α-D-glucopyranose being linked through its reducing group to C-2 of β-D-fructofuranose.

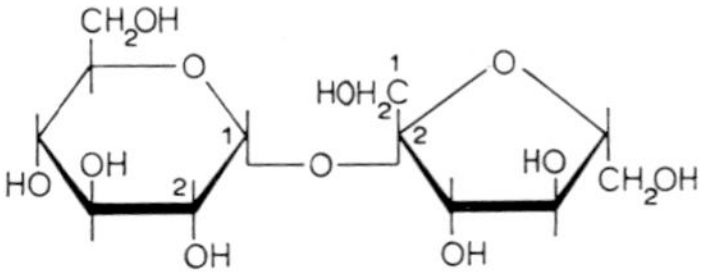

(CVIII)

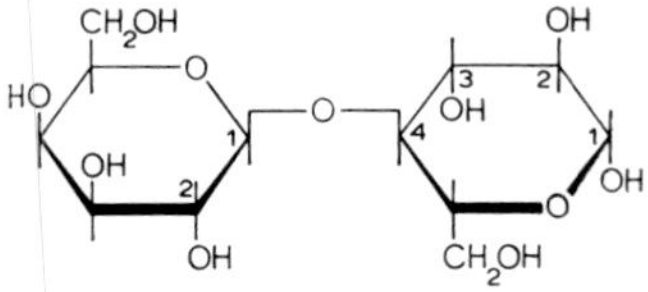

(CIX)
(β-form)

Linkage to the hydroxyl group of a second sugar yields a reducing disaccharide. Lactose (CIX), the reducing disaccharide found in milk, contains a unit of β-D-galactopyranose linked glycosidically to C-4 of a glucose residue. The process may be repeated with the production of oligosaccharides (two to ten monosaccharide units) or polysaccharides ($>$ ten monosaccharide residues). As in all glycosidations a molecule of water is eliminated each time union occurs.

Examples of the animal glycosides are the cerebrosides and gangliosides[54]; in the former a galactosyl residue is linked to the amino alcohol, sphingosine,

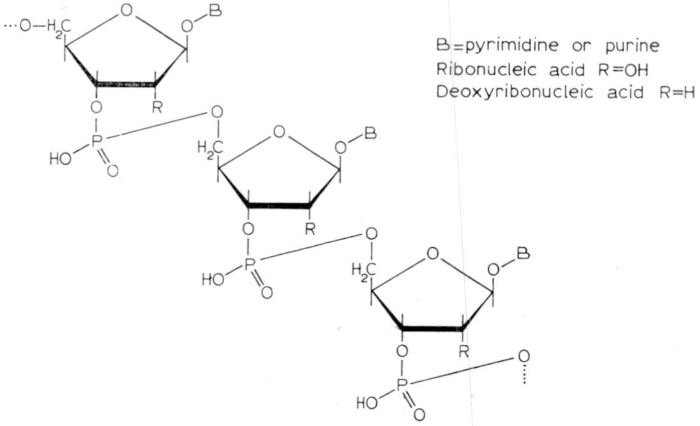

B = pyrimidine or purine
Ribonucleic acid R=OH
Deoxyribonucleic acid R=H

Portion of a nucleic acid molecule

and this in turn is joined through the amino group to a long-chain fatty acid. The nucleoproteins, present in all living cells, contain nucleic acids[55] (see previous page). These latter substances are composed of nitrogen glycosides

(CX)

of pyrimidines or purines linked to D-ribofuranose (or 2-deoxy-D-ribo-furanose) which in turn is linked to other residues through ester phosphate groups in the complex molecule of the nucleic acid. In addition many co-enzymes, such as adenosine di- and triphosphate (ADP and ATP) and uridine 5'-diphosphate glucose (UDPG) (CX), concerned in energy transfers and in the interconversions of sugars in their natural environments, are nitrogen glycosides.

(c) Determination of the ring size in monosaccharides

There are several well-established methods for the determination of the ring size, such as oxidative degradation of the methylated sugars and a com-parison with the lactones of the sugar acids[56] or oxidation of the glycoside by periodate and characterisation of the products of oxidation[57].

In the former method the free hydroxyl groups of the methyl glycosides are blocked by methyl ether groups. Hydrolysis of the glycosidic methoxyl is followed by hypohalite oxidation. This leads to the formation of a lactone with, of necessity, the same ring structure as the original glycoside. The size of the lactone ring can be determined by its ease of hydrolysis (p. 2) and in some instances by its rotation (p. 42). The methylated lactone (or with ketoses the hydrolysis product of the methylated glycoside) may be oxidised to dibasic acids. The application of this method to aldopyranosides and ketofuranosides is illustrated by the sequence of reactions given on p. 31.

Oxidation by periodate is one of the most widely used techniques in structural investigations of carbohydrates. In most cases this involves measurement of the quantity of periodate reduced, and of the rate of forma-tion and the amount of the simple end products of oxidation: formic acid, formaldehyde, carbon dioxide and ammonia (from amino-sugars, p. 56). This may also be accompanied by isolation of the carbohydrate fragment which remains after release of the above fragments. The precise mechanism of the reaction is not clear, but a most important factor is the pH of the

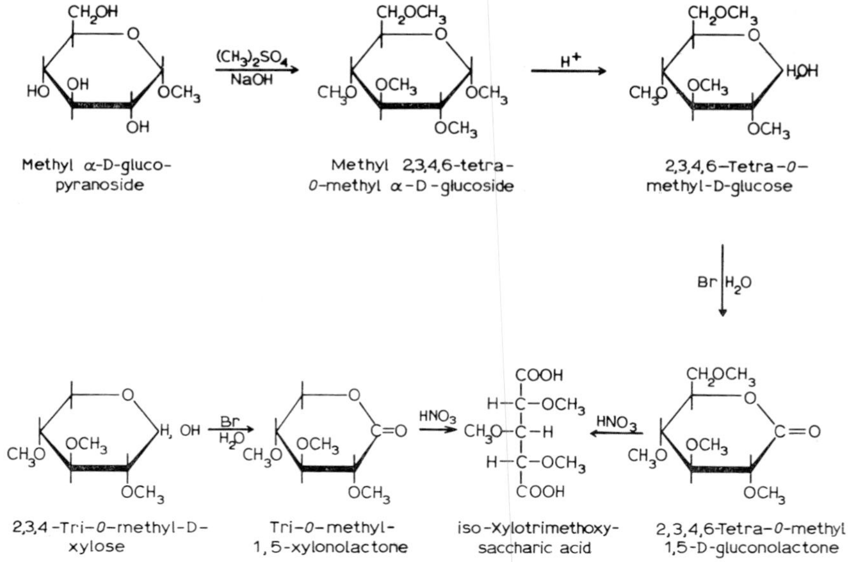

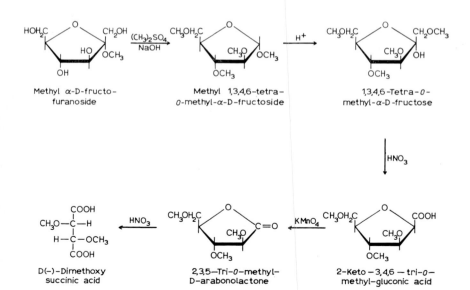

(CH3)2SO4
NaOH
H+
Br H2O
Br
H2O
HNO3
HNO3
Methyl α-D-gluco-pyranoside
Methyl 2,3,4,6-tetra-O-methyl α-D-glucoside
2,3,4,6-Tetra-O-methyl-D-glucose
2,3,4-Tri-O-methyl-D-xylose
Tri-O-methyl-1,5-xylonolactone
iso-Xylotrimethoxy-saccharic acid
2,3,4,6-Tetra-O-methyl 1,5-D-gluconolactone

(CH3)2SO4
NaOH
H+
HNO3
KMnO4
HNO3
Methyl α-D-fructo-furanoside
Methyl 1,3,4,6-tetra-O-methyl-α-D-fructoside
1,3,4,6-Tetra-O-methyl-α-D-fructose
D(–)-Dimethoxy succinic acid
2,3,5-Tri-O-methyl-D-arabonolactone
2-Keto-3,4,6-tri-O-methyl-gluconic acid

References p. 63

reaction mixture. In unbuffered periodate aldoses are oxidised in the ring form, fission taking place at the hemiacetal α-glycol group. This results in the formation of a formyl ester which is stable at this pH and until hydrolysis occurs complete oxidation is prevented. In ketoses the C-2 hemiacetal is attached to two α-glycol groups at C-1 and C-3 respectively and periodate cleaves both the C-1—C-2 and the C-2—C-3 linkages. Temperature also affects the rate at which oxidation takes place.

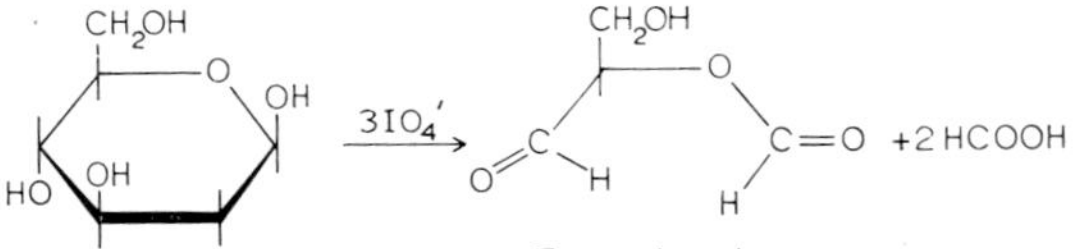

Formyl ester

The glycosidic link is immune to attack by periodate and this reaction can be used not only to establish the ring size of glycosides but also the configuration of the glycosidic link. α-D-Hexopyranosides reduce two moles of periodic acid, release a mole of formic acid and all yield the same diglycollic dialdehyde derivative (CXI). This has lost the asymmetric centres at C-2,

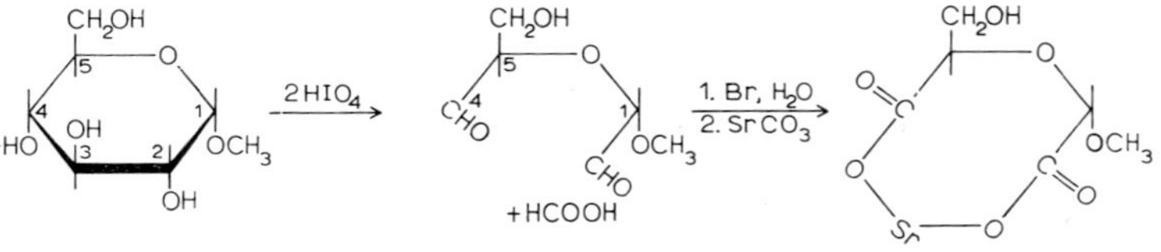

Methyl α-D-Glucoside   (CXI)   (CXII)

C-3 and C-4, while those at C-1 and C-5 are unchanged. In the case of β-D-hexopyranosides the configuration on C-1 is reversed in the dialdehyde. Examination of the rotation of the products showed that the anomeric stereochemical structures allocated by Hudson were correct. These dialdehydes may be characterised by oxidation to the diglycollic acid and crystallisation as the strontium salt. α-Glycopyranosides yield strontium

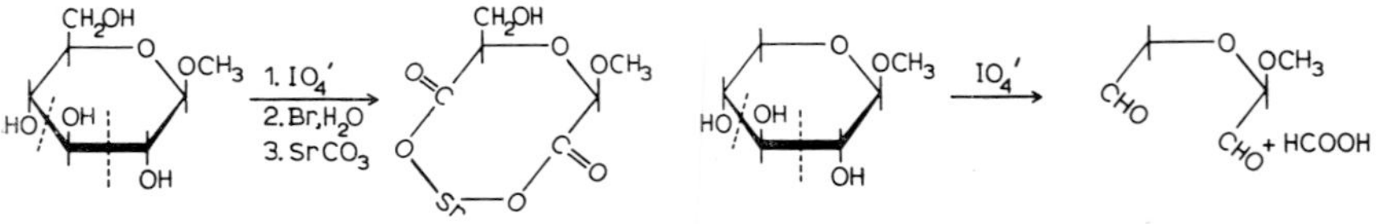

(CXIII)   (CXIV)   (CXV)   (CXVI)

D'-methoxy-D-hydroxy methyldiglycollate (CXII) and from β-glycopyranosides (CXIII) strontium L'-methoxy-D-hydroxy methyldiglycollate (CXIV) is derived. When the methyl D-pentopyranosides (CXV) are oxidised, the same quantity of periodate is reduced and monosubstituted diglycollic dialdehydes (CXVI) are produced.

Hexofuranoside rings (CXVII) may be distinguished since the C-2—C-3 and the C-5—C-6 carbon bonds are cleaved by periodate and a mole of formaldehyde is released instead of the mole of formic acid which is derived from the hexopyranosides.

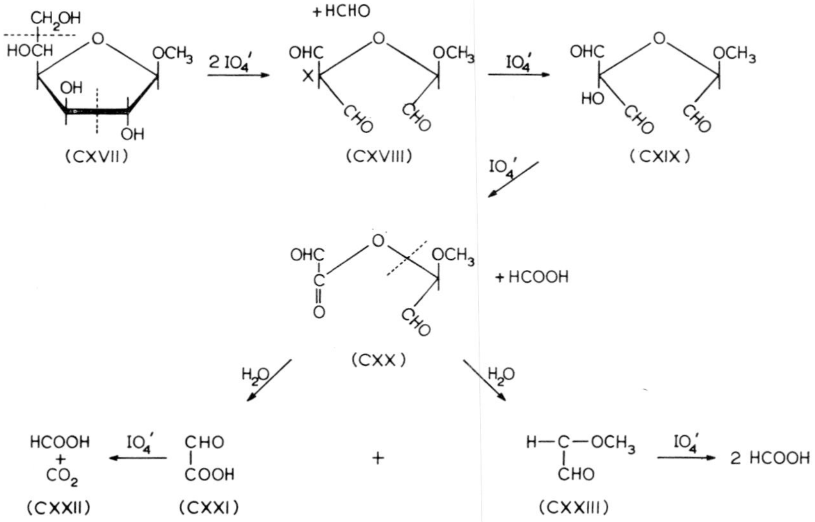

The trialdehyde (CXVIII) formed contains a malondialdehyde group which in the presence of excess periodate is further oxidised at the activated hydrogen atom (X) attached to C-4[58] (CXIX–CXXIII).

In contrast pentofuranosides (CXXIV) reduce one mole of periodic acid and release neither formic acid nor formaldehyde.

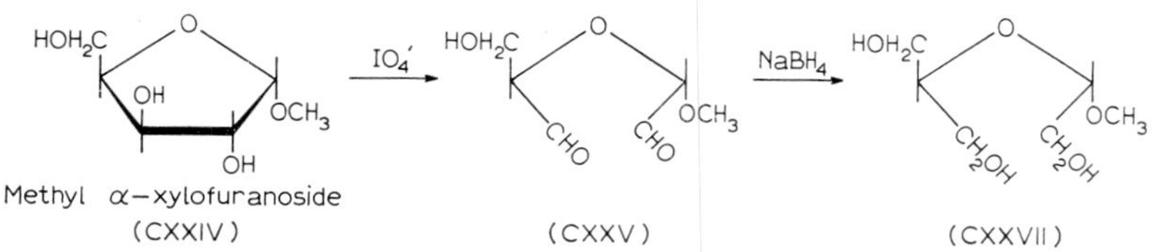

Methyl α−xylofuranoside
(CXXIV)   (CXXV)   (CXXVII)

Evidence has been advanced that the dialdehydes (CXVI) exist as ring compounds of the form given below, that from the hexopyranoside being designated 2-D′-methoxyl-6-aldehydo-1,4-dioxane 3-ol (CXXVI). This is deduced from the isolation of glycerol and glyoxylic acid after reduction, oxidation and hydrolysis[59].

References p. 63

The relatively unstable dialdehydes (CXVI) and (CXXV) may be stabilised by reduction with sodium borohydride to dihydric and trihydric (CXXVII) alcohols respectively.

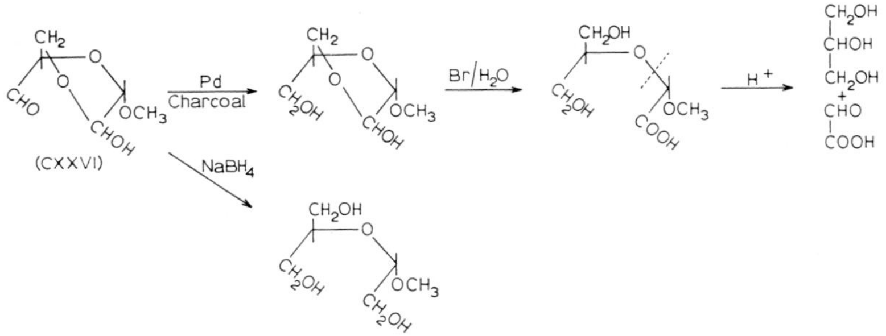

(d) Conformation of pyranose forms of monosaccharides

Whereas the furanose ring forms of sugars exist as planar rings it should be emphasized that this is not so in the pyranose sugars. If the normal valency angles are to be maintained in the latter then a non-planar conformation must be adopted[*].

There is a close similarity between the pyranose rings of monosaccharides and the cyclohexane ring, since the presence of an oxygen atom in the sugar ring causes little change in molecular geometry. Consequently many of the concepts established for the cyclohexane ring[60] may be applied to the pyranose sugars. Confirmation of this assumption has been obtained by recent work in a number of laboratories[61].

In order to be free from angle strain the rings assume the "chair" and the flexible conformations, examples of the latter being the "boat" and the "skew" forms. The chair conformation is the most stable form; it has a lower energy content than the flexible forms because the more staggered

Chair   Boat   Skew

arrangement of the addenda reduces their non-bonded interactions (repulsions)[62]. Consequently the chair conformations are the generally preferred

---

[*] The conformation of a molecule may be defined as the various arrangements in space which can arise by rotation about single bonds. It is generally impossible to isolate the different conformations of a molecule as the energy barriers between them are too small.

conformations for the sugars although during the course of a reaction a molecule may be excited and take up a less favoured conformation but one which is necessary before reaction can occur. Six of the carbon to hydrogen and hydroxyl bonds in the chair conformation are parallel to the three-fold axis of symmetry of the ring and are termed axial (a) while the other six extend outward and are called equatorial (e). Pyranose sugars can exist in two alternative interchangeable chair conformations designated C1 and 1C (CXXVIII, CXXIX). (CXXVIII) is transformed into (CXXIX) by moving C-1 up and C-4 down and it will be seen that the hydroxyl groups which are axial in the C1 conformation become equatorial when the sugar changes to the 1C conformation. When considering the preferred conformation for any sugar it should be remembered that the greatest repulsive effects are due to the hydroxyl groups; conformations in which large substituents are axial are avoided whenever possible and in this connection the bulkiness of the CH_2OH group should be remembered. It follows that the preferred chair form for each sugar is that which has the maximum number of hydroxyl groups or their substituents in the equatorial position.

The relationship between the Haworth formulae and the two chair forms for the more common pyranose sugars is illustrated in the following formulae. In drawing conformational formulae the direction of the bonds is determined by the tetrahedral valencies of the carbon atoms and the glycosidic carbon links in the C1 conformation must be drawn as in (CXXX) and not as in (CXXXI).

In each of these pyranose sugars (see p. 36) it may be observed that there are a fewer number of axial hydroxyl groups and less repulsive interactions in the C1 conformations, which is consequently the preferred form for these sugars. If both conformations have a similar number of axial hydroxyl groups or substituents then a mixture of the two conformations is probably present.

Although other interfering factors such as dipole interactions and hydrogen bonding make it difficult in many cases to predict the preferred conformation, this method of analysis has proved of value in a number of carbohydrate problems[63]. It has led to predictions, not only of preparative and structural results, but also of relative rates of reactions and the extent to which reversible reactions proceed. It is also of value in the interpretation of the relative stabilities of isomeric sugar derivatives. The equilibrium between α-D-galactose 1-phosphate and α-D-glucose 1-phosphate in which the hydroxyl groups at C-4 are respectively axial and equatorial in the stable C1 conformation favours the glucose derivative. The greater proportion of β-D-glucose compared with α-D-glucose in the mutarotation equilibrium can be similarly explained. However, as already mentioned, other factors must also be considered. For example, dipole interactions between the ring oxygen

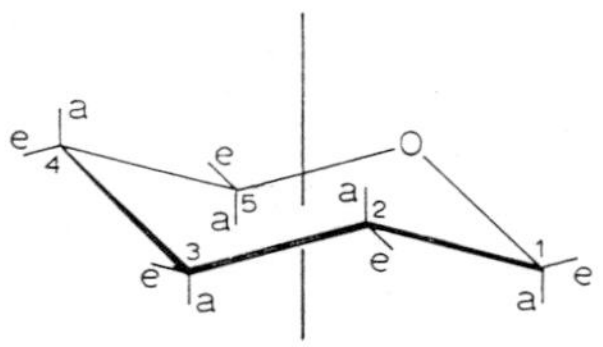

C1

(CXXVIII)

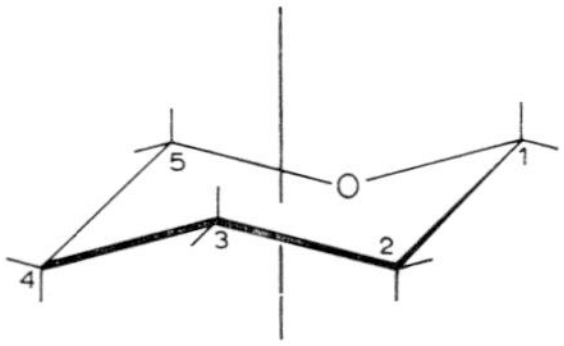

1C

(CXXIX)

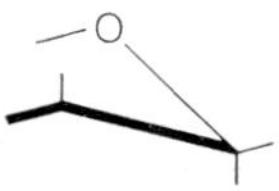

(CXXX)

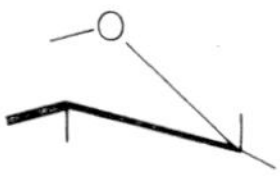

(CXXXI)

C1   1C

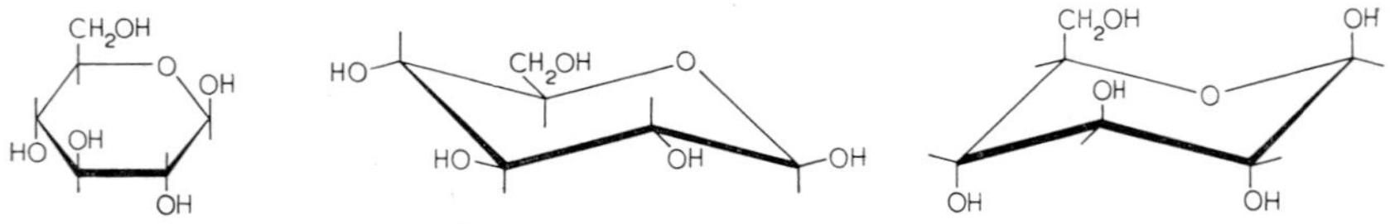

β-D-glucopyranose

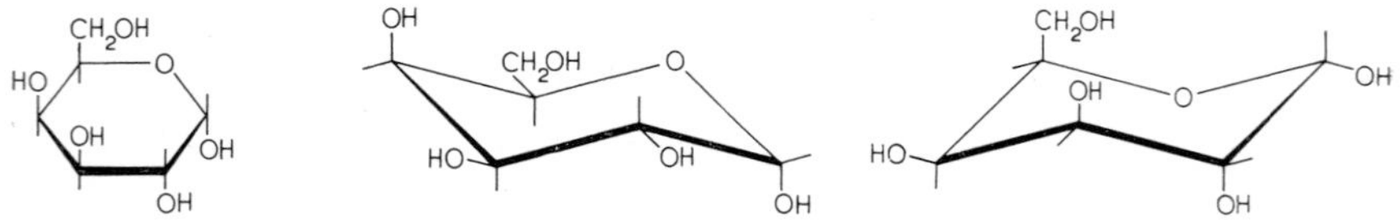

α-D-galactopyranose

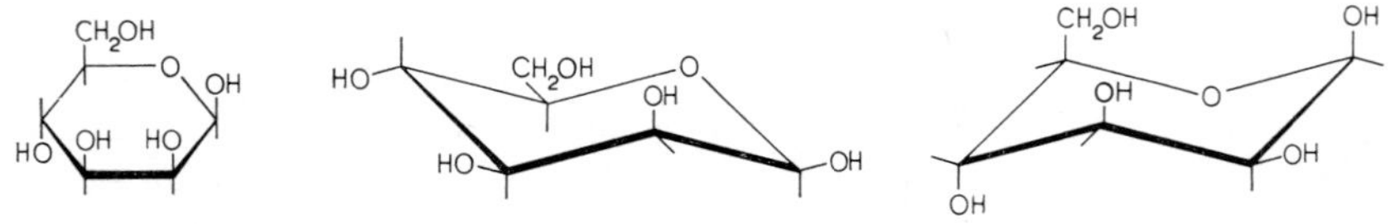

β-D-mannopyranose

and the oxygen on C-1 interfere in the equilibrium of methyl α- and β-glycosides in non-aqueous solvents and a higher proportion of the α-form is
favoured. This simultaneous operation of different kinds of steric and
electronic effect clearly shows that generalisations in sugar chemistry based
on conformational considerations should be viewed with great caution.

5. Interconversions

The main sugars are naturally occurring and from these by a series of interconversions the others may be synthesised.

(a) Pentoses to hexoses

```
                                    COOH              C=O
                                     |                 |
                                 H—C—OH            H—C—OH              CHO
                                     |                 |                 |
                            H₂O   (CHOH)₃    heat    CHOH  O   Na/Hg   H—C—OH
                              ↗                →         |     →          |
 CHO          CN                 CH₂OH            CH——             (CHOH)₃
  |          (C—HOH)                                   |                 |
(CHOH)₃  HCN   |                    +               CHOH            CH₂OH
  |       →  (CHOH)₃                                   |
CH₂OH         |                    COOH            CH₂OH
            CH₂OH            H₂O    |                +
(CXXXII)    (CXXXIII)         ↘  HO—C—H            C=O               CHO
                                     |                 |                 |
                                 (CHOH)₃    heat   HO—C—H   Na/Hg  HO—C—H
                                     |        →        |      →          |
                                 CH₂OH             CHOH  O          (CHOH)₃
                                                       |                 |
                                (CXXXIV)           CH——             CH₂OH
                                                       |
                                                   CHOH             (CXXXVI)
                                                       |
                                                   CH₂OH
                                                  (CXXXV)
```

Pentoses (CXXXII) may be converted to hexoses by the addition of hydro-
cyanic acid to the carbonyl group and hydrolysis of the two C-2 epimeric
cyanhydrins (CXXXIII) to the next higher C-2 epimeric pair of acids
(CXXXIV). Separation of the two acids, conversion to the lactones (CXXXV)
and reduction yields the respective sugars (CXXXVI)[64]. Reaction of a
sugar (CXXXVII) with nitromethane in the presence of sodium methoxide
produces the C-nitro-alcohols which are converted into the acid sodium

salt (CXXXVIII). Treatment with moderately strong acid yields two C-2 epimeric higher aldoses (CXXXIX) containing one more asymmetric C atom[65].

$$\underset{\text{(CXXXVII)}}{\overset{\displaystyle \overset{O}{\underset{|}{C-H}}}{\underset{|}{\underset{\displaystyle CHOH}{CHOH}}}} \;+\; CH_3NO_2 \;\xrightarrow{\text{NaOMe}}\; \underset{\text{(CXXXVIII)}}{\overset{\displaystyle H-C=N\overset{O}{\diagup}}{\underset{|}{\underset{\displaystyle ONa}{}}}\,\overset{\displaystyle }{\underset{\displaystyle }{}}}$$

$$\begin{array}{ccc}
H-C=N\diagdown^{O} & & H-C=N\diagdown^{O} \\
| \qquad \diagdown ONa & & | \qquad \diagdown ONa \\
H-C-OH & + & HO-C-H \\
| & & | \\
CHOH & & CHOH \\
| & & |
\end{array}$$

(CXXXVIII)

$$\xrightarrow{H^+}\;
\begin{array}{ccc}
H-C=O & & H-C=O \\
| & & | \\
H-C-OH & + & HO-C-H \\
| & & | \\
CHOH & & CHOH \\
| & & |
\end{array}$$

(CXXXIX)

(b) Hexoses to pentoses

There are various methods of degrading monosaccharides to the next lower member of the series. Wohl[66] (1893) devised a method which is virtually the reverse of the cyanhydrin ascent since it consists in the removal of hydrocyanic acid from the acetylated nitrile (CXLI) formed on acetylation

$$\underset{\text{(CXL)}}{\overset{\displaystyle H\cdot C=NOH}{\underset{|}{\underset{\displaystyle CHOAc}{\underset{|}{CHOAc}}}}} \;\xrightarrow[\text{NaOAc}]{\text{Ac}_2O}\; \underset{\text{(CXLI)}}{\overset{\displaystyle C\equiv N}{\underset{|}{\underset{\displaystyle CHOAc}{\underset{|}{CHOAc}}}}} \;\xrightarrow{\text{OH}'}\; HCN \;+\; \overset{\displaystyle CHO}{\underset{|}{}}$$

of the aldose oxime (CXL). There are a number of other methods of descending the series[67] including partial oxidation with periodate[68] and with lead tetra-acetate[69].

(c) Aldoses to ketoses

C-3 epimeric ketoses may be synthesised from the aldose with two carbons less, utilizing nitroethanol[65].

$$\underset{\text{Aldose}}{\overset{\displaystyle \overset{H}{\diagup}}{\underset{|}{\underset{\displaystyle CHOH}{\underset{|}{\overset{\displaystyle C=O}{\underset{|}{CHOH}}}}}}} \;+\; \underset{\text{Nitroethanol}}{\overset{\displaystyle CH_2OH}{\underset{|}{CH_2NO_2}}} \;\longrightarrow\;
\begin{array}{ccc}
CH_2OH & & CH_2OH \\
| & & | \\
CHNO_2 & & CHNO_2 \\
| & + & | \\
H-C-OH & & HO-C-H \\
| & & | \\
CHOH & & CHOH \\
| & & |
\end{array}$$

$$\xrightarrow[\text{2. H}_3O^+]{\text{1. NaOH}}\;
\begin{array}{ccc}
CH_2OH & & CH_2OH \\
| & & | \\
C=O & & C=O \\
| & + & | \\
H-C-OH & & HO-C-H \\
| & & | \\
CHOH & & CHOH \\
| & & |
\end{array}$$

Ketoses may also be prepared from the aldonyl chlorides (CXLII) containing one less carbon atom[70] by reaction with diazomethane to give diazomethyl ketones (CXLIII) which, on hydrolysis and careful deacetylation, yield ketoses.

$$
\begin{array}{ccccc}
\overset{\displaystyle O}{\underset{\displaystyle \|}{C}}-OH & \overset{\displaystyle O}{\underset{\displaystyle \|}{C}}-Cl & \begin{array}{c}CHN_2\\ |\\ C=O\end{array} & \begin{array}{c}CH_2OAc\\ |\\ C=O\end{array} & \begin{array}{c}CH_2OH\\ |\\ C=O\end{array}\\
|\\
(CHOAc)_4 & (CHOAc)_4 & (CHOAc)_4 & (CHOAc)_4 & (CHOH)_4\\
|\\
CH_2OAc & CH_2OAc & CH_2OAc & CH_2OAc & CH_2OH
\end{array}
$$

$$
\text{Penta-}O\text{-acetyl} \xrightarrow{PCl_5} (CXLII) \xrightarrow{CH_2N_2} (CXLIII) \xrightarrow{HOAc} \longrightarrow
$$

Penta-*O*-acetyl aldonic acid   (CXLII)   (CXLIII)

Aldoses may also be converted to ketones containing the same number of carbon atoms by treatment with hot pyridine or quinoline, ribose yielding ribulose.

$$
\begin{array}{ccc}
\begin{array}{c}CHO\\ |\\ H-C-OH\\ |\\ H-C-OH\\ |\\ H-C-OH\\ |\\ CH_2OH\\ \text{D-Ribose}\end{array} & \xrightarrow{\text{pyridine}} & \begin{array}{c}CH_2OH\\ |\\ C=O\\ |\\ H-C-OH\\ |\\ H-C-OH\\ |\\ CH_2OH\\ \text{D-Ribulose}\\ \text{D-Erythropentulose}\end{array}
\end{array}
$$

(d) Aldoses to other aldoses

On the other hand if an aldonic acid is treated with alkali, partial conversion to the C-2 epimer occurs. After separation, the pure epimeric acid can be converted to the γ-lactone by heating, and this on controlled reduction yields the corresponding aldose uncontaminated with ketose produced in the Lobry de Bruyn reaction (see p. 40). In this way a rare sugar such as talose may be synthesised from the aldonic acid of the comparatively abundant sugar, galactose[71].

$$
\begin{array}{c}COOH\\ |\\ H-C-OH\\ |\\ HO-C-H\\ |\\ HO-C-H\\ |\\ H-C-OH\\ |\\ CH_2OH\\ \text{D-Galactonic}\\ \text{acid}\end{array}
\xrightarrow{\text{pyridine}}
\begin{array}{c}COOH\\ |\\ HO-C-H\\ |\\ HO-C-H\\ |\\ HO-C-H\\ |\\ H-C-OH\\ |\\ CH_2OH\\ \text{D-Talonic}\\ \text{acid}\end{array}
\xrightarrow{\text{heat}}
\begin{array}{c}C=O\\ |\\ HO-C-H\\ |\\ HO-C-H\\ |\\ C-H\\ |\\ H-C-OH\\ |\\ CH_2OH\\ \text{D-Talono-}\gamma\text{-}\\ \text{lactone}\end{array}
\xrightarrow[Na/Hg]{H_2}
\begin{array}{c}\overset{\displaystyle H}{\underset{\displaystyle \|}{C}}=O\\ |\\ HO-C-H\\ |\\ HO-C-H\\ |\\ HO-C-H\\ |\\ H-C-OH\\ |\\ CH_2OH\\ \text{D-Talose}\end{array}
$$

References p. 63

(e) The action of alkali on monosaccharides

(i) The Lobry de Bruyn transformation[72]

Dilute alkali such as lime-water causes partial transformation to the C-2 epimeric aldose and the corresponding ketose. Glucose (CXLIV) gives an equilibrium mixture with fructose (CXLVII) and mannose (CXLVI) through the postulated intermediate 1,2-enol-form (CXLV).

$$
\begin{array}{ccccc}
 & & & & \text{CHO} \\
 & & & & | \\
 & & & & \text{HO—C—H} \\
 & & & & | \\
 & & & & \text{HO—C—H} \\
\text{CHO} & & \text{CHOH} & & | \\
| & & \| & & \text{H—C—OH} \\
\text{H—C—OH} & & \text{C—OH} & & | \\
| & & | & & \text{H—C—OH} \\
\text{HO—C—H} & \rightleftharpoons & \text{HO—C—H} & & | \\
| & & | & & \text{CH}_2\text{OH} \\
\text{H—C—OH} & & \text{H—C—OH} & & \text{(CXLVI)} \\
| & & | & & \\
\text{H—C—OH} & & \text{H—C—OH} & & \text{CH}_2\text{OH} \\
| & & | & & | \\
\text{CH}_2\text{OH} & & \text{CH}_2\text{OH} & & \text{C}=\text{O} \\
\text{(CXLIV)} & & \text{(CXLV)} & & | \\
 & & & & \text{HO—C—H} \\
 & & & & | \\
 & & & & \text{H—C—OH} \\
 & & & & | \\
 & & & & \text{H—C—OH} \\
 & & & & | \\
 & & & & \text{CH}_2\text{OH} \\
 & & & & \text{(CXLVII)}
\end{array}
$$

If the hydroxyl group on C-2 is substituted, then ketose formation is prevented since the substituent group cannot migrate to C-1, thus 2,3,4-tri-O-methylxylose (CXLVIII) yields only 2,3,4-tri-O-methyllyxose (CXLIX).

$$
\begin{array}{ccc}
\text{CHO} & & \text{CHO} \\
| & & | \\
\text{H—C—OCH}_3 & & \text{CH}_3\text{O—C—H} \\
| & & | \\
\text{CH}_3\text{O—C—H} & \rightleftharpoons & \text{CH}_3\text{O—C—H} \\
| & & | \\
\text{H—C—OCH}_3 & & \text{H—C—OCH}_3 \\
| & & | \\
\text{CH}_2\text{OH} & & \text{CH}_2\text{OH} \\
\text{(CXLVIII)} & & \text{(CXLIX)}
\end{array}
$$

(ii) Saccharinic acid formation

Dilute alkali may also cause degradation of reducing sugars and the enolisation may extend to the 2,3-dienol together with the production of such breakdown products as glyceraldehyde. Rearrangements can also take place with concentrated alkali with the formation of saccharinic acids[73]. D-Glucose (CLI) yields saccharinic acid (CL) with dilute alkali and a mixture of iso- (CLII) and *meta*-saccharinic acid (CLIII) with more concentrated alkali.

(CL) (CLI) (CLII) (CLIII)

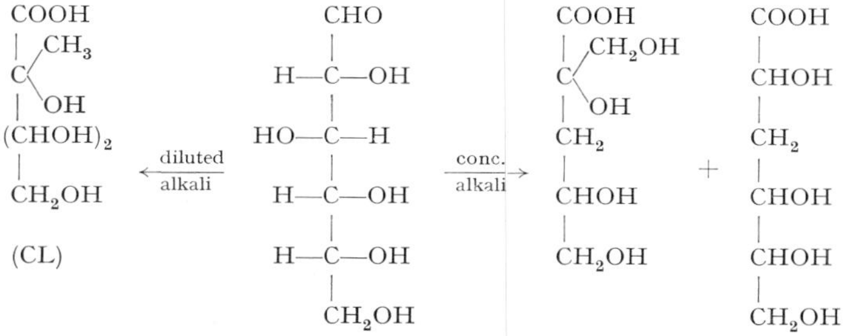

(f) The action of acids

Whereas dilute acid has little effect on dilute aqueous solutions of monosaccharides at room temperature, with more concentrated solutions of the sugars and at higher temperatures condensation can occur to give di- and higher saccharides. The process is known as *reversion*. D-Glucose and D-mannose give predominantly 1,6′-glycosidic linkages and L-arabinose yields mainly the 1,3′-linked disaccharide[74], although in all these cases and from D-xylose other glycosidic links such as 1,1′, 1,2′, 1,4′ and 1,5′ have been reported in lesser amount. Whereas only β-disaccharides were separated and characterised from L-arabinose, both α- and β-forms were separated from the other sugars.

Degradation of monosaccharides with strong acids at higher temperatures also occurs, the recognisable end product from pentoses being 2-furfuraldehyde (CLIV) and from keto- and aldohexoses 5-hydroxymethyl-2-furfuraldehyde (CLV) which degrades further to levulinic acid (CLVI) and formic acid[75]; ketoses undergoing this degradation more readily than aldoses.

(CLIV) (CLV) (CLVII)

References p. 63

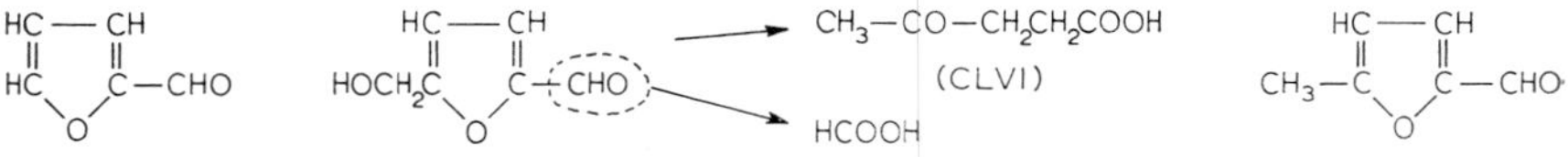

6-Deoxy-hexoses are similarly degraded by hot acid to 5-methyl furfur-aldehyde (CLVII).

The three derivatives of furfuraldehyde (CLIV, CLV and CLVII) form the basis of a number of colour tests for monosaccharides (p. 56) and are also responsible for many of the coloured products produced with different sprays on paper chromatograms (p. 56). It is probable that these furan compounds are responsible for the Maillard reaction[76], or "browning" effect when aqueous solutions of reducing sugars are heated with amino acids, a reaction which is believed to occur in food preservation. Indeed (CLV) is an important precursor in the formation of the brown colour which develops when aqueous solutions of glycine are heated with glucose.

(g) Oxidation and reduction

The aldehydic or hemiacetal group is the most easily oxidised portion of the monosaccharide molecule. All aldopyranoses (CLVIII) are oxidised with aqueous buffered bromine solution (pH 5.6). The initial product is the 1,5-lactone (CLIX) which then hydrolyses to the aldonic acid[77] (CLX). Evaporation of the aqueous solution yields the γ-lactone (CLXI), but from certain solvents such as pyridine which inhibit lactone formation the

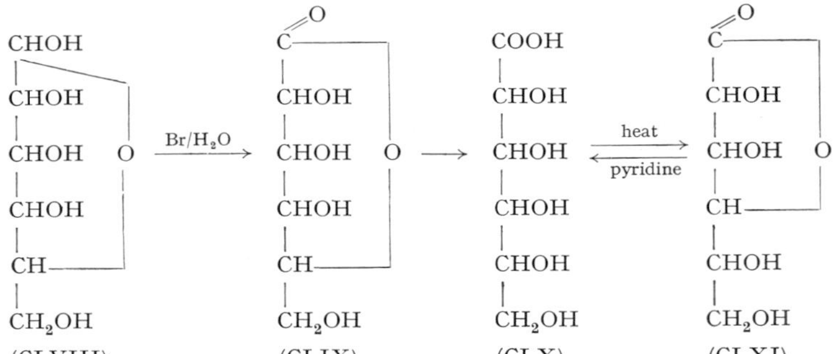

free acid can be isolated. An empirical rule established by Hudson[78] states that all monosaccharide lactones which possess an appreciable rotation display a higher positive optical rotation than the free acid if the lactone ring is on the right side in the Fischer projection formula and conversely lactones are more laevorotatory than the acid when their ring is on the left side in this formula.

The greater ease with which β-D-glucose is oxidised to gluconic acid compared with the α-form supports the contention that axial hydroxyls are less accessible to attack than equatorial hydroxyl groups (p. 35). Ketoses are not readily oxidised by bromine water; if oxidation occurs, cleavage of the carbon chain takes place.

```
      O                        O                        O
     //                       //                       //
    C                        C                        C
    |                        |                        |
  H—C—OH                    H—C—OH                   H—C—OCH₃
    |          O        O    |                        |
 HO—C—H                    HO—C—H                 CH₃O—C—H        O
    |                        |                        |
  H—C                        C—H                  CH₃O—C—H
    |                        |                        |
  H—C—OH                    H—C—OH                   H—C
    |                        |                        |
  CH₂OH                     CH₂OH                    CH₂OCH₃
```

| 1,4-D-Glucono-lactone $[\alpha]_D +68°$ | 1,4-D-Galactono-lactone $[\alpha]_D -77°$ | Tetra-O-methyl-1,5-D-galactonolactone $[\alpha]_D +145°$ |

Aldonic acids usually yield crystalline lactones, amides and other derivatives and have proved of value in the characterisation of sugars. No appreciable amounts of aldonic acids have been found in plants or animals, although certain bacteria are capable of oxidising glucose and other aldoses to the corresponding aldonic acids. Lactones have proved to be powerful inhibitors in certain enzymic reactions involving substances having structures related to the inhibitors[79].

Strong oxidising agents such as nitric acid (d 1.4) convert not only the hemiacetal but also the primary alcoholic group in aldoses to carboxyl groups. The resulting saccharic (aldaric) acid (CLXII) from glucose can be isolated as the 1,4:3,6-(γ)-dilactone (CLXIII). The low solubility of galactaric

```
   CHOH                        COOH                    α      C=O
    |                           |                             |
  H—C—OH                      H—C—OH              β    H—C—OH
    |              HNO₃         |                   γ         |       O
 HO—C—H   O      ──────→    HO—C—H        ──→          C—H
    |                           |                             |
  H—C—OH                      H—C—OH                  H—C
    |                           |                  O    |       γ
  H—C                         H—C—OH                  H—C—OH β
    |                           |                             |
  CH₂OH                       COOH                     C=O    α
```

(CLXII)   (CLXIII)

(mucic) acid in water has been used for the quantitative determination of galactose. Its isolation, however, does not characterise the initial material as either D- (CLXIV) or L-galactose (CLXVI) since, due to the peculiar

References p. 63

symmetry of the galactose molecule both the D- and the L-sugars yield the same optically inactive dibasic acid (CLXV) on oxidation with nitric acid.

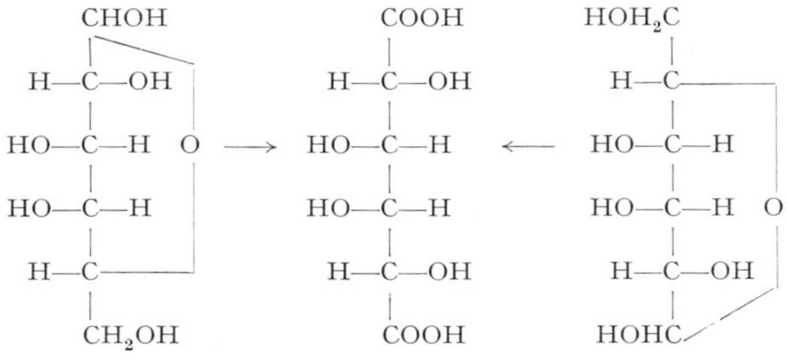

$$\text{(CLXIV)} \qquad \text{(CLXV)} \qquad \text{(CLXVI)}$$

Nitric acid oxidation of ketoses results in cleavage of the carbon–carbon links and the formation of lower chain carbon acids.

Uronic acids can be prepared by oxidation, *e.g.* with alkaline permanganate, of aldoses in which all the reactive groups except the primary alcoholic group, are blocked by substituents such as acetyl, isopropylidene etc.[80].

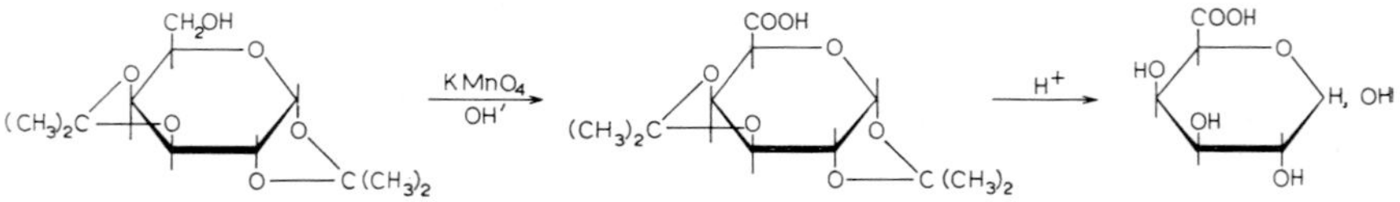

1,2:-3,4-Di-O-iso-propylidene-D-galactose

1,2:-3,4-Di-O-isopropylidene-D-galacturonic acid

D-Galacturonic acid

The reverse of the above oxidation reactions can be accomplished. Aldonic esters and lactones (but not the free acid) can be catalytically hydrogenated to glycitols. Sodium amalgam has been widely used for the reduction of lactones to sugars. In order to obtain good yields the reaction should be carried out at pH 3–3.5 with slight excess of sodium at temperatures below 15°. In this connection sodium borohydride has found wide application in recent years[81].

The ready reduction of monosaccharides to alcohols with sodium amalgam has already been mentioned (p. 2), but again sodium borohydride can also be used. The free aldoses can readily be reduced by this reagent to the corresponding glycitol (alditol) under the appropriate conditions. The reaction takes place in aqueous solution and is considered to be preceded by conversion to the straight-chain aldehydo form. Bragg and Hough[82] have carried out a quantitative study of this reaction on a number of monosaccharides, their methyl ethers, and lactones.

The tetrahydric alcohol, erythritol, (CLXVII) is found in algae, fungi and lichens, and the pentahydric alcohol, adonitol, (CLXVIII) occurs in *Adonis vernalis*. A number of the hexitols, particularly D-mannitol (CLXIX), and D-sorbitol (CLXX) are widely distributed in the vegetable kingdom[83].

CH_2OH	CH_2OH	CH_2OH	CH_2OH
H—C—OH	H—C—OH	HO—C—H	H—C—OH
H—C—OH	H—C—OH	HO—C—H	HO—C—H
CH_2OH	H—C—OH	H—C—OH	H—C—OH
	CH_2OH	H—C—OH	H—C—OH
		CH_2OH	CH_2OH
(CLXVII)	(CLXVIII)	(CLXIX)	(CLXX)

These two hexitols readily form mono- and di-anhydrides. The majority of sugar alcohols readily form acetal and ketal derivatives[84]. When the terminal groups in aldoses are made alike, loss of asymmetry of the molecules often occurs; the resulting aldaric acids and alditols, as for example, xylaric acid and galactitol, are optically inactive, non-resolvable *meso* forms. Fischer made use of this fact in his assignment of stereochemical formulae to the monosaccharides.

6. Esters

Sugar esters are relatively easy to prepare and in many instances are highly crystalline substances. The sugar normally reacts in the ring form. Consequently they are important in synthetic operations involving structural studies on monosaccharides, and also for the isolation and identification of sugars. They may be prepared by treatment of the sugar with the acid chloride or anhydride and a catalyst. The latter may be basic such as pyridine and sodium acetate, or acidic, for example zinc chloride and sulphuric acid. Esters are normally hydrolysed by alkali and less effectively with acid. Sugar acetates have provided valuable derivatives in the isolation of sugars from biological materials.

Acetylation of reducing sugars is complicated by the different ring and α- and β-forms of the sugar. Variations in the conditions of preparation give different isomers because an acetyl group replaces the anomeric hydroxyl. In general an acidic catalyst favours the formation of the β-acetate and a basic catalyst the α-form. Temperature also plays an important part. In pyridine and at a low temperature the α-aldohexopyranoses give the penta-O-acetyl-α-hexapyranoses, and the β-aldohexoses yield the penta-O-acetyl-β-sugar[85]. At higher temperatures and with an acid catalyst a 90% yield of the α-pentaacetate is formed from either isomer. The benzoyl derivatives

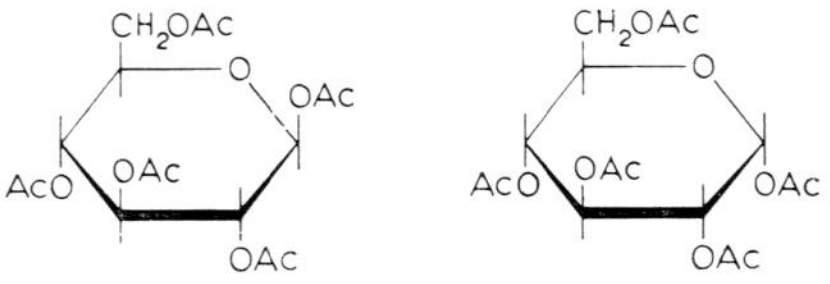

(CLXXI)

Penta-O-acetyl-β-glucose

(CLXXII)

Penta-O-acetyl-α-glucose

resemble the acetates and may be prepared by reaction of the sugars in pyridine with benzoyl chloride. It is possible to remove, selectively, the group in the glycosidic position.

The open-chain forms of the benzoyl and acetyl derivatives of aldose and ketose sugars are well-characterised crystalline substances which can be

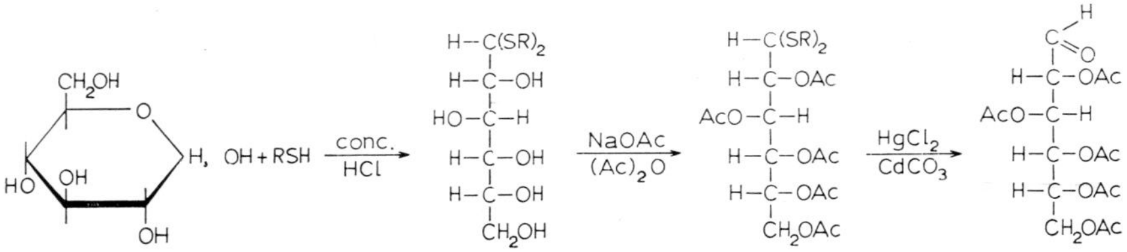

(CLXXIII)

2,3,4,5,6-Penta-O-acetyl-D-glucose

prepared from the sugar mercaptals (dithioacetals)[86] (CLXXIII) or oximes, in which the open chain is stabilised. These acyclic compounds have all the properties of true aldehydic and ketonic derivatives.

The acetyl group in a partially acetylated sugar is liable to migrate to another free hydroxyl, and usually one with a higher number, through the intermediate formation of a cyclic orthoester (CLXXIV). For this reason sugar acetates should be utilized with caution in structural investigations. The fully substituted derivatives, however, are of considerable value for the preparation of acetohalogenoses[87], derivatives in which the acetoxy radical on the potential reducing group in, for example, β-D-glucose penta-acetate is replaced by a halogen atom. The resulting acetyl glycosyl halides (CLXXV) are exceedingly valuable in synthetic work because of the ease with which the halogen atom may be replaced. Many different acyl groups

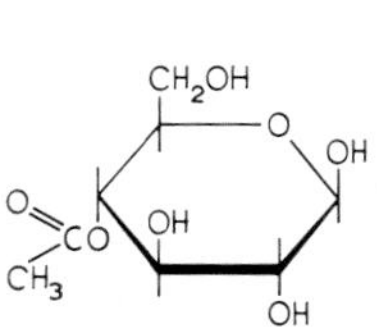

β-D-Glucose
4-0-acetate

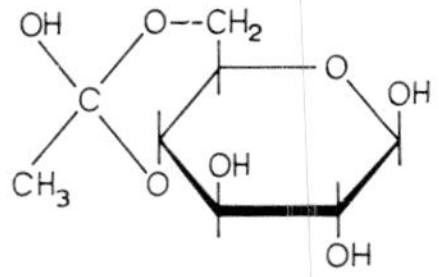

(CLXXIV)

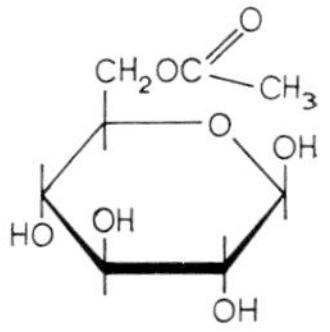

β-D-Glucose
6-0-acetate

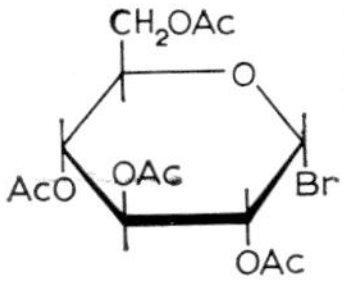

(CLXXV)
2,3,4,6-Tetra-0-acetyl-α-glucosyl bromide
(Acetobromo-α-D-glucose)

including phosphate (p. 28) and sulphate have been introduced into the sugar molecule by this means. The reaction is carried out in anhydrous inert solvent with alcohols or the silver salts of phenols or acids in the presence of silver carbonate or pyridine. The most commonly used aceto-halogen compounds are the chloride or bromide (CLXXVI) which exist in the α-form and replacement mostly occurs with Walden inversion and the forma-tion of a β-derivative (CLXXVII).

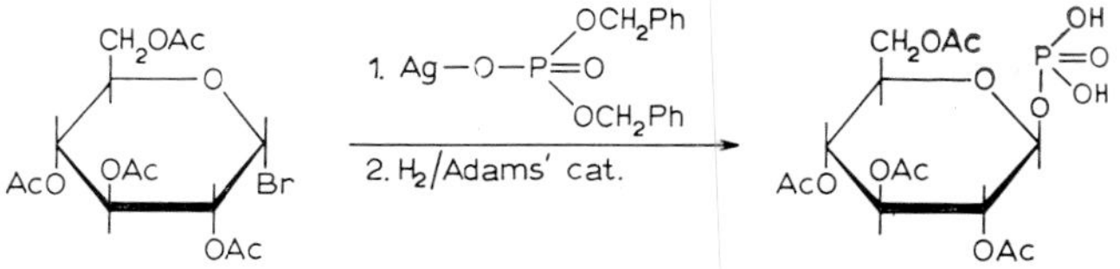

(CLXXVI)   (CLXXVII)

The esters of toluene p-sulphonic acid (tosyl) and methane sulphonic acid (mesyl)[88] of special interest because their removal can yield anhydro-sugars (p. 52), are prepared in the usual way by the action of the acid chloride in anhydrous pyridine solution. Hydrogenolysis with lithium aluminium hydride of the tosyl and mesyl groups from secondary hydroxyl groups can result in two different types of fission (a) and (b) with the formation respectively of the parent sugar and a new deoxy-sugar[89]. This reaction has proved of particular value in the synthesis of new ω-deoxy-sugars as fission of the tosyl group from the primary hydroxyl group in a

References p. 63

monosaccharide (CLXXVIII) proceeds according to (b) and yields the deoxy-sugar (CLXXIX)[90].

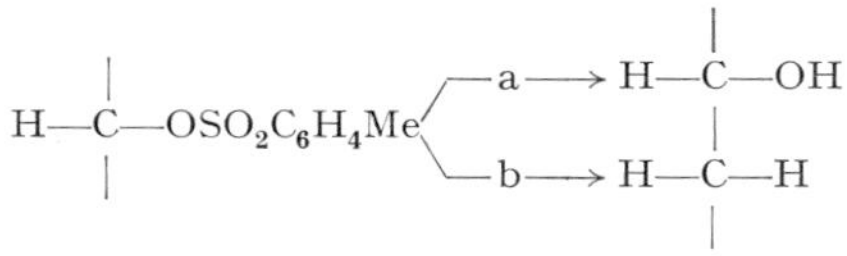

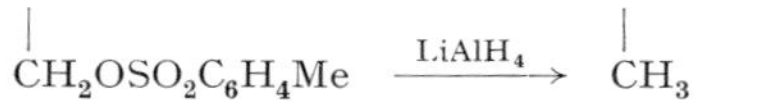

$$H—\overset{|}{\underset{|}{C}}—OSO_2C_6H_4Me \begin{cases} —a \longrightarrow H—\overset{|}{\underset{|}{C}}—OH \\ —b \longrightarrow H—\overset{|}{\underset{|}{C}}—H \end{cases}$$

$$\overset{|}{\underset{}{CH_2OSO_2C_6H_4Me}} \xrightarrow{\text{LiAlH}_4} \overset{|}{\underset{}{CH_3}}$$

(CLXXVIII)   (CLXXIX)

The formation of phosphoric esters[91] of carbohydrates is an essential stage in the biological synthesis, interconversion, and degradation of many pentoses and hexoses[92]. In the glucose series at least it is an essential step in the coupling together of the monosaccharide units to form ultimately amylose, amylopectin, and glycogen. α-D-Glucosyl phosphate-6-phosphate (D-glucose 1,6-diphosphate) has been established as the co-enzyme for the interconversion of glycosyl phosphate and 6-phosphate (ester) by phospho-glucomutase. Furthermore it has been established that phosphoric esters of glucosamine and its N-acetyl derivatives are concerned in the bio-synthesis of mucopolysaccharides.

In the early days metaphosphoric acid, mono- and tri-silver phosphates were the phosphorylating reagents utilized in the chemical synthesis of sugar phosphates. But their undesirable side reactions and the formation of di- and tri-esters have recently been avoided by the use of protected phosphorylating reagents such as dibenzyl and diphenyl phosphochloridates. The aromatic groups can readily be cleaved by hydrogenolysis in the presence of Adams' catalyst. In the preparation of partially phosphorylated sugars the most widely utilized protecting groups are acetyl, isopropylidene and trityl (CLXXX), the latter being removed with the phenyl groups on hydro-genolysis (CLXXX–CLXXXII).

1,3,4-Tri-O-acetyl-N-acetyl-β-D-glucosamine (CLXXXIII) on treatment

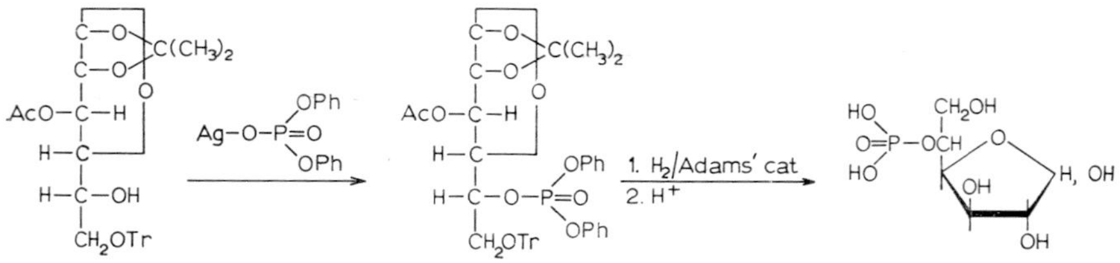

(CLXXX)   (CLXXXI)   (CLXXXII)

with diphenyl phosphochloridate yielded after hydrogenolysis and acidic hydrolysis the 6-phosphate[93] (CLXXXIV).

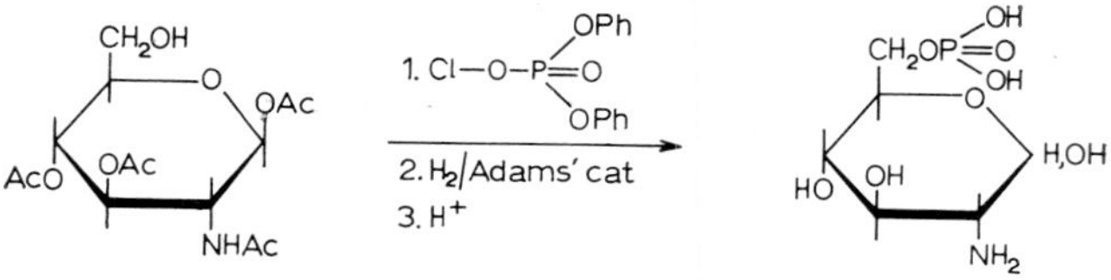

(CLXXXIII)   (CLXXXIV·

Sugar phosphates are most commonly isolated as their barium salts by precipitation with alcohol. These are readily converted into crystalline brucine and cyclohexylamine salts. Like all esters the phosphates are labile to alkali, glucose 6-phosphate being 60% hydrolysed by 0.2 N-alkali at 100° in 3 minutes.

The lability of the phosphate esters to acid varies with the position of the phosphate group in the sugar chain, the 6-phosphate being the most stable. Fairly drastic treatment which may even lead to the partial degradation of the sugar is necessary for the acidic hydrolysis of 6-phosphates. Similarly pentose 5-phosphates are hydrolysed many times more slowly than the other pentose ester phosphates. No change in configuration has so far been detected during acid hydrolysis of phosphate esters, but treatment of glucose and fructose 3-phosphates with phenylhydrazine in acetic acid caused inversion and the formation of 3,6-anhydro-D-allosazone. The use of heavy-oxygen water has shown that hydrolysis of phosphates occurs with fission of the phosphorus-oxygen bond (CLXXXV) unlike the hydrolysis of sulphonic esters where the C—O bond is broken.

(CLXXXV)

This probably explains the absence of anhydrides in the hydrolysis products of monosaccharide phosphate esters.

Migration of the phosphate group can occur on heating with acid through the intramolecular formation of an intermediate cyclic phosphate. All attempts to synthesise xylose 3-phosphate from xylose derivatives in which C-5 was substituted led to the preparation of the 5-phosphate. Removal of the C-5 blocking group was followed by the formation of the 3,5-cyclic phosphate (CLXXXVI) and this was cleaved preferentially at the 3 position with the formation of the 5-phosphate (CLXXXVII). Recent studies have revealed

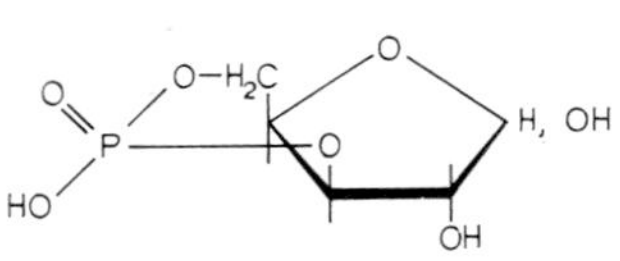

(CLXXXVI)   (CLXXXVII)   (CLXXXVIII)

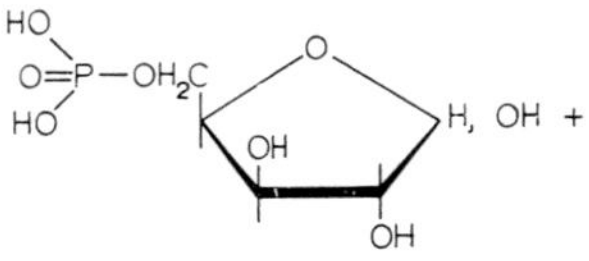

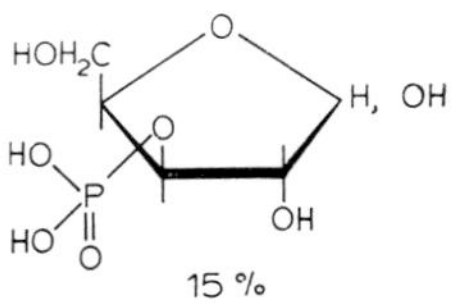

the presence of 15% of the 3-phosphate (CLXXXVIII). Cyclic phosphates (CLXXXIX) have been synthesised by Brown, Magrath, and Todd[94] by the addition of excess trifluoracetic anhydride in the cold to either the 2'- or 3'-phosphate of adenylic acid. Acid or alkali readily converts such derivatives to the two possible monophosphates (CXC, CXCI).

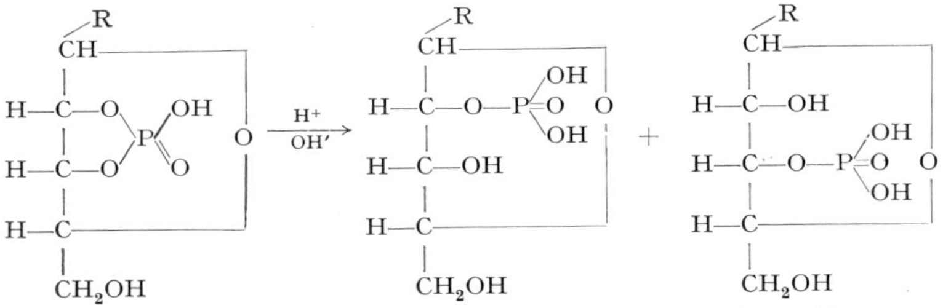

R = Adenine residue

(CLXXXIX)   (CXC)   (CXCI)

7. Acetals

The reaction of monosaccharides with acetone often results in a change in ring structure. If possible, the ketone reacts with two *cis* hydroxyl groups on contiguous carbon atoms and in order to do this a change from pyranose to furanose is sometimes necessary. In D-glucopyranose and D-xylopyranose this occurs with the production of 1,2:5,6-di-*O*-isopropylidene-D-gluco-furanose (CXCII) and 1,2:3,5-di-*O*-isopropylidene-D-xylofuranose (CXCIII) respectively. In α-D-galactopyranose (CXCIV) this is not necessary since the 1,2- and 3,4-hydroxyl groups provide two pairs of *cis* hydroxyls. Fructo-

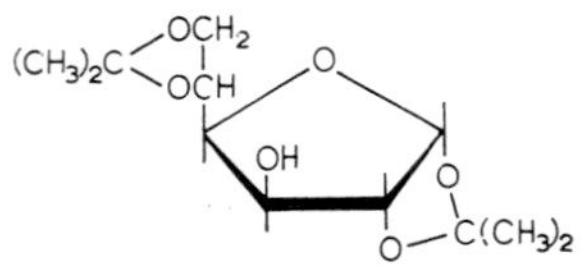

(CXCII) 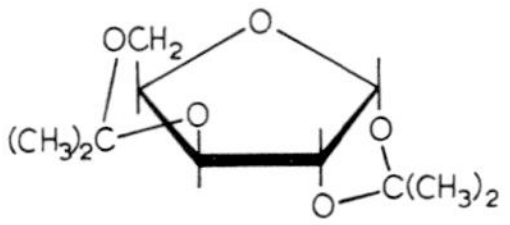   (CXCIII) 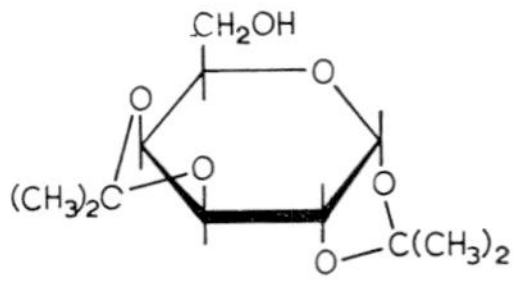   (CXCIV)

pyranose yields two di-isopropylidene derivatives in both of which the sugar retains the pyranose form (CXCV, CXCVI). The reaction is carried out in

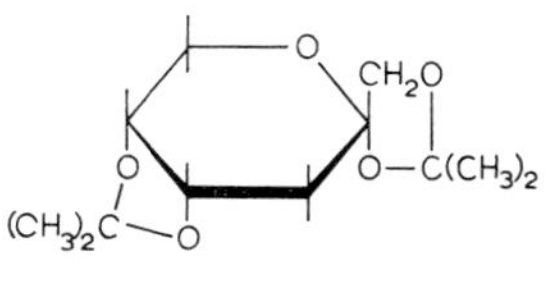

(CXCV)
α-form

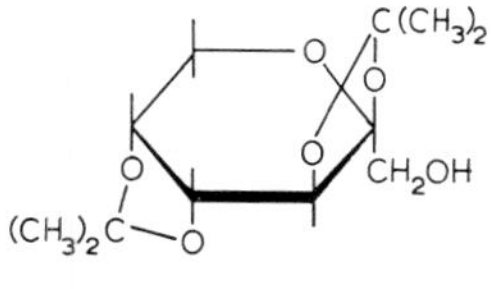

(CXCVI)
β-form

the presence of a dehydrating catalyst such as acid or anhydrous copper sulphate and the products are stable to alkali and labile to acid.

Bell[95] found that a mixture of natural monosaccharides could be separated into two groups by the use of these derivatives. The di-O-isopropylidene furanose sugars are hydrolysed to 1,2-mono-O-isopropylidene derivatives or free sugars by treatment with 0.1 N sulphuric acid at 20°. Extraction of the resulting solution with chloroform removes all the di-isopropylidene pyranose sugars and leaves the monoisopropylidene and free sugars in the aqueous solution. By this means arabinose, fructose, galactose and fucose may be separated from glucose, mannose, rhamnose and xylose.

Boric acid reacts comparably, and when D-glucose is shaken in an acetone solution containing sulphuric acid and orthoboric acid, a crystalline 1,2-O-iso-propylidene-D-glucofuranose 3,5-orthoborate separates. The extent of complexing of alkaline borate with the different hydroxyl groups varies with each sugar. Extensive use of this complexing, which can take place in aqueous solution, has been made in electrophoresis (ionophoresis), and in the separation of sugars on ion-exchange resins.

Aldehydes, e.g. benzaldehyde[96], may be condensed with sugars to form six-membered rings as in methyl 4,6-O-benzylidene-β-D-glucopyranoside

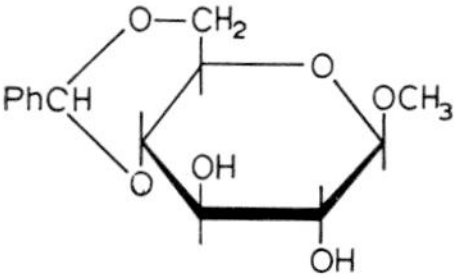

(CXCVII)

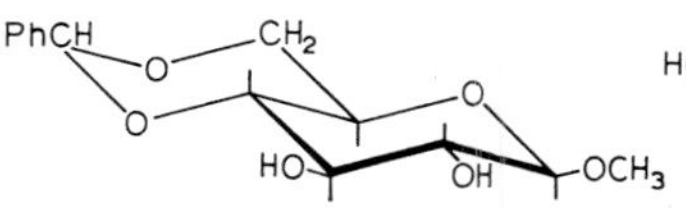

(CXCVIII)

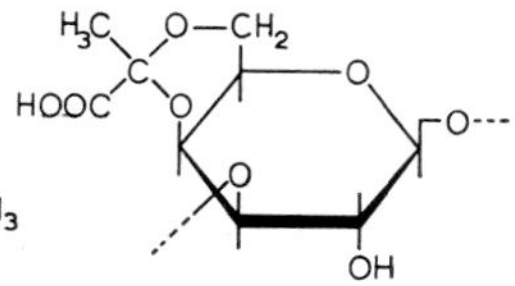

(CXCIX)

(CXCVII); the two fused rings forming a stable conformation (CXCVIII).

An interesting example of a natural cyclic ketal, formed by condensation of pyruvic acid with C-4 and C-6 of galactose is 4,6-O-(1'-carboxyethylidene)-D-galactose (CXCIX). This residue forms an integral part of the molecule of agar, a polysaccharide synthesised by several species of red algae.

8. Anhydro-sugars

It was stated earlier (p. 9) that internal etherification of monosaccharides yields anhydro-sugars. 1,2-, 2,3-(CC), 3,4-, and 5,6-epoxide rings, 2,4- and 3,5-propylene oxides (2,4-anhydro-D-glucose (CCI), and 3,5-anhydro-D-xylopyranose), and 1,4-, 2,5-, and 3,6- (CCII) butylene oxide rings are known.

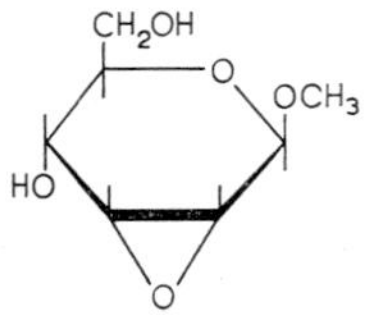

(CC)
Methyl – 2,3 –anhydro -/β–
D – allopyranoside

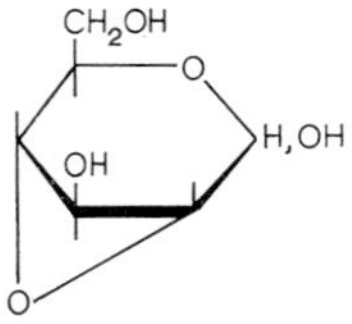

(CCI)

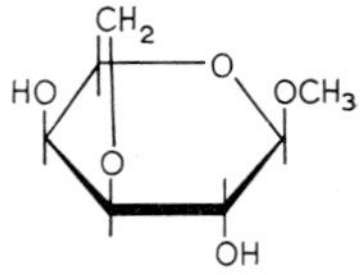

(CCII)
Methyl –3,6 –anhydro –/β –
D-galactose

Their preparation which is usually accompanied by Walden inversion involves removal of such substituents as amino (NH_2), halogen (F and Br), toluene p-sulphonyl, methane sulphonyl, and nitrate.

The most reactive class of sugar anhydride is the epoxide or ethylene oxide[97] in which adjacent carbon atoms are united by an oxygen bridge. These are usually prepared by the removal of the substituted sulphonate group by the action of sodium hydroxide in the cold and the reaction only takes place if there is, on an adjacent carbon atom, a hydroxyl group *trans* to the sulphonate group. Walden inversion occurs on the carbon atom which formerly carried the sulphonyl group. If the groups are *cis* or there are no free hydroxyl groups available then the sulphonic ester grouping is very difficult to remove and neither anhydride formation nor Walden inversion occurs. The essential character of this *trans* exchange is exemplified by treating methyl 4-O-methanesulphonyl-β-D-galacto- (CCIII) and -gluco- (CCIV) pyranosides with alkali. In the former case no reaction occurs and in the latter, methyl-3,4-anhydro-β-D-galactopyranoside (CCV) is formed.

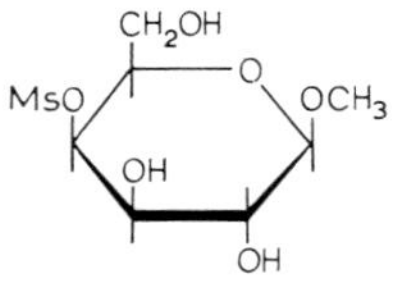

(CCIII)

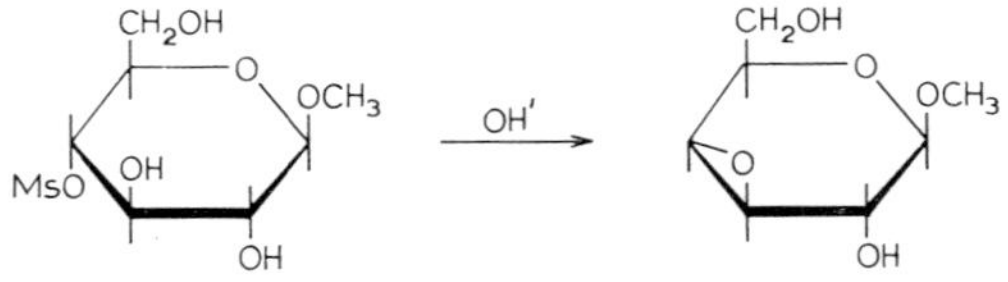

(CCIV)

(CCV)

The main interest in epoxide sugars lies in the fact that on treatment with alkali the ring opens, with another Walden inversion, and two products from the cleavage of each C–O bond may result[97]. The attacking ion, such as —OCH$_3$, enters from the side opposite the epoxide ring and inversion occurs at the carbon atom where fission occurs. Methyl-2,3-anhydro-4,6-dimethyl-β-D-mannoside (CCVI) on scission with sodium methoxide gives equimolecular quantities of methyl-2,4,6-tri-O-methyl-β-D-glucopyranoside (CCVII) and methyl-3,4,6-tri-O-methyl-β-D-altropyranoside (CCVIII). Although in some cases through steric and other factors only one of the possible

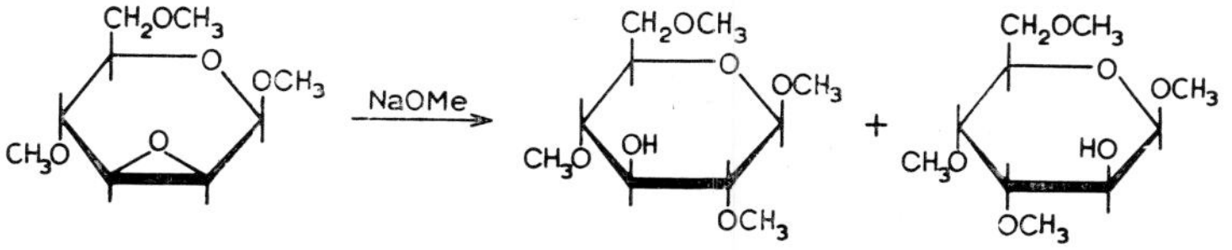

(CCVI)   (CCVII)   (CCVIII)

products is formed in isolable quantities, nevertheless these interconversions have proved of great value, not only for the synthesis of some of the rarer sugars but also in the assignment of structure. The formation of methyl β-D-glucopyranoside (CCX) by fission of the ring in 1,2-anhydro-

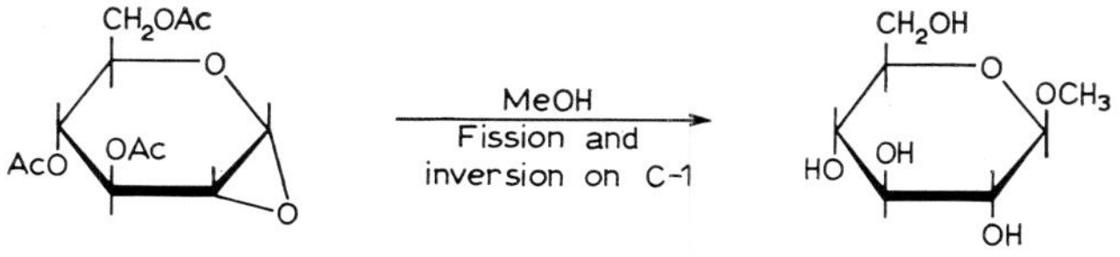

(CCIX)   (CCX)

3,4,6-tri-O-acetyl-α-D-glucopyranose (Brigls' anhydride) (CCIX), which is an intramolecular α-glucoside, confirms the anomeric structures assigned by Hudson. Use also was made of Brigl's anhydride to synthesise sucrose (α-D-glucopyranosyl-β-D-fructofuranoside) (yield 5.5 %) by heating it at 100°

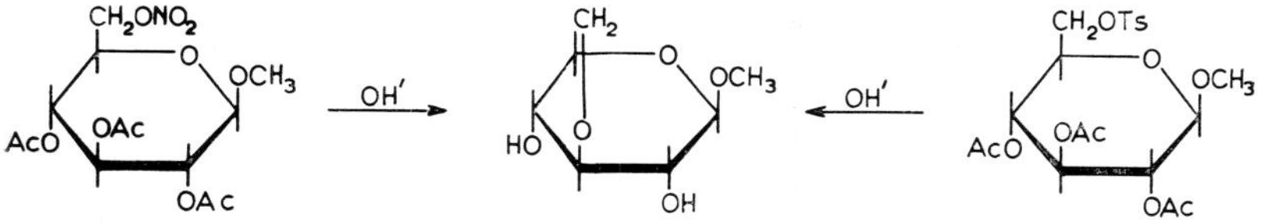

(CCXI)

(Ts≡tosyl)

for 104 hours with 1,3,4,6-tetra-O-acetyl-D-fructose. Under these circumstances the reaction took place with inversion.

3,6-Anhydro-sugars (CCXI) are readily formed by removal of the ester groupings from C-6 by the action of alkali. In these compounds which restore the colour to Schiff's reagent and give many of the colour reactions of ketose sugars (p. 56), the anhydro ring is of more importance than the sugar ring. It is stable to acid, alkali and oxidising agents. It is interesting to note that, although the pyranose ring may exist in the original 3,6-anhydro-sugar, it is impossible to prepare hexopyranosides from these derivatives, the furanoside being the invariable product. If a trace of acid is added to methyl 3,6-anhydro-α-glucopyranoside (CCXII), it is converted into the corresponding furanoside (CCXIII). Unless steric factors prevent their formation, as,

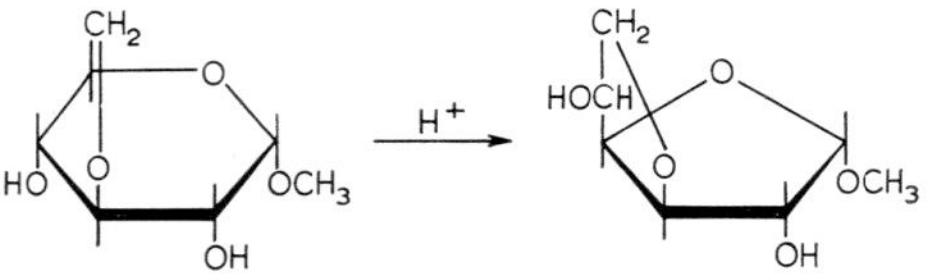

(CCXII)   (CCXIII)

for example, in the galactose series, it is clear that two five-membered rings fused together are more stable than a five- and a six-membered ring.

Besides the 1,2-anhydro-sugars of the internal glycoside type, 1,6-anhydrides known as glycosans (CCXV, CCXVI)[99] are formed on alkaline hydrolysis of phenyl β-glycosides (CCXIV) or by heating polysaccharides

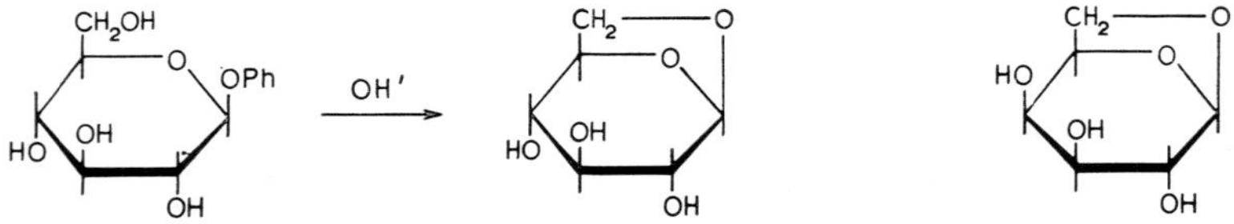

(CCXIV)   (CCXV)   (CCXVI)
β-Glucosan   β-Galactosan
(Laevoglucosan)

such as starch or ivory nut mannan in the dry state under reduced pressure. These anhydrides are often crystalline substances. They are non-reducing, and on heating with dilute acid are hydrolysed back to the free sugar. The products of the pyrolytic vacuum distillation of starch and of galactose contain 1,6-anhydro-β-D-glucofuranose (CCXVII) and -α-D-galactofuranose (CCXVIII) respectively. Whereas the constitution of β-glucosan (CCXV)

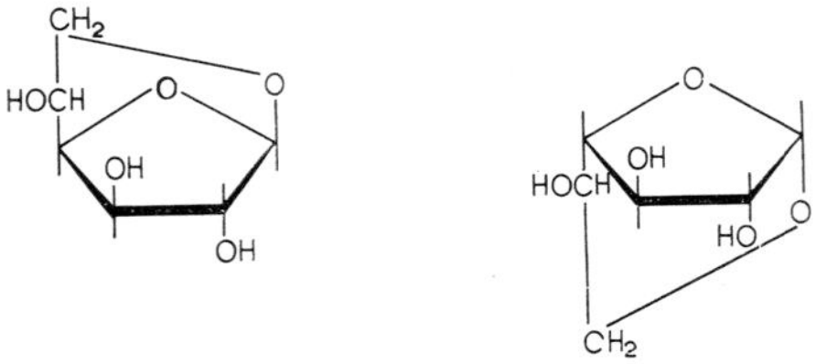

(CCXVII)   (CCXVIII)

was established by reaction with periodate, the two furanose 1,6-anhydrides (CCXVII, CCXVIII), in spite of the presence of adjacent hydroxyl groups on C-2 and C-3, are immune to attack by this reagent.

9. Amino-sugars

The common naturally occurring amino-sugars are glucosamine (2-amino-2-deoxy-D-glucose) (CCXIX) and galactosamine (2-amino-2-deoxy-D-galactose) (CCXXI)[100a]. In addition there are a few unusual examples synthesised by the *Actinomyces* species of moulds, talosamine found in cartilage and a curious C-linked mannosamine (CCXX) present in neuraminic acid. These substances, which are always found in combination, have the normal properties of reducing sugars and form O- and N-derivatives with acylating agents, the latter being considerably more stable than the former. The amino-sugars are readily protonated and form crystalline stable salts. The proximity of the amino group to the potential reducing group makes glycoside formation difficult and it is usual to substitute the amino group before glycosidation. Furthermore glycosaminides with a free amino group are

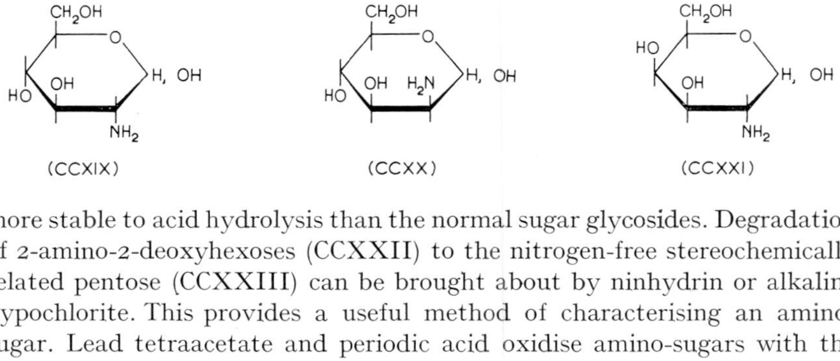

(CCXIX)   (CCXX)   (CCXXI)

more stable to acid hydrolysis than the normal sugar glycosides. Degradation of 2-amino-2-deoxyhexoses (CCXXII) to the nitrogen-free stereochemically related pentose (CCXXIII) can be brought about by ninhydrin or alkaline hypochlorite. This provides a useful method of characterising an amino-sugar. Lead tetraacetate and periodic acid oxidise amino-sugars with the

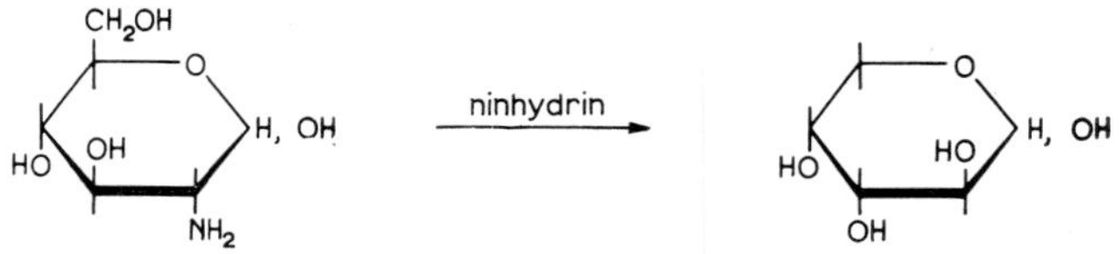

(CCXXII)   (CCXXIII)
D–Glucosamine   D–Arabinose

liberation of ammonia and fission of the C–C link. Careful control of the oxidation conditions is necessary to prevent over-oxidation[100b].

The purple colour given by 2-amino-2-deoxy-sugars with Erhlich's reagent

References p. 63

(p-dimethylamino-benzaldehyde) has been developed as a colorimetric method (Elson-Morgan reaction) for the quantitative estimation of glucos-

$$\begin{array}{c} | \\ \text{CHNH}_2 \\ | \\ \text{CHOH} \\ | \end{array} \xrightarrow{\text{NaIO}_4} \begin{array}{c} | \\ \text{CHO} \\ | \\ \text{CHO} \\ | \end{array} + \text{NH}_3$$

amine and galactosamine[101]. It should be noted that 4-O-methyl-substituted derivatives do not give a purple colour with this reagent.

The amino-sugars will be dealt with more fully in Chapter III.

10. Separation and identification of monosaccharides

(a) Qualitative

There are a number of well-known colour tests for monosaccharides, such as condensation of the acid degradation products[75] with phenolic substances. Perhaps the most frequently cited example of this is the Molisch test in which carbohydrates give a purple colour with α-naphthol in the presence of concentrated sulphuric acid. The presence of ketoses and of 3,6-anhydro-hexoses is often detected by the characteristic red colour rapidly developed with acid resorcinol (Seliwanoff test), and the presence of 2-deoxypentoses may be shown by the deep blue colour they yield with diphenylamine after degradation with acid to 5-hydroxy-levulinaldehyde. Before an individual sugar can be identified, however, it must be isolated as a pure substance in crystalline form or converted to a characteristic crystalline derivative. The derivative the author considers the best for the characterisation of the better known monosaccharides is given in Table I (p. 57).

Until the application of chromatography the separation of individual monosaccharides from a mixture was exceedingly difficult. If present in sufficient quantity in a pure form it is sometimes possible to crystallise out a proportion of a particular sugar from a mixture.

Chromatography[102] has proved an invaluable tool in the detection and separation of monosaccharides. When development is complete, the paper is dried and sprayed with reagents[103] such as aniline phthalate or alkaline silver nitrate which give coloured and black spots respectively at the final positions of the individual sugars in the mixture. Although each sugar has a characteristic rate of movement in a particular solvent, this varies under different conditions, particularly temperature, and it is advisable to run authentic samples of sugars as controls on each chromatogram. Even when

TABLE I

MONOSACCHARIDES OF RELATIVELY COMMON OCCURRENCE IN NATURAL PRODUCTS*

Sugar	m.p.	[α]D	Derivative	m.p.	Free	Occurrence combined
Aldopentose						
L-Arabinose	160°	+105°	Benzoylhydrazone[119]	203°	Heartwood of many conifers	Glycosides, hemicelluloses, gums, green algal and bacterial polysaccharides
D-Ribose	87°	−24°	p-Bromophenyl-hydrazone[20]	164°		Nucleic acids, nucleotides
D-Xylose	145°	+19°	Dibenzylidene dimethyl acetal[121]	211°		Glycoside: primverose; xylan from *Rhodymenia palmata*, and from green alga *Caulerpa filiformis*. In hetero polysaccharides of hemicelluloses, gums, mucilages and spp. of green algae
Ketopentose						
D-Ribulose	syrup	−16°	o-Nitrophenyl-hydrazone[122]	169°		Phosphorylated in animals, plants and yeasts
L-Xylulose	syrup	+35°	p-Bromophenyl-hydrazone[123]	128°	Urine in pentosuria	
Aldohexose						
D-Galactose	165°	+83.5°	Diethyl mercaptal[124]	142°	Ivy berries, galactosaemic blood and urine	Snail and beef galactogen, glycosides with glycerol in certain algae, gangliosides, cerebrosides, milk oligosaccharides, hemicelluloses and mucilages, blood group-specific substances
L-Galactose	165°	−84°	Diethyl mercaptal[124]	142°		Snail galactogen, agar and carrageenin. Flax seed mucilage, and Chagual and other gums

(continued on p. 58)

TABLE I (*continued*)

Sugar	m.p.	[α]$_D$	Derivative	m.p.	Free	Occurrence combined
D-Glucose	83–86° monohydrate	+52°	Dichlorophenyl hydrazone[125]	160°	Fruits, plant juices, honey, blood, cerebrospinal fluid, urine	Many oligosaccharides, notably sucrose, cellulose, starch, glycogen, laminarin, isolichenin and hemicelluloses
D-Mannose	132°	+15°	Phenylhydrazone[126]	199–200°	Small amounts in sphagnum moss and in peat	Mannans Tagua palm seed, *Phytelephas macrocarpa*, tubers of Orchidaceae and in red seaweed, *Porphyra* spp.
D-Talose	128–132°	+20°	Methylphenyl hydrazone[127]	154°		Antibiotic hygromycin B
Ketohexose						
D-Fructose	102–104°	−92°	2,5-Dichlorophenylhydrazone[125] Di-isopropylidene[128]	154°	Fruit juices, blood of foetal ungulates	Oligosaccharides notably sucrose. Inulins and levans
L-Sorbose	159–161°	−43°	2,5-Dichlorophenylhydrazone[125]	117°	Fermented juice	Lichen *Rocella linearis*
D-Tagatose	134–135°	−5°	1,2:3,4-di-isopropylidene[129]	66°		Gum exudate *Sterculia setigera*
Ketoheptose						
D-Mannoheptulose	152°	+29°	p-Bromophenyl-hydrazone[130]	179°	Avocado pear *Persea gratissima*	
Sedoheptulose	Syrup	+2°	Sedoheptulosan[131]	155°	*Sedum* spp. Trace amounts may be present in all green plants	
Deoxy-sugar						
2-Deoxy-D-ribose	97°	−58°	N-Phenylglycosyl-amine (anilide)[132]	174°		Deoxyribonucleic acids

(continued on p. 59)

TABLE I (continued)

Sugar	m.p.	$[\alpha]_D$	Derivative	m.p.	Free	Occurrence combined
L-Fucose	145°	−76°	Methylphenyl-hydrazone[133]	172°		Human milk oligosaccharides. Some bacterial polysaccharides, blood group-specific subs., fucoidin and glycoproteins
L-Rhamnose	94° hydrate	+9°	Benzoyl-hydrazone[119]	186°	Leaves *Rhus toxicodendron* (poison ivy)	Glycosides, gums, mucilages, bacterial and algal polysaccharides
Branched sugar						
Apiose	gum	+9°	Di-*O*-isopropyl-idene[134]	83°		In glycosidic union in Umbelliferae, Compositeae, Leguminoseae families, in *Hevea brasiliensis*, (Euphorbiaceae) and in leaves and fibre of *Posidonia australis*

* For full references, further details and rarer monosaccharides see D. J. BELL in M. FLORKIN AND H. S. MASON (Eds.), *Comparative Biochemistry*, Vol. III, Academic Press, New York, 1962, Chapter 7; *Encyclopedia of Plant Physiology*, W. RUHLAND (Ed.), Springer, Berlin, 1958.

References p. 63

spots with identical speeds developed in a number of different solvents have been obtained from the material and the control, this can only be taken as an indication that a particular sugar is present in a solution. Confirmatory evidence for the identity of a sugar may be obtained from ionophoretograms run in borate or other buffers[104]. Neither of these techniques, however, distinguishes between D- and L-sugars. For complete identification of a sugar it is necessary after separation to convert it into a characteristic crystalline derivative (p. 57) or if crystalline itself it may be characterised by its melting point, optical rotation and X-ray powder diffraction lines.

Preparative separation may be achieved chromatographically on Whatman (3 MM or No. 17) paper or on a column of powdered cellulose. Celite, silicic acid, charcoal and similar substances have also been used as the support for column separation of monosaccharides[105a] and here adsorption plays an important part. In order to obtain good separation, care in the packing of the column and in the choice of absorbent and eluting solution is necessary. If cellulose is utilized then evidence of the best solvent can be obtained from preliminary paper chromatograms. An important recent development has been the use of gas chromatography for the separation of methylated methyl glycosides and of sugar acetates[105b].

(b) Quantitative

A large number of quantitative determinations of sugars based on their reducing power have been developed. Oxidation with Fehling's solution results in the precipitation of cuprous oxide which can be determined iodometrically[106] or spectrophotometrically[107]. The reduction of ferricyanide ions by sugars in alkaline solution has also been developed on a quantitative basis[108]. The quantitative reduction of periodate has also been utilized for determination of monosaccharides[109]. Recent methods involve elution after development of the coloured spot, from a paper chromatogram and photometric determination of the depth of colour[110]. The quantity of sugar is then read off a standard graph prepared by eluting definite weights of the particular sugar on a paper chromatogram. This method has also been extended to the determination of fully and partially methylated sugars[111]. Any method for the determination of sugars must be applied with caution to a biological fluid since interfering substances frequently occur in protein-free filtrates and tissue fluids etc.

The use of radioactive ^{14}C as a tracer for carbohydrates in biological syntheses has been widespread[112]. The distribution of radioactivity among a number of labelled sugars in a mixture of monosaccharides can be of considerable importance to the investigator. The separation of radioactive components and their subsequent localisation by auto-radiographic techniques is well known. This is often a tedious process and a much simpler procedure is the use of an automatic scanning device whereby the activity of individual ^{14}C-labelled sugars in a solution can be measured after development on a paper chromatogram[113].

Radioactive D-glucose and other monosaccharides have been isolated from plants and animals fed with ^{14}C-labelled compounds. Chemical methods for the determination of the position of the ^{14}C in the monosaccharide are based mainly on periodate and lead tetraacetate degradation, conversion of the resulting formaldehyde and formic acid to carbon dioxide and radio assay of this in the form of barium carbonate. As examples of this procedure may be cited oxidation of methyl glucopyranoside (CCXXIV)[114], of potassium glucuronate (CCXXIX)[115] and of D-fructose[116]. Periodate releases C-3 as formic acid from (CCXIV) and this is then converted to carbon dioxide and assayed. The residual dialdehyde can then be oxidised by bromine to the di-acid which is isolated as the strontium salt (CCXXV). Hydrolysis of (CCXXV) with mineral acid yields glyoxylic acid (C-1 and C-2) (CCXXVI) and glyceric acid (C-4, C-5, and C-6) (CCXXVII). Separation of the latter and a second oxidation with periodate yields formaldehyde (from C-6), formic acid (from C-5) and carbon dioxide (from C-4). Heating to 250° of the derived dinitrophenylhydrazone (CCXXVIII) of the glyoxylic acid (CCXVI) gives carbon dioxide (from C-2 of the original glucose).

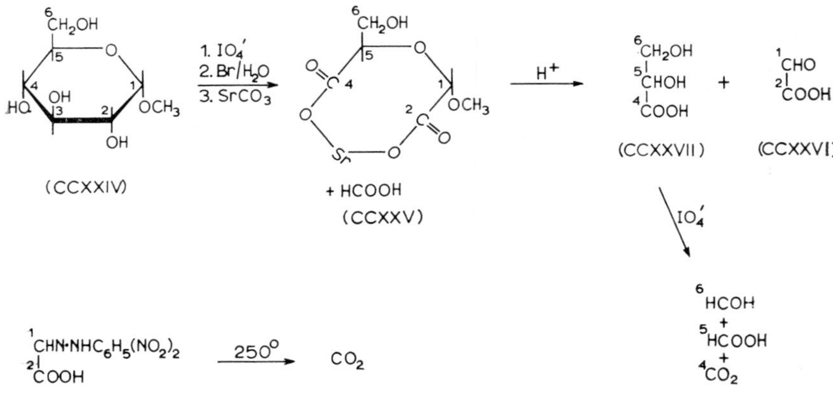

Similar oxidation of potassium gluconate (CCXXIX) and assay of the various fragments determines the radioactivity of C-1, of C-6, and of the combined activity of C-2, C-3, C-4 and C-5.

The German chemists, Weygand, Fehr and Klebe[117] have developed a chemical method for degrading glucose and determining the radioactivity

References p. 63

of each carbon atom which could be applied to all aldo-hexoses and pentoses. Every substance tested was determined by burning to carbon dioxide by means of potassium chlorate and copper oxide.

The location of radioactivity in glucose has also been determined enzymatically[118]. *Leuconostoc mesenteroides* splits glucose into carbon dioxide (C-1), ethanol (C-2 and C-3) and α-hydroxypyruvic acid (C-4, C-5 and C-6). These latter two substances can be degraded stepwise into carbon dioxide so that each carbon atom in glucose is assayed separately. By a series of purely chemical reactions Kohn and Dmuchowski have devised a method for the isolation of each individual carbon atom of glucose as barium carbonate[135]. This procedure could be extended to other sugars.

$$
\begin{array}{ccccc}
\overset{1}{\text{COOK}} & & \overset{1}{\text{CO}_2} \\
| & & \\
\text{H---C---OH} & & + \\
| & & \\
\text{HO---C---H} & & \\
| & \xrightarrow[\text{pH 5.8}]{\text{IO}_4'} & \\
\text{H---C---OH} & & 4\text{HCOOH} \xrightarrow{\text{HgCl}_2} 4\text{CO}_2 \\
| & & \\
\text{H---C---OH} & & + \\
| & & \\
\overset{6}{\text{CH}_2\text{OH}} & & \overset{6}{\text{HCHO}} \longrightarrow \text{HCOOH} \xrightarrow{\text{HgCl}_2} \text{CO}_2 \\
\text{(CCXXIX)}
\end{array}
$$

$$
\begin{array}{llllll}
1 & \text{H---C=O} & \text{CO}_2 & & & \\
  & | & + & & & \\
2 & \text{H---C---OH} & \text{CH}_3 & \text{CH}_3 & \text{CH}_3\text{NH}_2 \longrightarrow \text{CO}_2 \\
  & | & | & | & + \\
3 & \text{HO---C---H} \xrightarrow[\text{mesenteroides}]{\text{Leuconostoc}} & \text{CH}_2\text{OH} & \text{COOH} & \text{CO}_2 \\
  & | & + & & \\
4 & \text{H---C---OH} & \text{COOH} & \text{CO}_2 & \\
  & | & | & + & \\
5 & \text{H---C---OH} & \text{CHOH} \longrightarrow \text{COOH} & \text{CO}_2 \\
  & | & | & | & + \\
6 & \text{CH}_2\text{OH} & \text{CH}_3 & \text{CH}_3 & \text{CH}_3\text{NH}_2 \longrightarrow \text{CO}_2 \\
\end{array}
$$

ACKNOWLEDGEMENT

The author has pleasure in acknowledging her indebtedness to Dr. D. J. Bell for many helpful suggestions and criticisms.

REFERENCES

[1] W. Pigman (Ed.), *The Carbohydrates*, Academic Press, New York, 1957; E. G. V. Percival and E. E. Percival, *Structural Carbohydrate Chemistry*, J. Garnet Miller, London, 1962; F. Micheel and A. Klemer, *Chemie der Zucker und Polysaccharide,* Geest and Portig, Leipzig, 1956.

[2] *Chem. Eng. News*, 31 (1953) 1776.

[3] *J. Chem. Soc.*, (1952) 5108.

[4] K. Kiliani, *Ber.*, 21 (1888) 915; 19 (1886) 3029.

[5] K. Kiliani, *Ber.*, 18 (1885) 3066.

[6] E. Fischer, *Ber.*, 17 (1884) 579.

[7] L. Mester, *Adv. Carbohydrate Chem.*, 13 (1958) 115.

[8] L. F. Fieser and M. Fieser, *Organic Chemistry*, Reinhold, New York, 1956, p. 353.

[9] S. Bayne and J. A. Fewster, *Adv. Carbohydrate Chem.*, 11 (1956) 43.

[10] C. S. Hudson, *J. Org. Chem.*, 9 (1944) 470.

[11] G. P. Ellis, *Adv. Carbohydrate Chem.*, 14 (1959) 63.

[12] G. P. Ellis and John Honeyman, *Adv. Carbohydrate Chem.*, 10 (1955) 95.

[13] J. E. Hodge, *Adv. Carbohydrate Chem.*, 10 (1955) 169.

[14] A. L. Raymond, *Adv. Carbohydrate Chem.*, 1 (1945) 129.

[15] J. M. Bobbit, *Adv. Carbohydrate Chem.*, 11 (1956) 1.

[16] A. S. Perlin, *Adv. Carbohydrate Chem.*, 14 (1959) 9.

[17] W. N. Haworth and C. R. Porter *J. Chem. Soc.*, (1929) 2796; (1930) 649; W. N. Haworth, C. R. Porter and A. C. Waine, *J Chem. Soc.*, (1932) 2254.

[18] T. Purdie and J. C. Irvine, *J. Chem. Soc.*, (1903) 1021.

[19] W. N. Haworth, *J. Chem. Soc.*, (1915) 8.

[20] I. E. Muskat, *J. Am. Chem. Soc.*, 56 (1934) 3653; H. S. Isbell, H. L. Frush, B. H. Bruckner, G. N. Kowkabany and G. Wampler, *Anal. Chem.*, 29 (1957) 1523.

[21] K. Freudenberg and R. M. Hixon, *Ber.*, 56 (1923) 2119.

[22] F. Smith and R. Montgomery in D. Glick (Ed.), *Methods of Biochemical Analysis,* Vol. 3, Interscience, London, 1956, p. 153.

[23] K. Hess and F. Neumann, *Ber.*, 68 (1935) 1371.

[24] S. Allen, T. G. Bonner, E. J. Bourne and N. M. Saville, *Chem. & Ind. (London)*, (1958) 630.

[25] C. M. McCloskey, *Adv. Carbohydrate Chem.*, 12 (1957) 148.

[26] E. Fischer, *Ber.*, 24 (1891) 1836, 2683; C. S. Hudson, *J. Chem. Educ.*, 18 (1941) 353.

[27] T. Reichstein, *Helv. Chim. Acta*, 31 (1948) 1669; 28 (1945) 1.

[28] J. M. Bijvoet, A. F. Peerdeman and A. J. van Bommel, *Nature*, 168 (1951) 271.

[29] E. Fischer, *Untersuchungen über Kohlenhydrate und Fermente*, Springer, Berlin, 1909.

[30] A. P. MacLennan and D. A. L. Davies, *Bull. soc. chim. biol.*, 42 (1960) 1373.

[31] B. L. Horecker and A. H. Mehler, *Ann. Rev. Biochem.*, 24 (1955) 230.

[32] G. R. Noggle in Pigman (Ed.), *Carbohydrates*, Academic Press, New York, 1957, p. 733.

[33] N. K. Richtmyer and J. W. Pratt, *J. Am. Chem. Soc.*, 78 (1956) 4717.

[34] C. S. Hudson, *Adv. Carbohydrate Chem.*, 4 (1949) 57; F. Shafizadeh, *Adv. Carbohydrate Chem.*, 11 (1956) 263; W. G. Overend, *Science Progr.*, 187 (1959) 419.

[35] W. G. Overend and M. Stacey, *Adv. Carbohydrate Chem.*, 8 (1953) 65.

[36] T. Reichstein *et al.*, *Helv. Chim. Acta*, 25 (1942) 1611; 27 (1944) 1203; 31 (1948) 1630, 2061; 33 (1950) 446; 36 (1953) 302.

[37] W. J. Whelan, *Ann. Rev. Biochem.*, 29 (1960) 113; O. Lüderitz, *Bull. soc. chim. biol.*, 42 (1960) 1355.

[38] R. U. Lemieux and M. L. Wolfrom, *Adv. Carbohydrate Chem.*, 3 (1948) 337.

[39] P. W. Kent, *Research (London)*, 3 (1950) 427; R. Kuhn, *Angew. Chem.*, 69 (1957) 23; A. B. Foster and D. Horton, *Adv. Carbohydrate Chem.*, 14 (1959) 214.

[40] G. Blix in Wolfrom (Ed.), *Carbohydrate Chem. of Substances of Biological Interest,* Pergamon, London, 1959, p. 98; A. Gottschalk, *Bull. soc. chim. biol.*, 42 (1960) 1387.

[41] R. Kuhn in Wolfrom (Ed.), *Carbohydrate Chem. of Substances of Biological Interest,* Pergamon, London, 1959, p. 72.

[42] F. Zilliken and M. W. Whitehouse, *Adv. Carbohydrate Chem.*, 13 (1958) 242.

[43] W. N. HAWORTH, *The Constitution of Sugars*, Edward Arnold, London, 1929.
[44] C. S. HUDSON, *J. Am. Chem. Soc.*, 31 (1909) 66.
[45] R. S. CAHN, *J. Chem. Soc.*, (1954) 3702.
[46] C. S. HUDSON, *Adv. Carbohydrate Chem.*, 4 (1949) 57.
[47] T. LOWRY, *Optical Rotatory Power*, Longmans, London, 1935, p. 273.
[48] S. M. CANTOR AND Q. P. PENISTON, *J. Am. Chem. Soc.* 62 (1940) 2113; W. G. OVEREND, A. R. PEACOCKE AND J. B. SMITH, *Chem. & Ind. (Lndon)*, (1957) 113.
[49] C. S. HUDSON, *J. Am. Chem. Soc.*, 31 (1909) 66.
[50] J. CONCHI, G. A. LEVVY AND C. A. MARSH, *Adv. Carbohydrate Chem.*, 12 (1957) 157.
[51] C. E. BALLOU, *Adv. Carbohydrate Chem.*, 9 (1954) 59.
[52] McILROY, *The Plant Glycosides*, Arnold, London, 1951; A. STOLL AND E. JUCKER in RUHLAND (Ed.), *Encyclopedia of Plant Physiology*, Springer, Berlin, 1958, p. 534; S. VEIBEL in RUHLAND (Ed.), *Encyclopedia of Plant Physiology*, Springer, Berlin, 1958, p. 780.
[53] M. KALCKAR, *Biochim. et Biophys. Acta*, 12 (1953) 250.
[54] F. ZILLIKEN AND M. W. WHITEHOUSE, *Adv. Carbohydrate Chem.*, 13 (1958) 242; E. KLENK AND W. GIELEN, *Bull. soc. chim. biol.*, 42 (1960) 1395.
[55] E. CHARGAFF AND J. N. DAVIDSON (Eds.), *Nucleic Acids*, Academic Press, New York, 1955, p. 1; G. R. BARKER, *Adv. Carbohydrate Chem.*, 11 (1956) 285; A. TODD, *Proc. Chem. Soc.*, (1960) 290; P. DOTY, *Biochem. Symposia Cambridge (Engl.)*, 21 (1962) 8.
[56] E. L. HIRST AND C. B. PURVES, *J. Chem. Soc.*, 123 (1923) 1352; E. L. HIRST, *J. Chem. Soc.*, (1926) 350.
[57] J. R. DYER, *Methods of Biochem. Anal.*, 3 (1956) 111; J. M. BOBBIT, *Adv. Carbohydrate Chem.*, 11 (1956) 1; W. J. WHELAN, *Ann. Rev. Biochem.*, 29 (1960) 106; J. E. COURTOIS, *Anales real soc. españ. fis. y quim. (Madrid)*, 56B (1960) 93.
[58] C. F. HUEBNER, S. R. AMES AND E. C. BUBL, *J. Am. Chem. Soc.*, 68 (1946) 1621; C. S. HUDSON *et al.*, *J. Am. Chem. Soc.*, 73 (1951) 3742.
[59] F. SMITH *et al.*, *J. Am. Chem. Soc.*, 79 (1957) 693; 80 (1958) 939, 4681; 82 (1960) 4321.
[60] D. H. R. BARTON AND R. C. COOKSON, *Quart. Rev. (London)*, 10 (1956) 44; W. KLYNE, *Progress in Stereochemistry*, Vol. 1, Butterworth, London, 1954, p. 36.
[61] R. E. REEVES, *Adv. Carbohydrate Chem.*, 6 (1951) 107; R. U. LEMIEUX *et al.*, *J. Am. Chem. Soc.*, 80 (1958) 6098; J. HONEYMAN AND C. J. G. SHAW, *J. Chem. Soc.*, (1959) 2454. R. J. FERRIER AND W. G. OVEREND, *Quart. Revs. (London)*, 13 (1959) 265.
[62] S. J. ANGYAL AND J. A. MILLS, *Rev. of Pure and Applied Chem. (Australia)*, 2 (1952) 185.
[63] J. A. MILLS, *Adv. Carbohydrate Chem.*, 10 (1955) 1.
[64] C. S. HUDSON, *Adv. Carbohydrate Chem.*, 1 (1945) 2.
[65] J. C. SOWDEN, *Adv. Carbohydrate Chem.*, 6 (1951) 291.
[66] A. WOHL, *Ber.*, 26 (1893) 730; F. WEYGAND AND R. LÖWENFELD, *Ber.*, 83 (1950) 559.
[67] M. R. A. WEERMAN, *Rec. trav. chim.*, 37 (1917) 16; O. RUFF, *Ber.*, 32 (1899), 553, 3672; D. L. MacDONALD AND H. O. L. FISCHER, *J. Am. Chem. Soc.*, 74 (1952) 2087.
[68] C. SCHÖPF AND H. WILD, *Ber.*, 87 (1954) 1571; G. W. HUFFMAN, B. A. LEWIS, F. SMITH AND D. R. SPRIESTERSBACH, *J. Am. Chem. Soc.*, 77 (1955) 4346.
[69] A. S. PERLIN *et al.*, *J. Am. Chem. Soc.*, 76 (1954) 2595; *Can. J. Chem.*, 34 (1956) 541.
[70] M. L. WOLFROM, R. L. BROWN AND E. F. EVANS, *J. Am. Chem. Soc.*, 65 (1943) 1021.
[71] E. FISCHER AND I. W. FAY, *Ber.*, 28 (1895) 1975.
[72] C. A. LOBRY DE BRUYN AND W. ALBERDA VAN ECKENSTEIN, *Rec. trav. chim.*, 14 (1895) 203; J. C. SPECK JR., *Adv. Carbohydrate Chem.*, 13 (1958) 63.
[73] J. C. SOWDEN, *Adv. Carbohydrate Chem.*, 12 (1957) 35.
[74] W. WHELAN, *Ann. Rev. Biochem.*, 29 (1960) 111.
[75] F. H. NEWTH, *Adv. Carbohydrate Chem.*, 6 (1951) 83; E. F. L. ANET, *Chem. & Ind. (London)*, (1962) 262.
[76] G. P. ELLIS, *Adv. Carbohydrate Chem.*, 14 (1959) 63.
[77] H. S. ISBELL AND W. W. PIGMAN, *J. Research Natl. Bur. Standards*, 10 (1933) 337; 18 (1937) 141; I. R. L. BARKER, W. G. OVEREND AND C. W. REES, *Chem. & Ind. (London)*, (1960) 1297, 1298.
[78] C. S. HUDSON, *J. Am. Chem. Soc.*, 32 (1910) 338.
[79] G. A. LEVVY AND C. A. MARSH, *Adv. Carbohydrate Chem.*, 14 (1959) 411.

[80] R. A. Edington and E. Percival, *J. Chem. Soc.*, (1953) 2473.

[81] H. S. Isbell and H. Frush, *J. Amer. Chem. Soc.*, 78 (1956) 2844; M. L. Wolfrom and H. B. Wood, *J. Am. Chem. Soc.*, 73 (1951) 2933.

[82] P. D. Bragg and L. Hough, *J. Chem. Soc.*, (1957) 4348.

[83] R. Lohmar and R. M. Goepp Jr., *Adv. Carbohydrate Chem.*, 4 (1949) 211; L. F. Wiggins, *Adv. Carbohydrate Chem.*, 5 (1950) 191.

[84] S. A. Barker and E. J. Bourne, *Adv. Carbohydrate Chem.*, 7 (1952) 137.

[85] C. S. Hudson, *J. Ind. Eng. Chem.*, 8 (1916) 380; R. Barker, *J. Org. Chem.*, 25 (1960) 1670; V. Prey and A. Aszalos, *Monatsh. Chem.*, 91 (1960) 729.

[86] M. L. Wolfrom, *J. Am. Chem. Soc.*, 51 (1929) 2188.

[87] L. J. Haynes and F. H. Newth, *Adv. Carbohydrate Chem.*, 10 (1955) 207.

[88] R. S. Tipson, *Adv. Carbohydrate Chem.*, 8 (1953) 108.

[89] R. Allerton and W. G. Overend, *J. Chem. Soc.*, (1954) 2629.

[90] H. Schmid and P. Karrer, *Helv. Chim. Acta*, 32 (1949) 1371.

[91] A. B. Foster and W. G. Overend, *Quart. Revs. (London)*, 11 (1957) 61.

[92] L. Hough and J. K. N. Jones, *Adv. Carbohydrate Chem.*, 11 (1956) 185.

[93] J. M. Anderson and E. Percival, *J. Chem. Soc.*, (1956) 814.

[94] D. M. Brown, D. I. Magrath and A. R. Todd, *J. Chem. Soc.*, (1952) 2708.

[95] D. J. Bell, *J. Chem. Soc.*, (1947) 1461.

[96] K. Freudenberg, H. Toepffer and C. C. Andersen, *Ber.*, 61 (1928) 1750.

[97] S. Peat, *Adv. Carbohydrate Chem.*, 2 (1947) 137.

[98] R. U. Lemieux and G. Huber, *J. Am. Chem. Soc.*, 75 (1953) 4118.

[99] R. J. Dimler, *Adv. Carbohydrate Chem.*, 7 (1952) 37.

[100a] P. W. Kent and M. W. Whitehouse, *Biochemistry of the Amino Sugars*, Butterworth, London, 1955; A. B. Foster and D. Horton, *Adv. Carbohydrate Chem.*, 14 (1959) 213; W. J. Whelan, *Ann. Rev. Biochem.*, 29 (1960) 114.

[100b] M. Cantley and L. Hough, *Biochem. J.*, 77 (1960) 6P.

[101] K. Paech and M. V. Tracey (Eds.), *Modern Methods of Plant Analysis*, Vol. 2, Springer, Berlin, 1955, p. 269.

[102] N. Kowkatany, *Adv. Carbohydrate Chem.*, 9 (1954) 304; A. B. Foster, *Ann. Rev. Biochem.*, 30 (1961) 45.

[103] D. J. Bell in K. Paech and M. V. Tracey (Eds.), *Modern Methods of Plant Analysis*, Vol. 2, Springer, Berlin, 1955, p. 1; R. W. Bailey and E. J. Bourne, *J. Chromatog.*, 4 (1960) 206.

[104] A. B. Foster, *Adv. Carbohydrate Chem.*, 12 (1957) 81; B. A. Lewis and F. Smith, *J. Am. Chem. Soc.*, 79 (1957) 3929.

[105a] W W. Binkley, *Adv. Carbohydrate Chem.*, 10 (1955) 55.

[105b] C. T. Bishop and F P. Cooper, *Can. J. Chem.*, 38 (1960) 388; H. W. Kircher, *Anal. Chem.*, 32 (1960) 1103; S. W. Gunner, J. K. N. Jones and M. B. Perry, *Can. J. Chem.*, 39 (1961) 1892; R. J. Ferrier, *Chem. & Ind. (London)*, (1961) 831.

[106] M. Somogyi, *J. Biol. Chem.*, 160 (1945) 61.

[107] N. Nelson, *J. Biol. Chem.*, 153 (1944) 375.

[108] H. C. Hagedorn and B. H. Jensen, *Biochem. Z.*, 135 (1923) 46; C. S. Hanes, *Biochem. J.*, 23 (1929) 99.

[109] E. L. Hirst and J. K. N. Jones, *J. Chem. Soc.*, (1949) 1659.

[110] C. M. Wilson, *Anal. Chem.*, 31 (1959) 1199.

[111] W. C. Schaefer and J. W. van Cleve, *Anal. Chem.*, 28 (1956) 1290.

[112] S. Gurin, *Adv. Carbohydrate Chem.*, 3 (1948) 229; S. Aranoff, A. Benson, W. Z. Hassid and M. Calvin, *Science*, 105 (1947) 664; J. C. Sowden, *Science*, 109 (1949) 229; H. L. Frush and H. S. Isbell, *J. Research Natl. Bur. Standards*, 50 (1953) 133.

[113] R. Roberts and F. J. Carleton, *Anal. Chem.*, 28 (1956) 11.

[114] B. Boothroyd, S. A. Brown, J. A. Thorn and A. C. Neish, *Can. J. Biochem. and Physiol.*, 33 (1955) 62; M. J. Abercrombie and J. K. N. Jones, *Can. J. Chem.*, 38 (1960) 1999.

[115] F. Eisenberg Jr., *J. Am. Chem. Soc.*, 76 (1954) 5152.

[116] C. Brice and A. S. Perlin, *Can. J. Biochem. and Physiol.*, 35 (1957) 7.

[117] F. Weygand, K. Fehr and J. F. Klebe, *Z. Naturforsch.*, 146 (1959) 217.

[118] J. EDELMAN, V. GINSBURG AND W. Z. HASSID, *J. Biol. Chem.*, 213 (1955) 843.
[119] E. L. HIRST, J. K. N. JONES AND F. A. WOODS, *J. Chem. Soc.*, (1947) 1048.
[120] P. A. LEVENE AND R. S. TIPSON, *J. Biol. Chem.*, 115 (1936) 731.
[121] J. K. N. JONES AND L. J. BREDDY, *J. Chem. Soc.*, (1945) 738.
[122] C. GLATTHAAR AND T. REICHSTEIN, *Helv. Chim. Acta*, 18 (1935) 80.
[123] L. VON VARGHA, *Ber.*, 68 (1935) 24.
[124] M. L. WOLFROM, *J. Am. Chem. Soc.*, 52 (1930) 2466.
[125] I. MENDL AND C. NEUBERG, *Arch. Biochem. Biophys.*, 35 (1952) 326.
[126] C. L. BUTLER AND L. H. CRETCHER, *J. Am. Chem. Soc.*, 53 (1931) 4358.
[127] P. A. LEVENE AND R. S. TIPSON, *J. Biol. Chem.*, 93 (1931) 631.
[128] D. J. BELL, *J. Chem. Soc.*, (1947) 1461.
[129] T. REICHSTEIN AND W. BOSSHARD, *Helv. Chim. Acta*, 17 (1934) 753.
[130] F. B. LaFORGE, *J. Biol. Chem.*, 28 (1917) 511.
[131] F. B. LaFORGE AND C. S. HUDSON, *J. Biol. Chem.*, 30 (1917) 61.
[132] R. E. DERIAZ, W. G. OVEREND, M. STACEY, E. G. TEECE AND L. F. WIGGINS, *J. Chem. Soc.*, (1949) 1879.
[133] W. A. P. BLACK *et al.*, *J. Soc. Chem. Ind. (London)*, 69 (1950) 317.
[134] D. J. BELL, N. E. HARDWICK, F. A. ISHERWOOD AND R. S. CAHN, *J. Chem. Soc.*, (1954) 3702.
[135] P. KOHN AND B. L. DMUCHOWSKI, *J. Biol. Chem.*, 235 (1960) 1867.

Chapter II

Aldonic, Uronic, Oxoaldonic and Ascorbic Acids

ELIZABETH PERCIVAL

Chemistry Department, University of Edinburgh (Great Britain)

Aldoses and reducing oligosaccharides are relatively easily oxidised without loss of carbon to acids, and four types of acidic monosaccharides, namely aldonic, *oxo*aldonic, hexuronic, and ascorbic acids, have been isolated from natural environments.

1. Aldonic acids[1]

Aldonic acids (II) are the products of the oxidation of the aldehydic or hemiacetal group $(+)$ of an aldose sugar (I). D-Gluconic acid as its 6-phos-

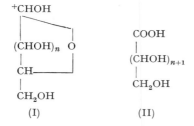

(I)   (II)

phate occurs as a metabolic intermediate in animals, plants, and micro-organisms, and the free acid is frequently found as a product of the aerobic oxidation of glucose by glucose oxidases present in many fungi and bacteria[2].

(a) Preparation of aldonic acids

(i) From natural products

Many organisms, as has been stated, will oxidise glucose to gluconic acid. From the mycelia or culture media, in which have been grown such fungi as *Penicillium luteum*, *Aspergillus niger* and *Penicillium notatum*, the oxidising enzyme has been isolated. *Pseudomonas ovalis* grown on 10% glucose solution converts 92% of the substrate to gluconic acid[3]. The enzyme action is specific and has been used for the detection and estimation of D-glucose in the presence of other sugars[4].

(ii) Chemical syntheses

(1) The most widely used chemical method of preparation of these acids is oxidation of the parent sugar with bromine water or nitric acid, the latter under mild conditions. Oxidation with bromine was first carried out in 1861 by Hlaswetz[5]. This oxidation of aldoses, and in particular of glucose (because of the wide commercial use of gluconic acid), has been studied by many workers. The standard method is that of Kiliani and Kleeman[6] in which yields of 50–70% of the various acids are obtained. Unchanged aldose, always present in the final solution, hinders crystallisation of the derived acid, and isolation is usually achieved by conversion to a salt and crystallisation or alcoholic precipitation of the latter. The acids are not readily extracted from aqueous solution, and their salts are usually water-soluble. The removal of hydrobromic acid as it is formed by the addition of calcium carbonate accelerates the oxidation by bromine and the best yields have been obtained by the use of bromine in a buffered solution at pH 5–6 produced by the addition of calcium or barium benzoate[7]. If the reaction is allowed to go on for 40–50 days over-oxidation occurs with the production in low yields of 5-oxo-acids[8] (see p. 83).

Essentially the same reaction is induced by electrolytic oxidation in the presence of calcium carbonate and a small amount of bromide as catalyst, the latter being constantly converted to bromine[9].

Generally α-isomers are oxidised much more slowly than the β-isomers and Barker, Overend and Rees[10] consider that the α-form of the sugar is anomerised to the β-form before it is oxidised, and it is the anomerisation which is the rate-determining step. It is interesting that the oxidation of D-glucose by glucose oxidase is considered to involve the β-anomer.

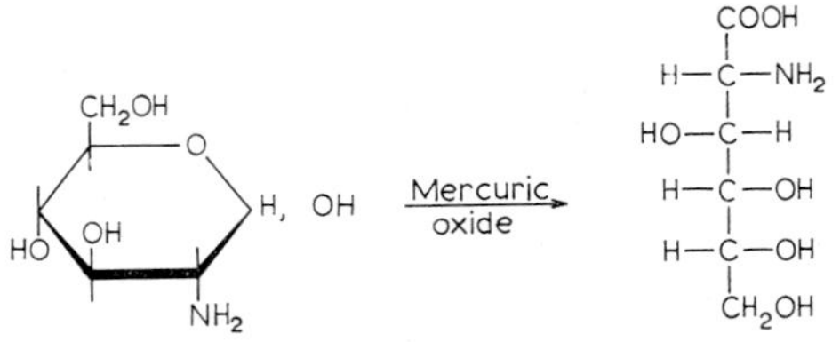

It has been found that L-rhamnose and 2-amino-2-deoxy-D-glucose (III) are oxidised more slowly than the other aldoses, and in the case of the latter substance mercuric oxide is the preferred oxidant[11a], a 62% yield of glucos-aminic acid (IV) being obtained.

The oxidation of disaccharides and trisaccharides, for example, lactose (V) to lactobionic acid (VI), has proved of value in structural studies since hydrolysis yields an aldose (VII) and an aldonic acid (VIII), the latter being

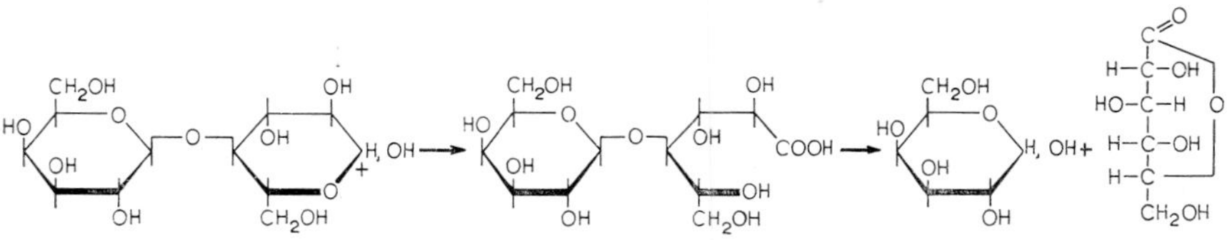

(V)   (VI)   (VII)   (VIII)

derived from the residue which carried the free reducing group (+) in the parent disaccharide. The separation of gluconic acid (VIII) from the products of oxidation of lactose proved that it was not the glucose but the galactose (VII) residue which was glycosidically linked in lactose.

It is apparently the ring forms of the aldoses that are oxidised under these conditions. Pyranoses yield initially δ-lactones (X) and furanoses γ-lactones (XI): both types of lactone may be described as intramolecular esters. In

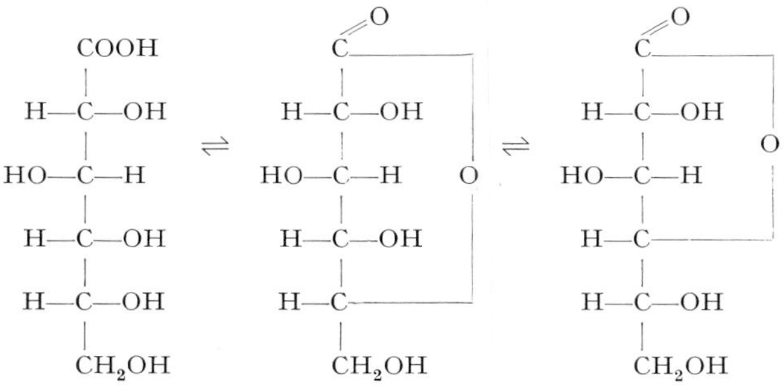

(IX)   (X)   (XI)

solution the aldonic acids (IX) and the lactones (X, XI) equilibrate to a mixture of all three forms, the relative proportions of which depend upon the particular sugar. The final equilibrium is also affected by the concentration, pH, and temperature of the solution. Equilibrium is reached slowly at room temperature and may take weeks but the process is accelerated by the presence of H_3O^+. The more rapid hydrolysis of δ-lactones in comparison with the γ-lactones provides a method for their identification (see Chapter I, pp. 2, 42). Infrared also permits a differentiation between these two types of lactone[11b]. The free aldonic acid may be isolated by concentration of the aqueous solution at low temperatures. D-Gluconic acid has m.p. 131°, $[\alpha]_D$ —6.7°. It is very soluble in water and moderately soluble in alcohol. The lactones are formed on dehydration by distillation with butanol or dioxane or by heating to 70–100° in high vacuum[12]. They can be recrystallised from anhydrous solvents. δ-Gluconolactone is a white odourless powder, m.p. 153°, $[\alpha]_D$ +61.7°. The γ-lactone has m.p. 136°, $[\alpha]_D$ +68°. In glucosaminic acid (IV) lactone formation does not occur unless the amino group is substituted.

(2) Oxidation of aldoses with alkaline hypoiodite under carefully controlled conditions can lead to a stoichiometric yield of aldonic acids. This reaction has been used both as a measure of the amount of aldose present in a solution and for the preparation of aldonic acids. Determination of the iodine con-

$$RCHO + I_2 + 3NaOH \longrightarrow RCOONa + 2NaI + 2H_2O$$

sumed is a quantitative measurement of the aldehydic group and hence of the amount of aldose present[13]. Moore and Link[14] prepared a number of aldonic acids in good yield by oxidation of methanol solutions of the aldoses with potassium hypoiodite.

(3) Aldonic acids may also be prepared from an aldose with one carbon atom less by the Kiliani cyanhydrin synthesis (see Chapter I, p. 37). A new asymmetric centre is produced and two epimeric acids in varying amounts[15].

Oxidation of ketoses leads to cleavage of the carbon chain, sometimes with the formation of lower aldonic acids, or more generally to extensive degradation.

(b) *Properties of the aldonic acids*

Aldonic acids and lactones are stable substances which are not degraded by mineral acid to furfural etc., and they possess all those properties of the parent sugars associated with the alcoholic hydroxyl groups. They are optically active substances, the acids mostly have small rotations, but the lactones, because of ring formation, possess considerably larger rotations. Hudson[16] correlated the rotation of a large number of these derivatives and found that the stereochemistry of the hydroxyl groups at C-4 and C-5 have a strong influence on the rotations of the lactones. From this he formulated the "lactone rule" that if the hydroxyl group involved in lactone formation lies on the right side in the Fischer projection formula then the lactone is more dextrorotatory than the free acid. If the hydroxyl group is on the left then the lactone will be more laevorotatory. D-Galactonic acid has laevorotatory γ-(XII) and dextrorotatory (XIII) δ-lactones and D-gulono-γ-lactone (XIV) is laevorotatory. This rule has proved of value in

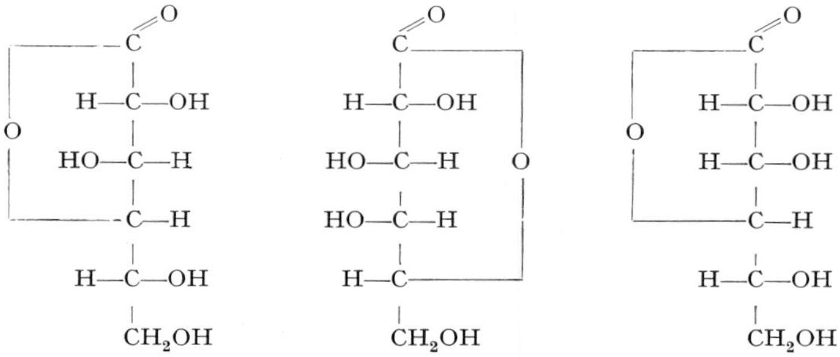

$$
\begin{array}{ccc}
\text{(XII)} & \text{(XIII)} & \text{(XIV)} \\
[\alpha]_D -78° & [\alpha]_D +166° & [\alpha]_D -55°
\end{array}
$$

configurational studies especially in the allocation of structure to new acids formed by the cyanhydrin synthesis (see Chapter 1, p. 37).

By heating an aldonic acid in aqueous pyridine or quinoline it is partially converted into the C-2 epimeric acid. Thus D-mannonic acid (XV) may be transformed into D-gluconic acid (XVI).

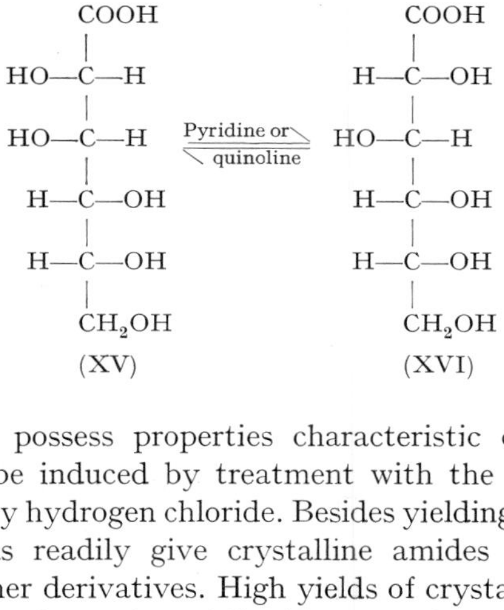

Pyridine or quinoline

(XV)   (XVI)

Aldonic acids also possess properties characteristic of carboxylic acids. Esterification can be induced by treatment with the appropriate alcohol containing 2–5 % dry hydrogen chloride. Besides yielding crystalline lactones and salts the acids readily give crystalline amides (XVII), hydrazides (XIX, XX) and other derivatives. High yields of crystalline amides (XVII) can be prepared by the action of liquid ammonia on the aldonolactones or the corresponding esters. Crystalline phenylhydrazides (XIX, XX) are formed by refluxing the lactone (XVIII) or acid with ethanol–benzene (2:1) for 10 h with a slight excess of freshly distilled phenylhydrazine. After removal of the solvent by evaporation the product generally crystallises. The configuration of C-2 affects the rotation of these acyclic derivatives. The amides and phenylhydrazides are dextrorotatory when the hydroxyl group

References p. 94

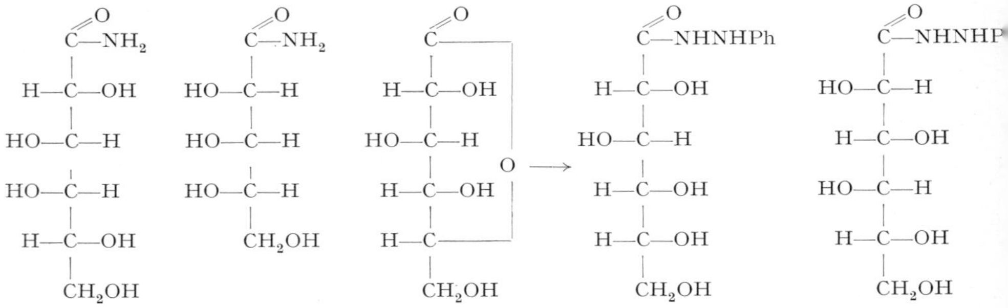

$\overset{O}{\overset{\parallel}{C}}-NH_2$	$\overset{O}{\overset{\parallel}{C}}-NH_2$	$\overset{O}{\overset{\parallel}{C}}-\!\!-\!\!-$	$\overset{O}{\overset{\parallel}{C}}-NHNHPh$	$\overset{O}{\overset{\parallel}{C}}-NHNHP$
H—C—OH	HO—C—H	H—C—OH	H—C—OH	HO—C—H
HO—C—H	HO—C—H	HO—C—H	HO—C—H	H—C—OH
HO—C—H	HO—C—H	H—C—OH	H—C—OH	HO—C—H
H—C—OH	CH$_2$OH	H—C—$\quad$	H—C—OH	H—C—OH
CH$_2$OH		CH$_2$OH	H—C—OH	H—C—OH
			CH$_2$OH	CH$_2$OH
(a)	(b)			
D-galacton-amide	L-ribonamide	D-glucono-lactone	D-gluconic phenylhydrazide	D-idonic phenylhydrazide
$[\alpha]_D +37°$	$[\alpha]_D -16°$		$[\alpha]_D +12°$	$[\alpha]_D -12.4°$
	(XVII)	(XVIII)	(XIX)	(XX)

on this carbon atom lies to the right in the Fischer projection formula and laevorotatory if it lies to the left[17]. For example, D-galactonamide (XVIIa) has $[\alpha]_D +37°$ and L-ribonamide (XVIIb) $[\alpha]_D -16°$. It follows that these derivatives may be used to establish the configuration of C-2. Regeneration of the lactone (XVIII) from the hydrazide (XIX) is induced by treatment with nitrous anhydride[18].

The acids may also be characterised as the crystalline benzimidazole derivative[19] (XXI) which is an optically active base and could be used for resolution of racemic mixtures.

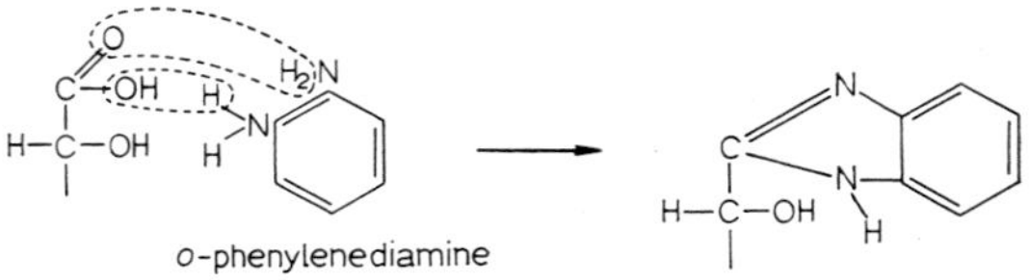

o-phenylenediamine

(XXI)

(c) Detection and estimation of aldonic acids

Chromatographic analysis of a solution of an aldonic acid reveals the presence of both acid and lactone if present, the latter being represented by the faster moving spot. Aldonic acids, amides, lactones and esters can be detected on a paper chromatogram in the form of their hydroxamic acid derivatives[20].

There is no well known method for the determination of aldonic acids. Several reactions might be utilised on a quantitative basis. The reduction of periodate by these acids has been measured, as has the enhanced optical rotation induced by the presence of the molybdate ion[21]. Cohen and Raff[22] using a specifically adapted strain of *Escherischia coli* describe a manometric method for the determination of D-gluconic acid on the μg scale.

(d) Uses of gluconic acid[23]

Gluconic acid is important in the pharmaceutical, food, animal feeding stuffs and general chemical industries. In the form of its salts, which are very soluble, it is a means of introducing trace elements into the diet. Ferrous gluconate, again soluble and devoid of any inorganic anions, is used in the treatment of iron-deficiency anaemia, and calcium gluconate can be given in cases of calcium deficiency. Gluconic acid besides finding use as an acid catalyst in the textile industry has also proved of value in the detergent and leather industries.

2. Uronic acids[24]

Uronic acids (**XXIII**) are derived from the aldoses (**XXII**) by oxidation of the terminal CH_2OH group to COOH. These acids have not so far been

$$
\begin{array}{ccc}
\text{CHO} & & \text{CHO} \\
| & & | \\
(\text{CHOH})_n & \longrightarrow & (\text{CHOH})_n \\
| & & | \\
\text{CH}_2\text{OH} & & \text{COOH} \\
(\textbf{XXII}) & & (\textbf{XXIII})
\end{array}
$$

found free in nature, but a number of them exist in glycosidic union in natural environments. D-Glucuronic acid is a common constituent of animal

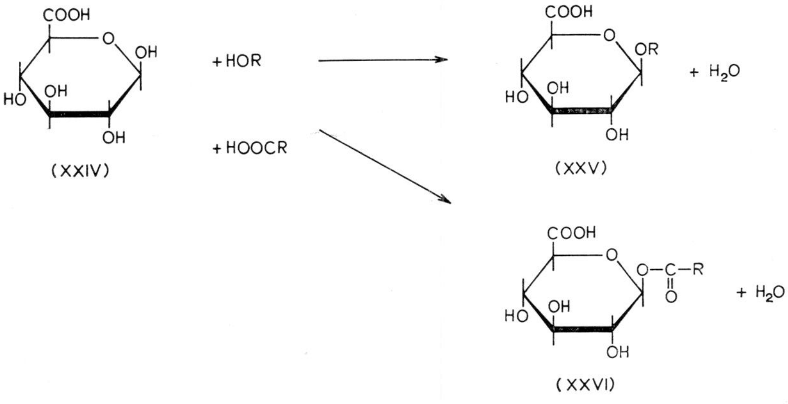

polysaccharides (polyuronides, mucopolysaccharides), with the exception of glycogen, and of glycoproteins. Animals can utilize D-glucuronic acid as a means of eliminating certain types of substance, such as phenols, sterols and aromatic carboxylic acids, some of which may be toxic, by generating a glycosidic link between a hydroxyl or carboxyl group and the glucuronic acid (XXIV). The product, a glucosiduronic acid (XXV, XXVI), is then excreted in the urine[25]. A molecule of water is eliminated in the glucuronoside formation. From the available evidence[26] it appears that *in vivo* the glucuronic acid is linked with uridine-diphosphate (UDP), and that glucosiduronic acid formation generally occurs according to the equation

$$\text{UDP-glucuronic acid} + \text{ROH} \longrightarrow \text{UDP} + \text{RO-glucuronic acid}$$

in which ROH may be regarded as the acceptor molecule. The reaction can then be regarded as a diversion from the synthesis of mucopolysaccharides to that of glucuronosides. The union in the latter is always by a β-linkage and the glucuronic acid is therefore readily liberated by β-glucuronosidases.

In the plant kingdom, either as the unsubstituted acid or its 4-O-methyl ether, D-glucuronic acid is a constituent of some of the so-called "xylan hemicelluloses", many bacterial polysaccharides, gum exudates, and green algal polysaccharides. D-Galacturonic acid forms the building unit of pectic acid (where some of the carboxyl groups may be esterified by methyl) and is also present with neutral sugars in many mucilages, and in a number of bacterial polysaccharides. Alginic acid, the major constituent of the brown seaweeds, comprises D-mannuronic acid residues together with variable amounts of L-guluronic acid. With the exception of L-iduronic acid which has been found in the animal polysaccharide, chondroitin sulphate B (β-heparin), these are the only uronic acids which have so far been found to occur in natural products.

(a) *Preparation of uronic acids*

(i) *From natural products*

The isolation of these acids from polyuronides by chemical means is difficult. The uronosyl (pyranosyluronic) link (XLIII, XLIV) (p. 78), is very resistant to acid hydrolysis and the drastic conditions necessary to break this linkage (prolonged action of $2\,N$ sulphuric acid at $100°$) degrades the uronic acid as it is released. In some instances 98% formic acid has proved to be a more satisfactory hydrolytic agent. Hydrolysis with the appropriate enzymes may be achieved. Indeed, D-galacturonic acid has been prepared from pectic acid by the use of enzymes.

Williams[27] prepared D-glucuronic acid biosynthetically by administering large doses of menthol to rabbits (3 g/rabbit) and separating the resulting glucosiduronate from the urine as the ammonium methyl glucosiduronate (25 g being obtained from six rabbits). Glucuronic acid may be isolated from this salt on treatment with acids. Glucosiduronates can also be isolated as the basic lead salt, and the glucuronic acid liberated with hydrogen sulphide.

(ii) Chemical synthesis

There are two general methods for the chemical syntheses of these acids (XXVIII), either reduction of the appropriate monolactone of an aldaric acid[28] (XXIX), or the oxidation of the primary alcoholic group of an aldose[28] (XXVII).

(XXVII) (XXVIII) (XXIX)

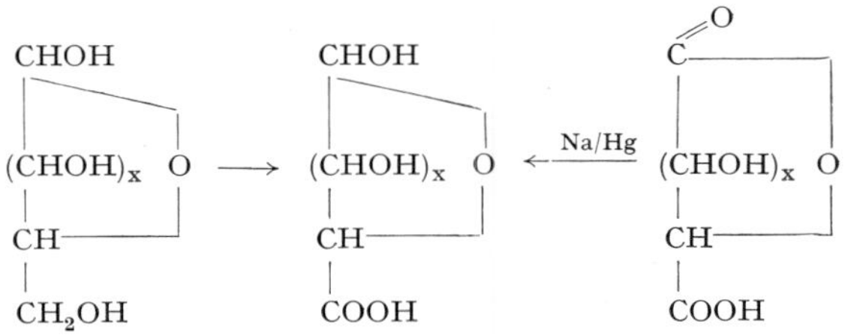

Reduction can be achieved by sodium amalgam in acid solution, D-glucosaccharolactone (XXX) yielding D-glucuronolactone (XXXI). Difficulty in obtaining good yields is probably due to the fact that the glucosaccharolactone is a mixture of 1,4- (XXX) and 3,6- (XXXII) lactones.

(XXX) (XXXI) (XXXII)

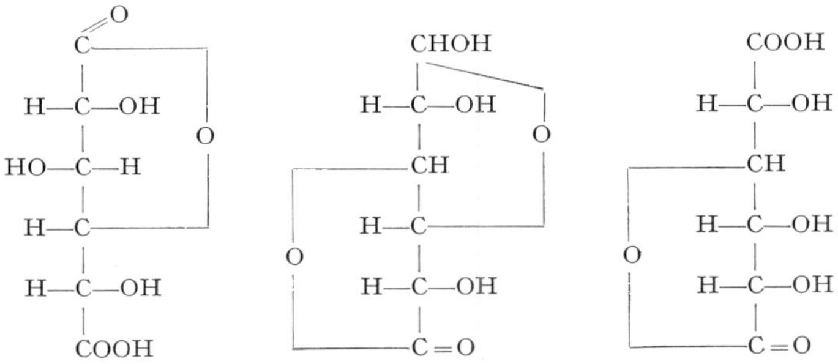

The alternative method for the preparation of uronic acids, the oxidation of aldoses, has been more widely used. This requires that the reaction be limited to the primary hydroxyl group and may be achieved either by protecting the secondary hydroxyl groups by substitution with different residues, or by the use of selective oxidants.

References p. 94

Potassium permanganate, a much used non-specific oxidant, requires that the other hydroxyl groups are protected. The protecting groups must be readily removable in order that degradation of the uronic acid may be avoided. Two types of substituents have been utilised. Isopropylidene, benzylidene and ethylidene residues, which are acid-labile and acetyl and benzoyl residues which are readily hydrolysed by alkali are suitable substituents. In the former examples the oxidations are carried out under neutral or alkaline conditions. A 70% yield of D-galacturonic acid (XXXIV) has been obtained by oxidation of 1,2:3,4-di-O-isopropylidene-D-galactose (XXXIII) with potassium permanganate in potassium hydroxide solution[29]. Oxidation of aldose acetates or benzoates is carried out with potassium permanganate in the presence of acetic acid. An 85% yield of tri-O-benzoyl-mannuronic acid (XXXVI) may be obtained by oxidation of methyl 2,3,4-tri-O-benzoyl-α-D-mannoside (XXXV) under these conditions[30].

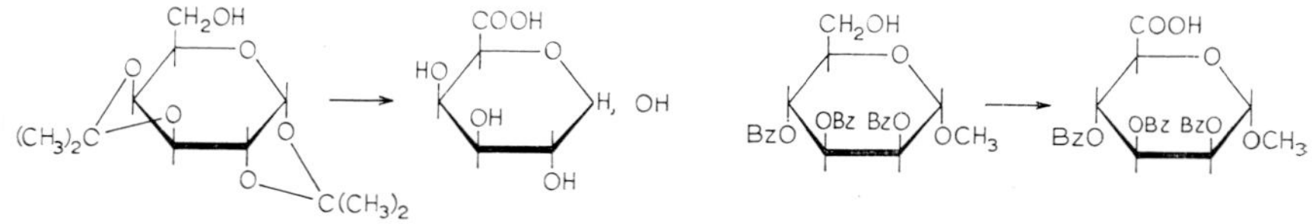

(XXXIII)   (XXXIV)   (XXXV)   (XXXVI)

Catalytic oxidation of partially substituted aldoses has also proved moderately satisfactory. An overall yield of 30% of D-glucuronolactone (XXXVIII) from D-glucose was obtained by catalytic oxidation of 1,2-O-isopropylidene-α-D-glucofuranose[31] (XXXVII) utilising a platinum-activated carbon

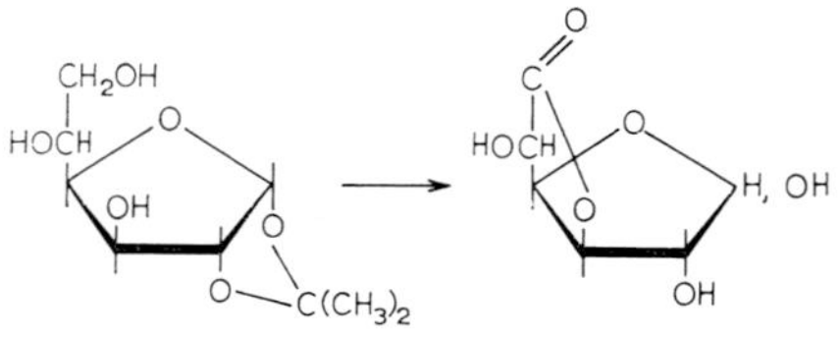

(XXXVII)   (XXXVIII)

catalyst and alkaline solution pH 8–9. α-D-Glucuronic acid 1-phosphate has been prepared by catalytic oxidation of glucose 1-phosphate and the β-isomer from acetobromoglucuronic acid methyl ester and silver phosphate[32].

Low yields of uronic acid usually result from the action of selective oxidants on glucosides and non-reducing acetals of the aldoses in which all the hydroxyl groups are free. However, a 56% yield of D-galacturonoside has been claimed for the oxidation of methyl α-D-galactopyranoside with nitrogen dioxide[33].

(b) *Properties of uronic acids*

The uronic acids possess many of the properties of the parent sugars. They exist as α- (**XXXIXa**) and β- (**XXXIXb**) anomers, and in pyranose (**XXXIXa**) and furanose (**XXXIXb**) forms. If it is stereochemically possible

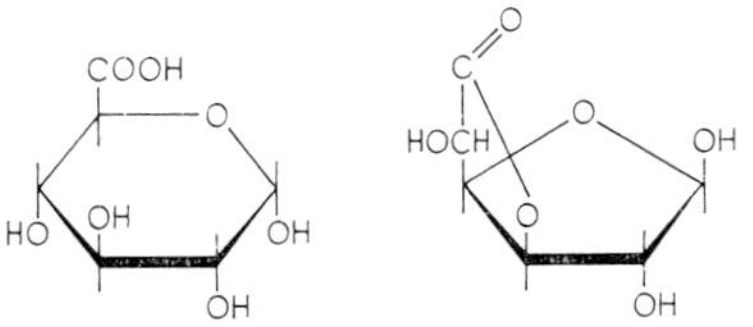

(XXXIX)   (XL)

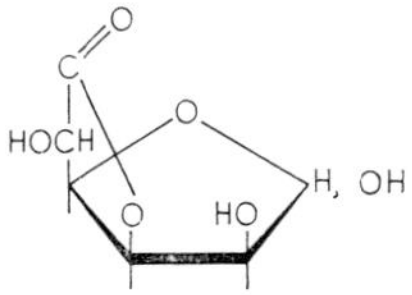

they tend to be converted to lactones. In fact glucuronic acid and mannuronic acid are generally isolated as the crystalline furanuronic 3,6-lactones, glucurone (**XXXIXb**), and mannurone (**XL**) depicted here as the furanuronic 3,6-lactone, but definite proof of this structure is still awaited. In the case of galacturonic acid, lactonisation is not easy since furanoid rings are difficult to accommodate, and a derivative containing a 5- and a 6-membered ring would be unstable.

Certain reactions typical of aldoses are less easily applicable to the uronic acids because of the modifying effect of the carboxylic group. The important nitrogen derivatives, including osazones, hydrazones and arylglycosylamines are less satisfactory for the characterisation of uronic acids. Such derivatives are apparently a mixture of the desired product with the corresponding amine salt or amide.

The uronic acids can be converted into glycosides by the standard methods. The methyl D-glucuronoside is isolated as the crystalline methyl β-D-furanosiduro-3 → 6-lactone (**XLI**), m.p. 139°, $[α]_D$ —57°. Methyl D-galacturonoside exists in the pyranose form (methyl D-galactosiduronide) (**XLII**). Like the aldoses, uronic acids link up glycosidically with aldoses

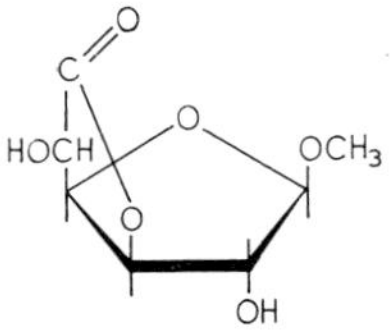

(XLI) 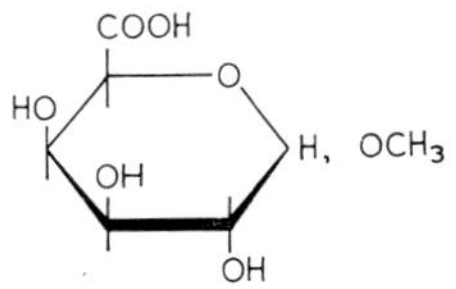   (XLII)

and uronic acids to yield di- (aldobiouronic acids) (**XLIII, XLIV**), tri- and poly-uronic acids.

When the reducing group of a uronic acid is protected by glycoside

References p. 94

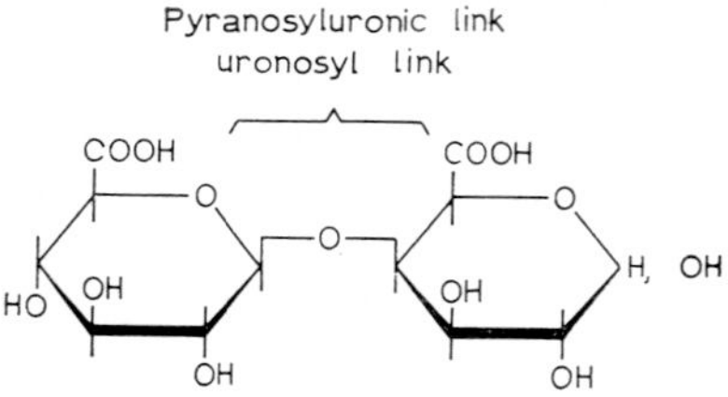

Pyranosyluronic link
uronosyl link

(XLIII)

Pyranosyluronic link
uronosyl link

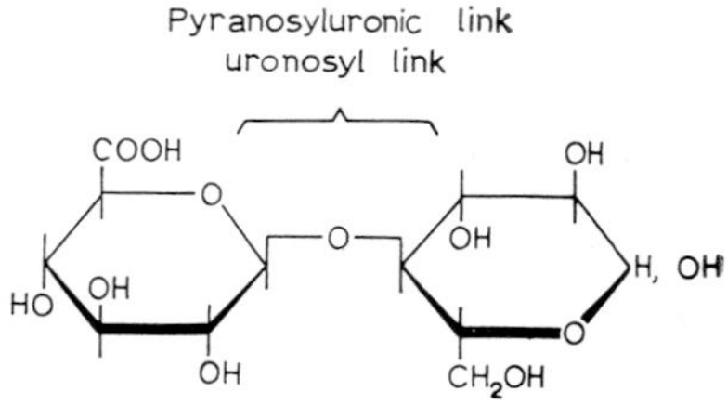

(XLIV)

formation, the product behaves as a simple hydroxycarboxylic acid. Metallic salts, alkyl esters, amides, and substituted amides are obtained by classical methods. Alkaloidal salts such as cinchonine and brucine have been used for identification. The methyl glycosyluronoamides (XLV) are the most easily crystallised derivatives. They are stable, readily recrystallised, have sharp

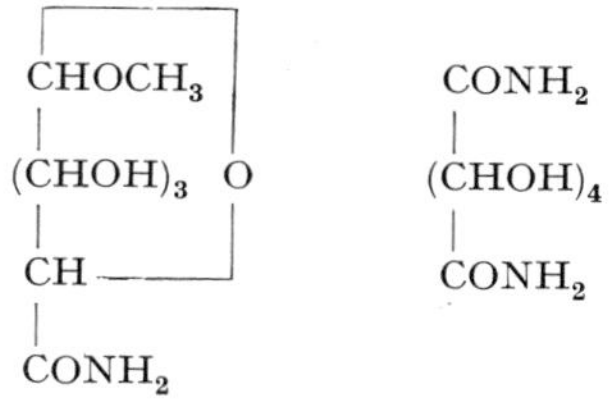

CHOCH$_3$
|
(CHOH)$_3$ O
|
CH
|
CONH$_2$
(XLV)

CONH$_2$
|
(CHOH)$_4$
|
CONH$_2$
(XLVI)

melting points and can be converted back to the free glycosyluronic acid. Benzimidazole derivatives (see p. 72) are also useful for characterising uronic acids. The secondary hydroxyl groups in uronic acids react to form esters, ethers and acetals as for the aldoses, and in the acetyl glycosyl halides (see Chapter I, p. 46) the halogen atom appears to have the same reactivity as in the corresponding derivatives of the aldoses[34].

The reducing group in uronic acids is oxidised by bromine water or nitric acid to the corresponding aldaric acid which can readily be characterised

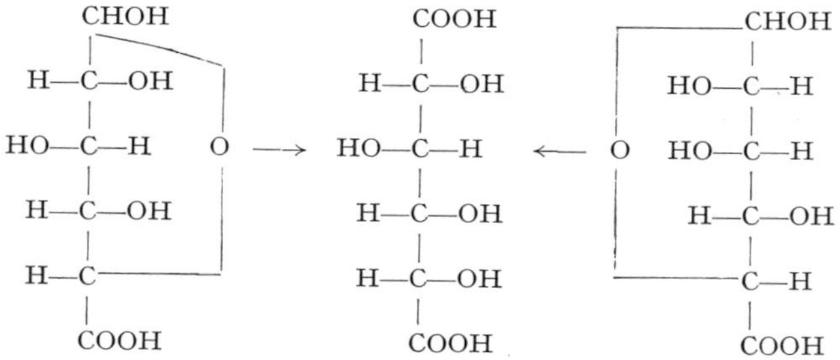

CHOH
|
H—C—OH
|
HO—C—H   O →
|
H—C—OH
|
H—C
|
COOH
(XLVII)

COOH
|
H—C—OH
|
HO—C—H   ← O
|
H—C—OH
|
H—C—OH
|
COOH
(XLVIII)

CHOH
|
HO—C—H
|
HO—C—H
|
H—C—OH
|
C—H
|
COOH
(XLIX)

as the crystalline diamide (XLVI). Owing to the symmetry of the product characterisation of a particular uronic acid by this means is not to be recommended. D-Glucaric acid (L-gularic) (XLVIII) is derived from both D-glucuronic (XLVII) and L-guluronic (XLIX) acids, and both D- (L) and L- (LII) galacturonic acids yield galactaric acid (mucic acid) (LI). Further-

```
        CHOH                      COOH                      CHOH
          |                         |                         |
     H—C—OH                    H—C—OH                    HO—C—H
          |                         |                         |
    HO—C—H      O   →       HO—C—H    ←— O         H—C—OH
          |                         |                         |
    HO—C—H                    HO—C—H                    H—C—OH
          |                         |                         |
     H—C                       H—C—OH                    C—H
          |                         |                         |
        COOH                      COOH                      COOH

         (L)                       (LI)                      (LII)
```

more the diamides from the different aldaric acids have similar melting points. A more recent and preferable method of characterising uronic acids is by reduction to the parent aldose with lithium aluminium hydride[35], or with sodium borohydride[36]; with both reagents it is essential that the reducing group be protected by glycoside formation. The immediate product is, therefore, the aldoside from which the corresponding aldose may be obtained by acid hydrolysis.

The methyl furanosides of the uronic acids appear to be similar in properties to the neutral aldofuranosides. As yet no reliable evidence has been advanced for the existence of furanosiduronic acid groups in natural products.

(c) Detection and estimation of uronic acids

Uronic acids can be separated and detected chromatographically[37]. Development of a paper chromatogram is usually carried out with an acid eluant and any of the sprays available for aldoses can be used for detection of the uronic acid. Those acids such as glucuronic, mannuronic and guluronic, which exist in solution as an equilibrium mixture of the acid and lactone, give two spots on the paper chromatogram, the faster spot corresponding to the lactone. Ionophoresis[38] has also proved of value in the separation and identification of uronic acids. These acids may be separated from one another and from neutral sugars on a preparative scale on ion-exchange resins[39]. Elution with increasing concentration of acetic or formic acid achieves separation. Mono-, di- and tri-uronic acids can also be separated by this means[40]. Pure samples of these acids have been separated from mixtures by the author[41] by the use of cellulose columns and elution with ethyl acetate–acetic acid–water.

The evolution of one mole of carbon dioxide from a mole of uronic acid on boiling with 12–19% hydrochloric acid has been developed as a quantitative method for the estimation of uronic acids[42], and this method has been adapted to the semi-micro scale[43]. The reaction mechanism is not fully understood, but has been postulated as proceeding according to the following equation:

$$
\begin{array}{cccccc}
\text{CHO} & \text{CHO} & \text{CHO} & \text{CHO} & \text{CH}\!-\!\text{CH} \\
| & | & | & | & \|\quad\| \\
(\text{CHOH})_4 \xrightarrow{\text{HCl}} & (\text{CHOH})_3 \longrightarrow & \text{C}\!-\!\text{OH} \xrightarrow{\text{H}_2\text{O}} & \text{C}\!- & \longrightarrow & \text{CH}\quad\text{C}\!-\!\text{CHO} \\
| & | & \| & \| & & \diagdown\!\text{O}\!\diagup \\
\text{COOH} & \text{CH}_2\text{OH} & \text{CH} & \text{CH} & & \text{furfural} \\
& + & | & | & \text{O} & + \\
& \text{CO}_2 & \text{CHOH} & \text{CHOH} & & \text{H}_2\text{O} \\
& & | & | & & \\
& & \text{CH}_2\text{OH} & \text{CH}_2\!- & &
\end{array}
$$

In the presence of strong mineral acids the uronic acids give specific colours with phenolic compounds such as naphthoresorcin, and a colorimetric method for the determination of uronic acids utilizing carbazole and sulphuric acid has been developed[44]. A similar method which depends on the colour produced with benzidene in glacial acetic acid has also been devised[45]. Alternatively the acids can be converted into the hydroxamic acids which give intensely coloured compounds with ferric salts. The intensity of colour can be measured and the method is sufficiently accurate to be used on the semi-micro scale[46]. Care should be observed in the interpretation of the results as other acids such as acetic acid derived from acetyl residues, interfere.

3. Oxoaldonic acids

5-(LIV) and 2-(LVI) Oxoaldonic acids (osonic, keto-uronic acids) are derived

$$
\begin{array}{cccc}
\text{COOH} & 1\ \text{COOH} & \text{CH}_2\text{OH} & 1\ \text{COOH} \\
| & | & | & | \\
\text{CHOH} & 2\ \text{CHOH} & \text{C}=\text{O} & 2\ \text{C}=\text{O} \\
| & | & | & | \\
\text{CHOH} \longrightarrow & 3\ \text{CHOH} & \text{CHOH} \longrightarrow & 3\ \text{CHOH} \\
| & | & | & | \\
\text{CHOH} & 4\ \text{CHOH} & \text{CHOH} & 4\ \text{CHOH} \\
| & | & | & | \\
\text{CHOH} & 5\ \text{C}=\text{O} & \text{CHOH} & 5\ \text{CHOH} \\
| & | & | & | \\
\text{CH}_2\text{OH} & 6\ \text{CH}_2\text{OH} & \text{CH}_2\text{OH} & 6\ \text{CH}_2\text{OH} \\
(\text{LIII}) & (\text{LIV}) & (\text{LV}) & (\text{LVI})
\end{array}
$$

by oxidation of the appropriate secondary or primary alcoholic groups in an aldonic acid (LIII) or ketone (LV) respectively. Besides existing in a straight-chain form these acids may be regarded as carboxy-keto-pyranoses (LVII) or -furanoses (LVIII), (LIX). Ultraviolet absorption spectra of the 2-oxogluconic acid and its salts substantiate this claim, no evidence for the presence of carbonyl groupings being obtainable[47].

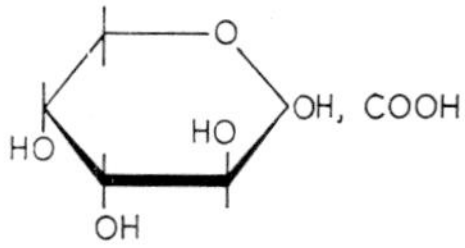

(LVII)

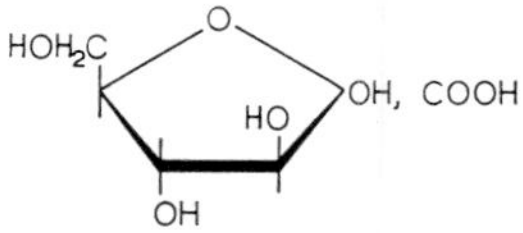

(LVIII)

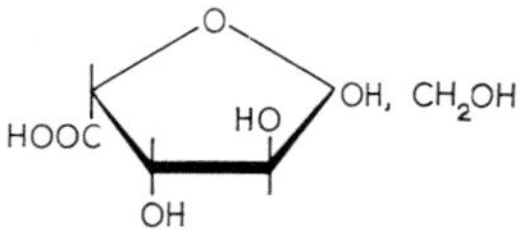

(LIX)

2-Oxo-D-gluconic acid
1-Carboxy-D-arabinopyranose
1-Carboxy-D-arabinofuranose

5-Oxo-D-gluconic acid
5-Carboxy-D-xylulose

Both 2- and 5-oxo-D-gluconic acid have been found as products of bacterial oxidation of glucose. The importance of the 2-oxo-acids (LX) lies in theii ready enolisation to ascorbic acid analogues (LXI).

COOH
|
C=O
|
$(CHOH)_3$
|
CH_2OH

(LX)

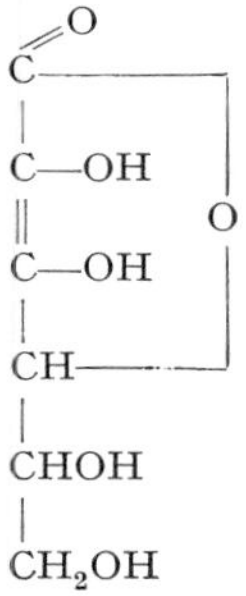

(LXI)

(a) *Preparation of oxoaldonic acids*[48]

(i) *Enzymic synthesis*

Both the 2- and 5-oxo-D-gluconic acids can be prepared by the action of bacteria. By the use of *Acetobacter suboxidans*, Stubbs[49] and his co-workers obtained a 90% yield of the 5-oxogluconic acid from a 10% glucose solution after 33 h. A year later yields of over 80% of the 2-oxo-acid from 10% glucose solutions were reported[50] utilising strains of *Pseudomonas*.

(ii) *Chemical synthesis*

2-Oxo-acids. Oxidation of (*a*) osones by bromine water, (*b*) ketoses with nitric acid and (*c*) aldonic acids with chlorates yields the corresponding

References p. 94

2-oxo-acid. (a) The success of the oxidation of osones (LXII) depends upon the purity of the starting material[51].

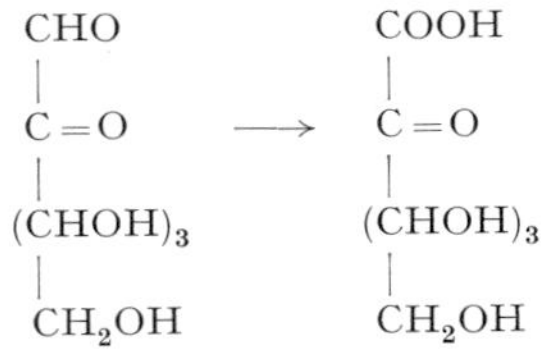

$$
\begin{array}{ccc}
\mathrm{CHO} & & \mathrm{COOH} \\
| & & | \\
\mathrm{C}=\mathrm{O} & \longrightarrow & \mathrm{C}=\mathrm{O} \\
| & & | \\
(\mathrm{CHOH})_3 & & (\mathrm{CHOH})_3 \\
| & & | \\
\mathrm{CH_2OH} & & \mathrm{CH_2OH} \\
(\mathrm{LXII}) & & (\mathrm{LXIII})
\end{array}
$$

(b) Careful control of the conditions is necessary during the oxidation of ketoses with nitric acid[52]. However, whenever it is possible to prepare the

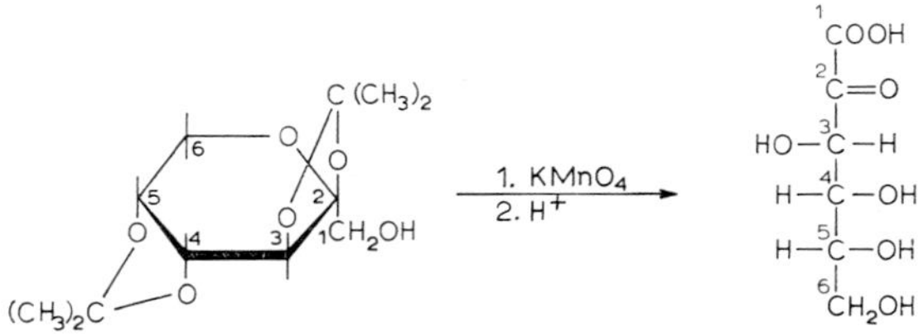

$$
\begin{array}{c}
\overset{1}{\mathrm{C}}\mathrm{OOH} \\
\overset{2}{\mathrm{C}}=\mathrm{O} \\
\mathrm{HO}-\overset{3}{\mathrm{C}}-\mathrm{H} \\
\mathrm{H}-\overset{4}{\mathrm{C}}-\mathrm{OH} \\
\mathrm{H}-\overset{5}{\mathrm{C}}-\mathrm{OH} \\
\overset{6}{\mathrm{C}}\mathrm{H_2OH}
\end{array}
$$

(LXIV)   (LXV)

isopropylidene derivative of the ketose in which all the hydroxyl groups, except the primary alcoholic grouping at C-1, are protected, as for example in 2,3:4,5-di-O-isopropylidenefructose (LXIV), the oxidation is much easier. Oxidation of (LXIV) with potassium permanganate in alkaline solution[53] readily yields 2-oxogluconic acid (LXV). (c) The preferential oxidation of the hydroxyl group on C-2 in aldonic acids has been achieved with chromic acid and with chlorates in the presence of a vanadium catalyst[54]. Oxidation of methyl D-gluconate (LXVI) gave a 60% yield of the methyl 2-oxo-D-

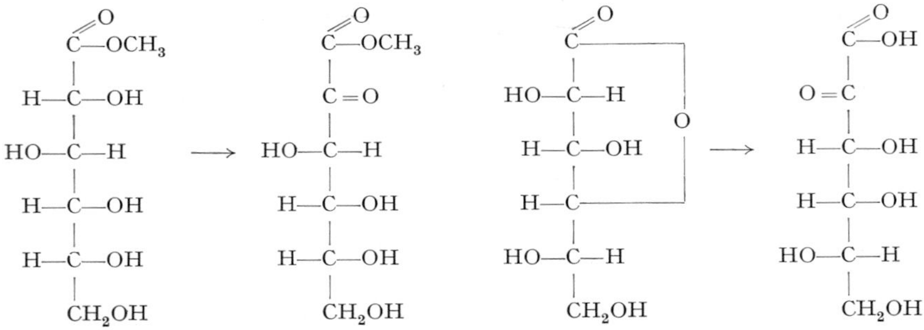

(LXVI)   (LXVII)   (LXVIII)   (LXIX)

gluconate (LXVII), and oxidation of L-galactono-γ-lactone (LXVIII) gave a 30% yield of the 2-oxo-L-galactonic acid (LXIX).

5-*Oxo-acids*. (*a*) Both D-glucuronic (LXX) and D-galacturonic (LXXII) acids are converted to the 5-oxo-L-aldonic acids (LXXI, LXXIII) by the carefully controlled action of calcium and strontium hydroxides[55].

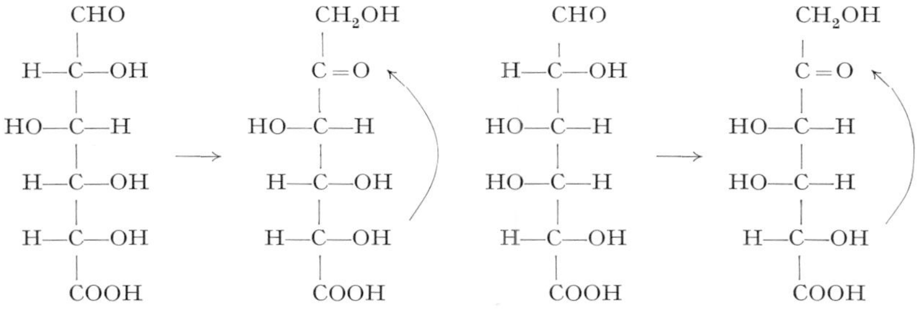

(LXX)   (LXXI)   (LXXII)   (LXXIII)

(*b*) As for the 2-oxo-acids, oxidation of the appropriate di-*O*-isopropylidene derivative with permanganate results in the formation of the 5-oxo-acid. An example of this is the conversion of 1,2:3,4-di-*O*-isopropylidene-D-tagatose (LXXIV) into 5-oxo-D-galactonic acid (LXXV)[56].

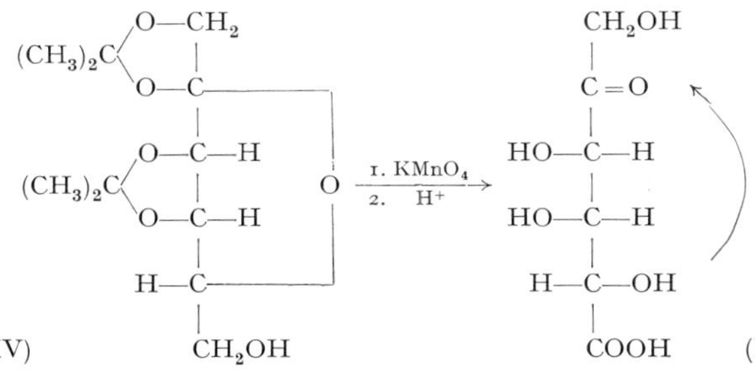

(LXXIV) CH_2OH COOH   (LXXV)

(b) *Properties of the oxoaldonic acids*

The oxoaldonic acids resemble the uronic acids in many of their properties, particularly in their colour reactions and in their decarboxylation on heating with 12% hydrochloric acid. They also show similarities with the ketoses, for example, in their behaviour toward oxidising agents[57].

(c) *Determination of oxoaldonic acids*

These acids in the absence of other reducing substances may be determined quantitatively by the Schaffer–Hartmann sugar method[49], and probably by other methods depending on oxido–reduction. 2-Oxogluconic acid has 87% and 5-oxogluconic acid 80% of the reducing power of glucose towards the Schaffer-Hartmann reagent. 5-Oxogluconic acid can be determined in the presence of the 2-isomer, glucose, fructose, and uronic acids by means of a modified Benedict reagent[58].

4. Ascorbic acids[59]

Ascorbic acids are characterised by the possession of an enediol structure (LXXVI) similar to reductic acid (LXXVIII) and reductone (LXXIX) and in some cases by antiscorbutic activity. It is this activity that has given ascorbic acids their importance and caused intensive investigation of their structure, properties and biological function. The most widely known ascorbic acid is vitamin C, the antiscorbutic vitamin. It was first isolated by Szent-Györgyi in 1928 from adrenal cortex. A rich source was later found in Hungarian paprika and also in rose-hips. He called it "hexuronic acid" and recorded that it was a strongly reducing substance with the molecular formula $C_6H_8O_6$.

Early studies showed that vitamin C has properties typical of an organic acid, but since these could be destroyed by the removal of two hydrogen atoms on oxidation by iodine (with the formation of dehydroascorbic acid, CX) they clearly were not due to the presence of a carboxyl group. This, coupled with the extreme instability of ascorbic acid to alkaline reagents

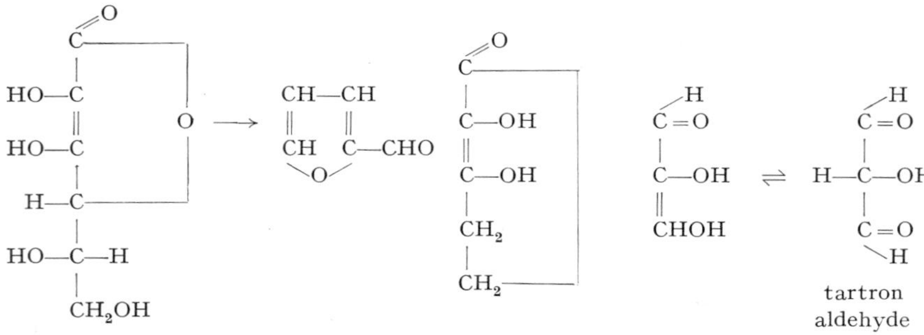

(LXXVI)   (LXXVII)   (LXXVIII)   (LXXIX)   (LXXX)

indicated that the acidity might be due to an activated hydroxyl group such as —C(OH)=C(OH)—. Further structural studies revealed that vitamin C has indeed the formula (LXXVI). Distillation with hydrochloric acid yielded furfural (LXXVII), showing that at least five of the six carbon atoms are present in an unbranched chain. The presence of an enolic structure was confirmed by the typical colour given with ferric chloride solution. Methylation yielded a tetra-*O*-methyl derivative (LXXXI) indicating the presence of four hydroxyl groups, and proof of the furanose-ring structure was obtained by cleavage of the double bond in the methylated material by ozone and the isolation of oxamide (LXXXII) and dimethoxyhydroxybutyramide (LXXXIII) after treatment of the ozonised material with ammonia.

(LXXXI) (LXXXII) (LXXXIII)

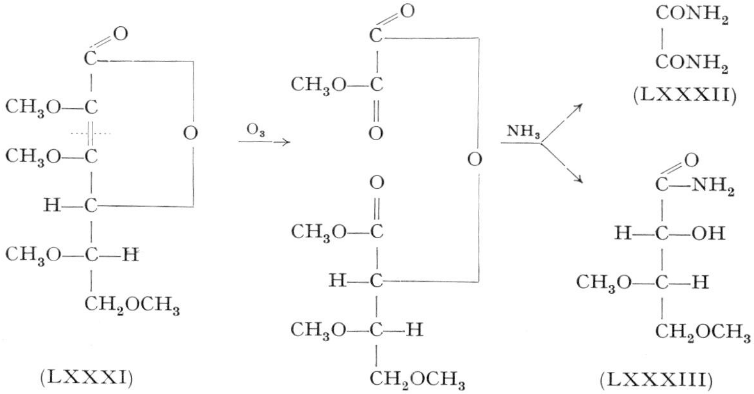

X-ray analysis supports this formulation. That ascorbic acid (LXXXIV) is derived from the L-series of sugars was shown by the isolation of trimethoxy-L-threonamide (LXXXV) after oxidation with permanganate, methylation and amide formation. Confirmation of the structure was obtained by synthesis[60].

(LXXXIV) (LXXXV)

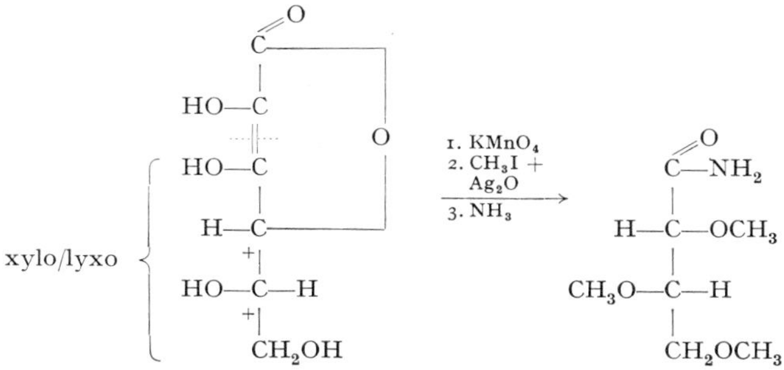

The nomenclature of these acids is somewhat confused. One system is based on the parent osone that could give rise to the particular acid, L-xylosone or L-lyxosone to vitamin C, which is often termed L-xylo- (L-lyxo-) ascorbic acid. (The xylo/lyxo portion is depicted in the bracket in the above formula (LXXXIV)). There are only two asymmetric carbon atoms (+) in the molecule and a better system in the author's opinion is to call it L-threo-hexoascorbic acid. A definitive name for this acid, based on carbohydrate rules (see Chapter I, p. 1), is 2-keto-L-threo-hexono-γ-lactone-2,3-enediol.

It has been found that only those acids in which the ring is on the right in the Fischer-projection formula possess antiscorbutic activity in guinea pigs; the extent of the activity depending on the particular acid; L-rhamno- and D-arabinoascorbic acids (LXXXVI, LXXXVII) having one fifth and

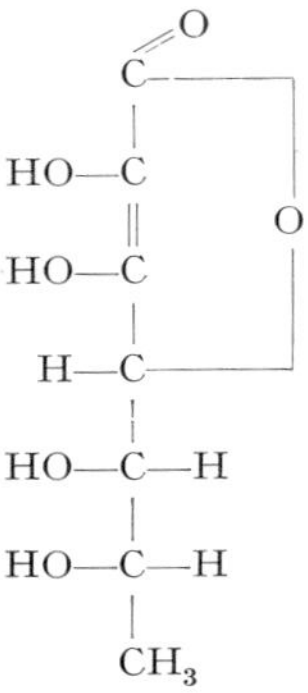

(LXXXVI) 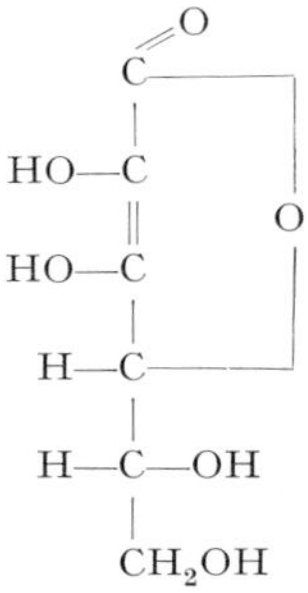   (LXXXVII) 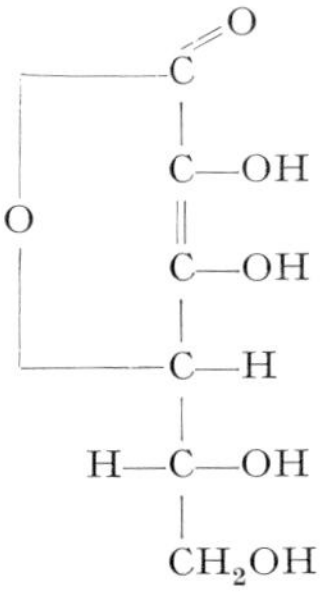   (LXXXVIII)

one twentieth of the activity respectively of L-xyloascorbic acid (vitamin C), and D-xyloascorbic acid (LXXXVIII) being devoid of activity.

(a) Preparation of ascorbic acids

There are four general chemical methods of synthesising these acids, two of which involve enolisation of 2-oxoaldonic acids.

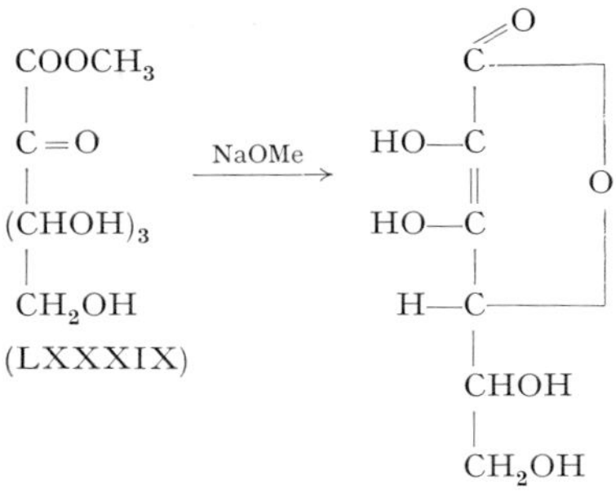

(*i*) By the action of sodium methoxide on the methyl esters of 2-oxo-aldonic acids (LXXXIX) an almost quantitative yield of the respective ascorbic acid (XC) is obtained.

Isbell[61] made use of this reaction to synthesise vitamin C from L-galactono-γ-lactone. The latter was first converted into the 2-oxo derivative (see p. 83). A commercial synthesis of ascorbic acid is also based on this isomerisation. Bertrand's sorbose bacterium, *Acetobacter xylinium*, converts sorbitol to L-sorbose (XCI) and this on condensation with acetone yields the 2,3:4,5-di-O-isopropylidene derivative (XCII). Oxidation and hydrolysis of this

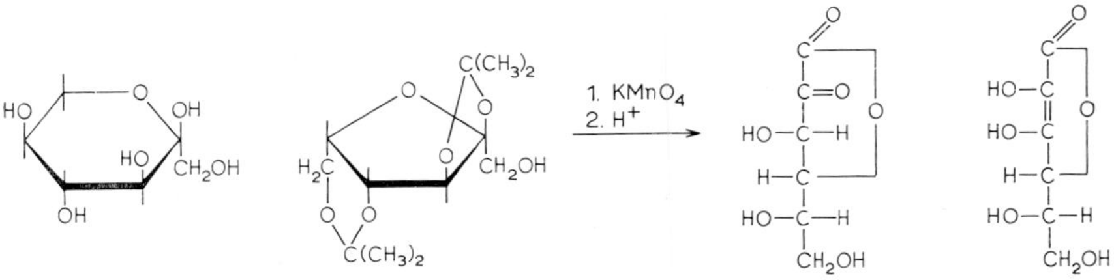

| (XCI) | (XCII) | 1. $KMnO_4$ 2. H^+ → | (XCIII) | (XCIV) |

material yields 2-oxo-L-gulonic acid (XCIII) which by enolisation is converted into vitamin C (XCIV).

    (*ii*) The original synthesis of ascorbic acid[60] (xyloascorbic acid) was from L-xylosone (L-lyxosone). Treatment of the osone (XCV) with calcium chloride and potassium cyanide leads to the formation of the "imino"-ascorbic acid (XCVII) and this on hydrolysis yields L-xyloascorbic acid

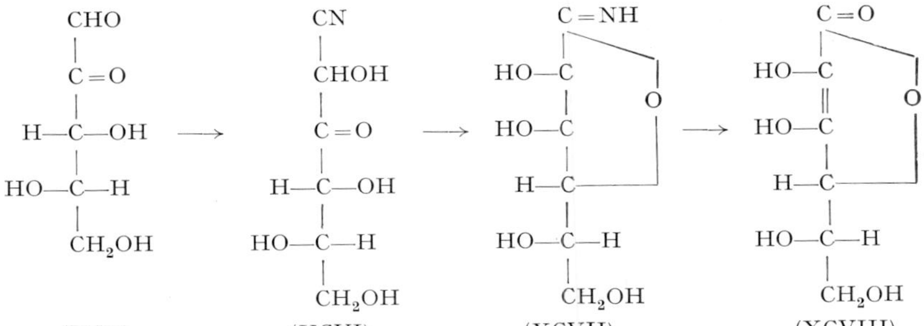

| (XCV) | (XCVI) | (XCVII) | (XCVIII) |

(XCVIII). Several analogues of ascorbic acid have been prepared by this method.

    (*iii*) Ascorbic acids (CII) may also be prepared by condensation of the appropriate hydroxy aldehyde, for example, D-xylose (C) with ethyl glyoxylate (XCIX) or ethyl mesoxylate[62]. The intermediate 3-oxo derivative is not isolated. This method is of wide application and can be used for the preparation of any of the analogues of ascorbic acid.

(*iv*) A method based on the Claisen condensation can also be used for the preparation of ascorbic acids. Condensation of ethyl benzoyloxyacetate (CIV) with the benzoyl derivative of a polyhydroxyester such as the ethyl

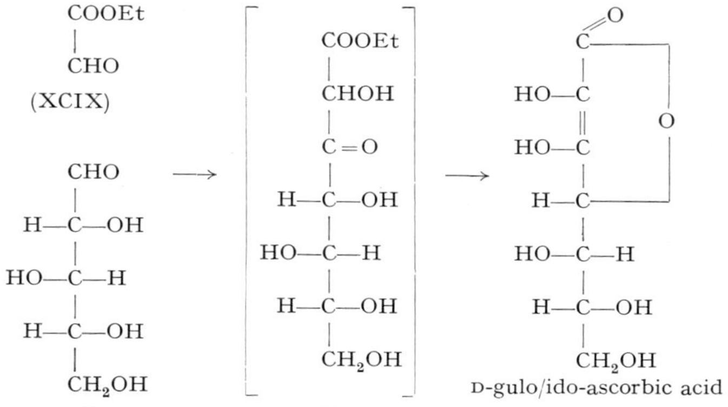

$$
\begin{array}{ccc}
\begin{array}{c}
\text{COOEt} \\
| \\
\text{CHO} \\
\text{(XCIX)}
\end{array}
&
&
\\
\\
\begin{array}{c}
\text{CHO} \\
| \\
\text{H—C—OH} \\
| \\
\text{HO—C—H} \\
| \\
\text{H—C—OH} \\
| \\
\text{CH}_2\text{OH} \\
\text{(C)}
\end{array}
\longrightarrow
\left[
\begin{array}{c}
\text{COOEt} \\
| \\
\text{CHOH} \\
| \\
\text{C}=\text{O} \\
| \\
\text{H—C—OH} \\
| \\
\text{HO—C—H} \\
| \\
\text{H—C—OH} \\
| \\
\text{CH}_2\text{OH} \\
\text{(CI)}
\end{array}
\right]
\longrightarrow
\begin{array}{c}
\text{D-gulo/ido-ascorbic acid} \\
\text{(CII)}
\end{array}
\end{array}
$$

ester of tetra-*O*-benzoyl-D-arabinonic acid (CIII) in the presence of potassium as a catalyst results in the formation of D-gluco/manno-ascorbic acid (CV)[63]. If two molecules of ethyl benzoyloxyacetate are condensed

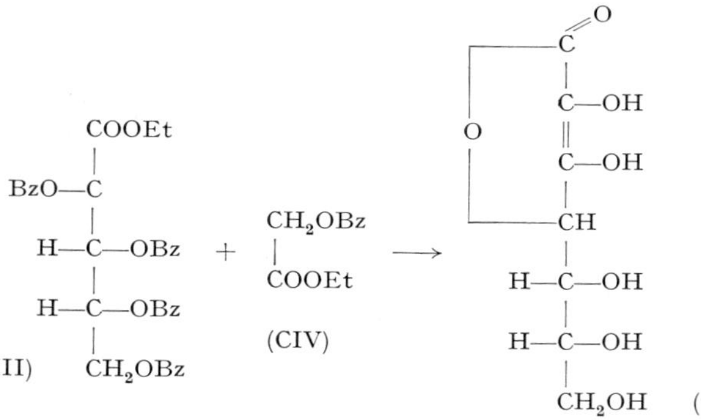

$$
\begin{array}{c}
\text{COOEt} \\
| \\
\text{BzO—C} \\
| \\
\text{H—C—OBz} \\
| \\
\text{H—C—OBz} \\
| \\
\text{(CIII)} \quad \text{CH}_2\text{OBz}
\end{array}
\; + \;
\begin{array}{c}
\text{CH}_2\text{OBz} \\
| \\
\text{COOEt} \\
\\
\text{(CIV)}
\end{array}
\longrightarrow
\begin{array}{c}
\text{C—OH} \\
\| \\
\text{C—OH} \\
| \\
\text{CH} \\
| \\
\text{H—C—OH} \\
| \\
\text{H—C—OH} \\
| \\
\text{CH}_2\text{OH} \quad \text{(CV)}
\end{array}
$$

under these conditions, the simplest analogue of ascorbic acid, hydroxy-tetronic acid (CVII) is obtained[64]. This acid is devoid of antiscorbutic activity.

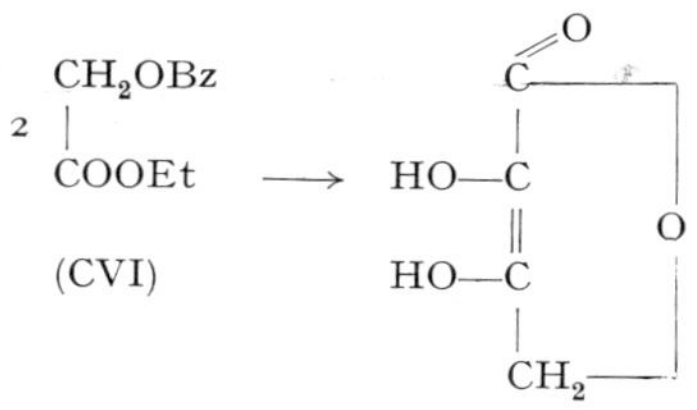

$$
2 \;
\begin{array}{c}
\text{CH}_2\text{OBz} \\
| \\
\text{COOEt} \\
\\
\text{(CVI)}
\end{array}
\longrightarrow
\begin{array}{c}
\text{C}\diagup^{\text{O}} \\
| \\
\text{HO—C} \\
\| \\
\text{HO—C} \\
| \\
\text{CH}_2 \quad \text{(CVII)}
\end{array}
$$

(b) Properties of ascorbic acids

Ascorbic acids are acidic, very strongly reducing, optically active, unstable compounds. The presence of the activated hydroxyl groups explains the reducing properties, acidity and the instability of these acids to alkaline reagents. In aqueous solution the hydrogen of the enol group on C-3 becomes ionised, yielding a solution with a pH of 3.0, and in this medium these acids behave as monobasic acids forming salts containing one monovalent metal atom or equivalent. In alkaline solution the hydrogen of the enol group on C-2 becomes dissociated and is replaced by metal.

 Ascorbic acids give most of the colour reactions associated with aldoses and in addition the colour with ferric chloride typical of an enolic compound. They are very readily oxidised to the dehydro form (CVIII) by titration

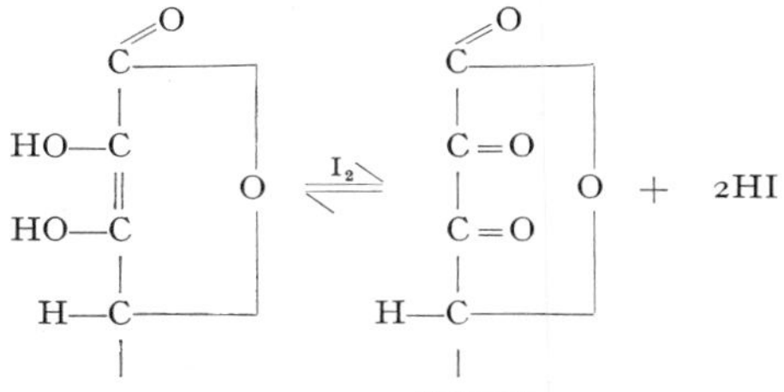

(CVIII)

with iodine, and two molecules of hydrogen iodide are produced. This is a reversible reaction and evaporation of the derived solution results in the oxidation of the hydriodic acid by the dehydroascorbic acid, liberation of iodine and the regeneration of ascorbic acid. Ascorbic acid (CIX) is converted to the dehydro form (CX) by any mild oxidising agents, and the latter is slowly transformed to 2,3-diketo-L-gulonic acid (CXI) in mild acid solution. This transformation is much more rapid in solutions at pH 1.0 or lower and in neutral and alkaline medium, and the resulting diketo-acid (CXI) has no

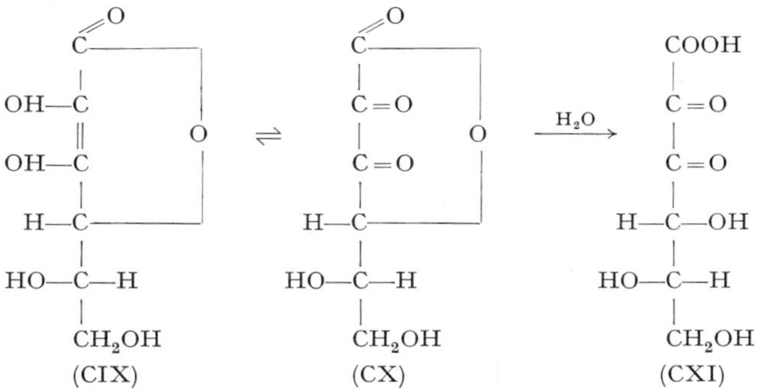

(CIX)   (CX)   (CXI)

antiscorbutic properties. In contrast to the dehydro-acid the diketo-acid cannot be reduced to ascorbic acid by hydrogen sulphide. The dehydro form may be stored as the methanol complex from which the parent acid is regenerated by dissolution in water.

L-Xyloascorbic acid is a white crystalline solid, m.p. 192°, $[\alpha]_D$ +23° (water), +48° (methanol). Its absorption spectrum has a maximum at 265 mμ and a small band between 350 and 400 mμ.

(c) Detection and determination of ascorbic acids[65]

Ascorbic acids can be detected on paper chromatograms (see Chapter I, p. 56) after elution with n-butanol–acetic acid–water or phenol–acetic acid–water[66], and spraying with silver nitrate, p-aminobenzoic acid or dichlorophenol-indophenol dye. By this means L-ascorbic acid can be separated from D-araboascorbic acid (a naturally occurring analogue), hydroxytartronic acid, reductic acid (LXXVIII) and reductone (LXXIX). An improved technique has been introduced by Chen et al.[67] in which the enediols are stabilised by extraction with saturated oxalic-acid solution, and the two chromatographic solvents are also stabilised by saturation with oxalic acid and omission of the acetic acid. The oxalic acid has an added advantage in that it removes interfering heavy metals by complexing with them. These authors extended this procedure to quantitative determinations by eluting the ascorbic acid from the paper chromatogram and estimating the quantity separated with indophenol (see below).

Quantitative determination of ascorbic acid in biological fluids and processed foods is hindered by interference by ferrous, cuprous and stannous ions, phenols, sulphydryl compounds, reductone (LXXIX), reductic acid (LXXVIII) and tartronaldehyde (LXXX). The most commonly used method of estimation is based on the rapid reduction of 2,6-dichlorophenol-indophenol ("indophenol") to its leuco form by ascorbic acid. This method, which was first introduced by Tillmanns, Hirsch and Hirsch[68], involves the titration of an acid extract of the tissue or vitamin with a dilute solution of the dye.

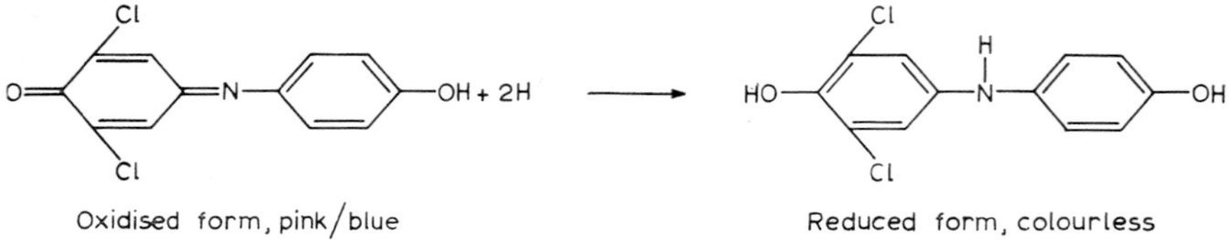

Oxidised form, pink/blue   Reduced form, colourless

The end-point of the titration is taken when the pink colour persists for 15 seconds after the addition of one drop of the indophenol solution. The method is not completely specific and is rendered inaccurate by the presence of the contaminants mentioned above, and various modifications have been introduced, including the addition of *p*-chloromercuribenzoic acid[69], to remove interfering sulphydryl-containing materials.

The procedure has been adapted to photometry. The photometric density of a solution of indophenol is measured before and after the addition of the ascorbic acid solution.

The quantity of dehydroascorbic acid in a solution may also be determined by this method. The difference in values before and after reduction with hydrogen sulphide gives the amount of the dehydro-acid. This, however, is often complicated by the presence of other products of the reduction and a better method consists in the conversion of the dehydroascorbic acid to the bis-2,4-dinitrophenylhydrazone and photometric determination of the red colour produced on treatment of the bis-hydrazone with concentrated sulphuric acid[70].

This procedure has also been adapted to differentiate between ascorbic acid, dehydroascorbic acid and diketogulonic acid[71]. These latter two substances form bis-2,4-dinitrophenylhydrazones (CXII), (CXIII), in which the hydrazine residues are coupled to C-2 and C-3. The differentiation entails (*I*) the reduction of the dehydro form to ascorbic acid by hydrogen sulphide

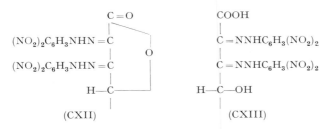

under conditions which do not reduce the diketo-acid, and (*2*) oxidation of ascorbic acid with bromine. The solution to be measured is divided into three aliquots, one is reduced with hydrogen sulphide, the second is left untreated, and the third is oxidised with bromine. The first aliquot yields on treatment with the hydrazine the bis-hydrazone of diketogulonic acid. The second aliquot is a mixture of the two bis-hydrazones and the third aliquot is that of ascorbic, dehydro- and keto-acids. By appropriate subtraction the values of each of the components may be obtained.

A high degree of specificity is claimed for this method. Any osazones of sugars that may be formed decompose in the concentrated sulphuric acid and for this reason a delay of 30 min after development of colour before measurement is recommended. Furthermore, thiourea or stannous chloride is added to avoid interference from non-ascorbic acid chromogens. Nevertheless, care should be exercised in its use in the determination of ascorbic acid in processed foods of high sugar content which may also contain sugar degradation products. There is a modification of this method for the determination of ascorbic acid in small amounts of blood[72].

(d) Biological function of ascorbic acid

Vitamin C is widely distributed in nature, especially in green vegetables and citrus fruits, conifer needles and potatoes. Some investigators consider that it is a universal constituent of plant tissue where it occurs normally in the reduced form. Approximately 5% of the total vitamin C is present in the plant in the dehydro form.

All the higher plants and most animals with the exception of man, the primates, and the guinea pig can synthesise ascorbic acid, but there is little reliable evidence that it can be synthesised by bacteria[73]. Oxygen appears to be necessary for ascorbic acid synthesis in plants and the process is apparently coupled either directly or indirectly to photosynthesis.

Several pathways for the biosynthesis of this acid have been advanced and these were reviewed by Mapson[73] in 1955. The most probable pathways appear to be[74]:

$$\text{D-glucose} \xrightarrow[\text{lactonisation}]{\text{oxidation at C-6}} \text{D-glucurono-}\gamma\text{-lactone} \xrightarrow[\text{C-1}]{\text{reduction}} \text{L-gulono-}\gamma\text{-lactone}$$

$$\xrightarrow[\text{C-3}]{\text{inversion}} \text{L-galactono-}\gamma\text{-lactone} \xrightarrow[\text{C-2 and C-3}]{\text{oxidation}} \text{L-ascorbic acid}$$

$$\nearrow \text{TPNH}$$

D-galacturonic acid

Nothing is known with certainty about metabolic pathways for the degradation of ascorbic acid or of its use in the plant. Although some biologists[75] consider that it is a catalyst in photosynthetic phosphorylation, this is by no means certain, and until more positive evidence is advanced it is safer to consider that this acid fulfils some as yet imperfectly known metabolic function in the active plant cell.

Much evidence has been presented[73] that the ascorbic acid is linked to other compounds such as proteins in the plant tissues, but conclusive proof of this has not been advanced, and many of the conclusions are based on faulty extraction procedures.

When plant tissues are damaged the ascorbic acid is oxidised by various enzymes, including ascorbic oxidase, to the dehydro form. It is difficult to prevent this change occurring during extraction. The presence of acids such as phosphoric and sulphuric have been found to be efficacious in this respect.

Finally mention should be made of the crystalline enolic substances (CXV–CXVII) resembling ascorbic acid, prepared by the enolisation by alkali of D-mannosaccharo-1,4:3,6- (CXIV), D-glucosaccharo-1,5:3,6- (CXVI), and 1,4:3,6- (CXVIII) dilactones[59].

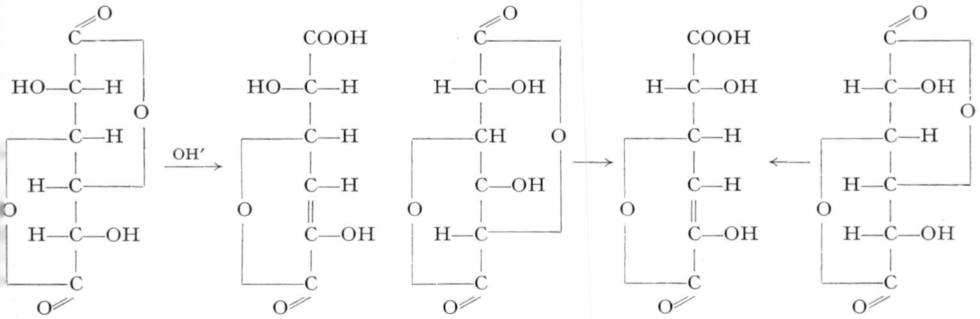

(CXIV)	(CXV)	(CXVI)	(CXVII)	(CXVIII)
C=O	COOH	C=O	COOH	C=O
HO—C—H	HO—C—H	H—C—OH	H—C—OH	H—C—OH
C—H	C—H	CH	C—H	C—H
H—C	C—H	C—OH	C—H	H—C
H—C—OH	C—OH	H—C	C—OH	H—C—OH
C=O	C=O	C=O	C=O	C=O

These substances differ from ascorbic acid in their retarded action with iodine and their inability to reduce silver nitrate solution. It is these substances which are responsible for the reducing properties displayed by the dilactones[76].

REFERENCES

1 J. W. GREEN, *Adv. Carbohydrate Chem.*, 3 (1948) 140; B. VOLLMERT, *Encyclopedia of Plant Physiology*, 6 (1958) 390.
2 J. H. BIRKINSHAW AND H. RAISTRICK, *Phil. Trans. Roy. Soc. London, Ser. B*, 220 (1931) 331; R. BENTLEY AND L. SLECHTA, *J. Bacteriol.*, 79 (1960) 346.
3 L. B. LOCKWOOD, B. TABENKIN AND G. E. WARD, *J. Bacteriol.*, 42 (1941) 51.
4 D. KEILIN AND E. F. HARTREE, *Biochem. J.*, 42 (1948) 221, 230; R. L. WHISTLER, L. HOUGH AND J. W. HYLIN, *Anal. Chem.*, 25 (1953) 1215.
5 H. HLASWETZ, *Ann. Chem. & Pharm.*, 119 (1861) 281.
6 H. KILIANI AND S. KLEEMAN, *Ber.*, 17 (1884) 1296.
7 C. S. HUDSON AND H. S. ISBELL, *J. Am. Chem. Soc.*, 51 (1929) 2225.
8 J. P. HART AND M. R. EVERETT, *J. Am. Chem. Soc.*, 61 (1939) 1822.
9 H. S. ISBELL, H. L. FRUSH AND F. J. BATES, *Ind. Eng. Chem.*, 24 (1932) 375.
10 I. R. L. BARKER, W. G. OVEREND AND C. W. REES, *Chem. & Ind. (London)*, (1960) 1297.
11a M. L. WOLFROM AND M. J. CRON, *J. Am. Chem. Soc.*, 74 (1952) 1715.
11b S. A. BARKER, E. J. BOURNE, R. M. PINKARD AND D. H. WHIFFEN, *Chem. & Ind.*, (1958) 658.
12 D. J. BELL in PAECH AND TRACEY (Eds.), *Modern Methods of Plant Analysis*, Vol. 2, Springer, Berlin, 1955, p. 46.
13 R. WILLSTÄTTER AND G. SCHUDEL, *Ber.*, 51 (1918) 780; C. A. BROWNE AND R. W. ZERBAN, *Physical and Chemical Methods of Sugar Analysis*, J. Wiley and Sons, New York, 1941, p. 896.
14 S. MOORE AND K. P. LINK, *J. Biol. Chem.*, 133 (1940) 273.
15 H. S. ISBELL AND R. SCHAFFER, *J. Am. Chem. Soc.*, 78 (1956) 1887.
16 C. S. HUDSON, *J. Am. Chem. Soc.*, 32 (1910) 338.
17 C. S. HUDSON, *J. Am. Chem. Soc.*, 40 (1918) 813.
18 A. THOMPSON AND M. S. WOLFROM, *J. Am. Chem. Soc.*, 68 (1946) 1509.
19 S. MOORE AND K. P. LINK, *J. Biol. Chem.*, 133 (1940) 300.
20 ABDEL AKHER AND F. SMITH, *J. Am. Chem. Soc.*, 73 (1951) 5859.
21 T. BENNET-CLARK, *Biochem. J.*, 28 (1934) 45.
22 S. S. COHEN AND R. RAFF, *J. Biol. Chem.*, 188 (1951) 501.
23 E. J. PRESCOTT, J. K. SHAE, J. P. PILELLO AND G. O. CRAGWALL, *Ind. Eng. Chem.*, 45 (1950) 338.
24 F. A. HENGLEIN, *Encyclopedia of Plant Physiology*, 6 (1958) 405.
25 H. G. BRAY, *Adv. Carbohydrate Chem.*, 8 (1953) 251; R. S. TEAGUE, *Adv. Carbohydrate Chem.*, 9 (1954) 186.
26 I. D. E. STOREY AND G. J. DUTTON, *Biochem. J.*, 59 (1955) 279.
27 R. T. WILLIAMS, *Nature*, 142 (1939) 641.
28 C. L. MEHLTRETTER, *Adv. Carbohydrate Chem.*, 8 (1953) 233.
29 H. M. SELL AND K. P. LINK, *J. Am. Chem. Soc.*, 60 (1938) 1813; R. A. EDINGTON AND E. PERCIVAL, *J. Chem. Soc.*, (1953) 2437.
30 R. A. EDINGTON, E. L. HIRST AND E. PERCIVAL, *J. Chem. Soc.*, (1955) 2281.
31 C. L. MEHLTRETTER, B. H. ALEXANDER, R. L. MELLIES AND C. E. RIST, *J. Am. Chem. Soc.*, 73 (1951) 2424; *U.S. Pat.*, 2,559,652 (1951).
32 O. TOUSTER AND V. H. REYNOLDS, *J. Biol. Chem.*, 197 (1952) 863.
33 K. MAURER AND G. DREFAHL, *Ber.*, 80 (1947) 94.
34 C. T. BISHOP, *Can. J. Chem.*, 31 (1953) 134.
35 B. LYTHGOE AND S. TRIPPETT, *J. Chem. Soc.*, (1950) 1983.
36 M. L. WOLFROM AND KIMIKI ANNO, *J. Am. Chem. Soc.*, 74 (1952) 5583.
37 D. J. BELL in PAECH AND TRACEY (Eds.), *Methods of Plant Analysis*, Vol. 2, Springer, Berlin, 1955, p. 1.
38 A. B. FOSTER, *Adv. Carbohydrate Chem.*, 12 (1957) 87.
39 J. X. KHYM AND D. G. DOHERTY, *J. Am. Chem. Soc.*, 74 (1952) 3190.
40 R. DERINGS AND H. DEUEL, *Helv. Chim. Acta*, 37 (1954) 657.
41 J. J. O'DONNELL AND E. PERCIVAL, *J. Chem. Soc.*, (1959) 2168.
42 R. M. McCREADY, H. A. SWENSON AND W. D. MACLAY, *Ind. Eng. Chem. Anal. Ed.*, 13 (1946) 290.

[43] B. LINDBERG, O. THEANDER AND A. JOHANSSON, *Svensk Papperstidn.*, 57 (1954) 41; D. M. W. ANDERSON, *Talanta*, 2 (1959) 73.
[44] E. G. V. PERCIVAL AND A. G. ROSS, *J. Soc. Chem. Ind. (London)*, 67 (1948) 420.
[45] J. K. N. JONES AND J. B. PRIDHAM, *Nature*, 172 (1953) 161.
[46] M. A. G. KAYE AND P. W. KENT, *J. Chem. Soc.*, (1953) 79.
[47] P. NIEDERHOFF, *Z. physiol. Chem.*, 181 (1929) 83.
[48] F. SMITH, *Adv. Carbohydrate Chem.*, 2 (1946) 84.
[49] J. J. STUBBS, L. B. LOCKWOOD, E. T. ROE, B. TABENKIN AND G. E. WARD, *Ind. Eng. Chem.*, 32 (1940) 1626.
[50] L. B. LOCKWOOD, B. TABENKIN AND G. E. WARD, *J. Bacteriol.*, 42 (1941) 51.
[51] C. NEUBERG AND T. KITASATO, *Biochem. J.*, 183 (1927) 485.
[52] W. N. HAWORTH, E. L. HIRST, J. K. N. JONES AND F. SMITH, *British Pat.*, 443, 901.
[53] H. OHLE AND R. WALTER, *Ber.*, 63B (1930) 843.
[54] P. P. REGNA AND B. P. CALDWELL, *J. Am. Chem. Soc.*, 66 (1944) 243.
[55] F. EHRLICH AND R. GUTTMANN, *Ber.*, 17 (1934) 573.
[56] T. REICHSTEIN AND W. BOSSHARD, *Helv. Chim. Acta*, 17 (1934) 753.
[57] H. OHLE, *Ber.*, 67 (1934) 155.
[58] E. MILLITZER, *J. Biol. Chem.*, 154 (1944) 325.
[59] F. SMITH, *Adv. Carbohydrate Chem.*, 2 (1946) 79; B. ABERG, *Encyclopedia of Plant Physiology*, 6 (1958) 479.
[60] E. L. HIRST *et al.*, *J. Chem. Soc.*, (1933) 1419; (1934) 62; T. REICHSTEIN, A. GRÜSSNER AND R. OPPENAUER, *Helv. Chim. Acta*, 16 (1933) 1019; 17 (1934) 510.
[61] H. S. ISBELL, *J. Research Natl. Bur. Standards*, 33 (1944) 45.
[62] B. HELFERICH AND O. PETERS, *Ber.*, 70B (1937) 465.
[63] F. MICHEEL AND H. HAARHOFF, *Liebigs Ann. Chem.*, 545 (1940) 28.
[64] F. MICHEEL AND F. JUNG, *Ber.*, 66B (1933) 1291.
[65] J. H. ROE, in D. GLICK (Ed.), *Methods of Biochemical Analysis*, Vol. 1, Interscience, London, 1954, p. 115; W. FRANKE in, PAECH AND TRACEY (Eds.), *Modern Methods of Plant Analysis*, Vol. 2, Springer, Berlin, 1955, p. 95.
[66] E. WEYGAND, *Arkiv Kemi*, 3 (1952) 11; L. W. MAPSON AND S. M. PARTRIDGE, *Nature*, 164 (1949) 479.
[67] Y.-T. CHEN, F. A. ISHERWOOD AND L. W. MAPSON, *Biochem. J.*, 55 (1953) 821.
[68] J. TILLMANNS, P. HIRSCH AND W. HIRSCH, *Z. Untersuch. Lebensm.*, 63 (1932) 1.
[69] J. A. OWEN, B. IGGO AND D. B. HORN, *Nature*, 174 (1954) 701.
[70] M. B. MILLS AND J. H. ROE, *J. Biol. Chem.*, 170 (1947) 159; J. H. ROE AND M. J. OESTERLING, *J. Biol. Chem.*, 152 (1944) 511.
[71] J. H. ROE, M. B. MILLS, M. J. OESTERLING AND C. M. DAMRON, *J. Biol. Chem.*, 174 (1948) 201.
[72] O. H. LOWRY, J. A. LOPEZ AND O. A. BESSEY, *J. Biol. Chem.*, 160 (1945) 609.
[73] L. W. MAPSON, *Vitamins and Hormones*, 13 (1955) 71.
[74] L. W. MAPSON AND F. A. ISHERWOOD, *Biochem. J.*, 56 (1954) 21; 59 (1955) 9.
[75] F. R. WHATLEY, M. B. ALLEN AND D. I. ARNON, *Biochim. Biophys. Acta*, 16 (1955) 605.
[76] J. W. W. MORGAN AND M. L. WOLFROM, *J. Am. Chem. Soc.*, 78 (1956) 1897.

Chapter III

Amino Sugars

H. EGGE

Max Planck Institute for Medical Research*, Heidelberg (Germany)

Amino sugars are sugars in which one or more OH-groups are replaced by NH_2. The nomenclature** follows the rules for the nitrogen-free carbo-hydrates. In addition to the systematic designations 2-amino-2-deoxy-D-glucose and 2-amino-2-deoxy-D-galactose, the shorter historical names D-glucosamine (chitosamine) and D-galactosamine (chondrosamine) are used.

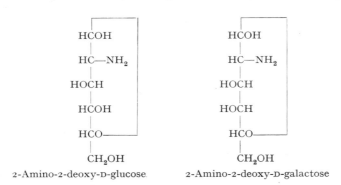

2-Amino-2-deoxy-D-glucose   2-Amino-2-deoxy-D-galactose

This shortened terminology is extended to all the 2-amino-2-deoxy-hexoses, -pentoses and -tetroses. Examples are: D-mannosamine, D-lyxosamine and D-threosamine.

If the lactolhydroxyl group is substituted by NH_2 at C-atom 1, one speaks of glycosylamines, or, by substitution with NHR, of N-glycosides. Glyc-amines are 1-amino-1-deoxy sugar alcohols. The nomenclature of the compounds found in nature, which are formed partly or entirely from amino sugars, is still not uniform[1].

---

* Director: Prof. Dr. RICHARD KUHN.

** *J. Chem. Soc.*, (1952) 5108.

The chemistry of the amino sugars begins with the discovery of glucosamine in a hydrolysate of lobster shells by Ledderhose[2,3] in the year 1876.
During the last decade the chemistry of the amino sugars has developed
vigorously. It is evident that as building stones of many of the higher and
high-molecular substances they play an important part in the metabolism
of micro-organisms, animals and man. The active development of this field
found concrete expression in a series of general and specialized publica-
tions[1,3-12]. In the tables of Horton[10] of the 2-amino-2-deoxyhexoses alone
more than 900 derivatives are listed. In this paper we want to show,
especially with the 2-amino-2-deoxyaldoses as an example, the general
chemistry of these compounds.

1. Syntheses

The following methods are especially used for the preparation of amino
sugars:
(*a*) addition of NH_3 to sugar epoxides;
(*b*) epimerization of 2-acetamido-2-deoxyaldoses;
(*c*) intramolecular rearrangement of *N*-glycosides (Amadori rearrangement,
    Heyns rearrangement);
(*d*) the HCN method (partial hydrogenation of aminonitriles);
(*e*) the nitromethane method.

(*a*) *Addition of NH₃ to sugar epoxides*

NH_3 is added to sugar epoxides in such a way, that the resulting NH_2-
and OH-groups are arranged in *trans* position. In rigid ring systems the
axial position predominates (Fürst–Plattner rule[13]).

The yield of the respective isomers which arise depends on the nature
(stereochemistry) of the epoxides.
    The first synthesis of D-glucosamine which proved its configuration was
carried out in the following way[14]: NH_3 was added to methyl-2,3-anhydro-
4,6-benzylidene-α-D-mannopyranoside. After removal of the protective
methyl and benzylidene groups a good deal of 3-amino-3-deoxyaltrose
and a little 2-amino-2-deoxyglucose were obtained. Instead of the benzyl-

idene compounds, as in the above mentioned example, 1,6-anhydrides can
also be used, since in these too the pyranose ring is no longer flexible and
the opening of the epoxides can proceed only in one direction[15,16].

(b) Epimerization of 2-acetamido-2-deoxyaldoses

The synthetic possibilities of obtaining 2- and 3-deoxyamino sugars by
addition of NH_3 were extended by Winstein's[17] discovery that N-acetyl-
O-tosyl(or O-mesyl)-trans-amino alcohols can be rearranged by solvolysis to
form N-acetyl-cis-amino alcohols:

$$
\begin{array}{ccc}
R_1 & & R_1 \\
| & & | \\
HC\!-\!NH\!-\!Ac & \xrightarrow[\text{KOAc, } p\text{-toluolsulfonic acid}]{\text{solvolysis}} & HC\!-\!NH\!-\!Ac \\
| & & | \\
Tos\!-\!O\!-\!CH & & HC\!-\!OH \\
| & & | \\
R_2 & & R_2
\end{array}
$$

In this way, for example, by addition of NH_3 to the 2,3-epoxides and subsequent epimerization, the following sugars were prepared: 3-amino-3-deoxy-
D-ribose from L-arabinose[18] and D-xylose[19]; 2-amino-2-deoxy-D-allose from
2-amino-2-deoxy-D-glucose[20], and 2-amino-2-deoxygulose from 2-amino-
2-deoxy-D-galactose[21].

A further synthetic possibility is the epimerization of 2-acylamido-
2-deoxyaldoses with dilute alkali[22]. The size of the acyl group and the
equatorial or axial position of the acylamino group are decisive for the
amounts of the respective epimers which arise[23]. From N-acetylglucosamine
a good yield of 2-acetamino-2-deoxy-D-mannose can be obtained in this way.

(c) Intramolecular rearrangement of N-glycosides
(Amadori rearrangement, Heyns rearrangement)

In the reaction of aldoses with arylamine by way of the Amadori rearrangement[24] the 1-arylamino-1-deoxyketoses (Amadori compounds) are obtained.
The catalytic hydrogenation of these compounds in acetic acid solution
gives a good yield of the 1-amino-1-deoxyketose (e.g. D-isoglucosamine),
with loss of the substituent to the nitrogen. By analogy, Heyns[26] rearranged
ketosylamine catalytically with weak acids (succinic acid, benzoic acid) to
the corresponding pairs of the 2-amino-2-deoxyaldoses. Strong acids lead,
by loss of the amino groups, to the corresponding ketoses. For example,
from fructosylamine (D-arabohexulosylamine), D-glucosamine und D-mannosamine are obtained.

```
   CH2OH              CH2OH               HCOH                HCOH
    |                  |                   |                   ⊕ |
 HOC—O—          ⊕H3NC—O—              HCNH3⊕             H3NCH
    |                  |                   |                   |
 HOCH               HOCH                HOCH          +     HOCH
    |         HCl      |       benzoic     |                   |
 HCOH      ←——       HCOH      ——→       HCOH               HCOH
    |                  |        acid       |                   |
 HCOH               HCOH                HCO—                HCO—
    |                  |                   |                   |
   CH2—               CH2—              CH2OH               CH2OH
```

(d) The HCN method (partial hydrogenation of aminonitriles)

Fischer and Leuchs[27] were the first who successfully synthesized an amino-sugar, *i.e.* D-glucosamine, in the following way: addition of HCN to D-arabinosylamine, hydrolysis of the aminonitrile with concentrated HCl to the corresponding acid, dehydration to the lactone and finally reduction to the aldose with sodium amalgam. Later, D-galactosamine[28] and N-methyl-L-glucosamine[29] were synthesized in an analogous way. The yields ranged from 0.3 to 1.5 %.

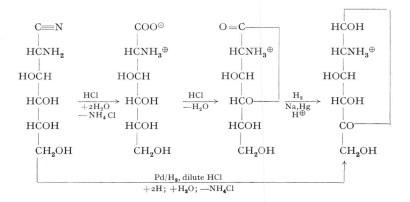

```
    C≡N               COO⊖               O=C—                HCOH
     |                 |                  |                   |
  HCNH2             HCNH3⊕            HCNH3⊕             HCNH3⊕
     |                 |                  |                   |
  HOCH              HOCH               HOCH                HOCH
     |      HCl        |       HCl        |       H2          |
  HCOH    ——→        HCOH    ——→       HCO—     ——→        HCOH
     |    +2H2O         |      —H2O        |     Na,Hg         |
  HCOH    —NH4Cl     HCOH               HCOH     H⊕         CO—
     |                 |                  |                   |
   CH2OH             CH2OH              CH2OH               CH2OH
                                                             ↑
         |——————————— Pd/H2, dilute HCl ———————————————|
                     +2H; +H2O; —NH4Cl
```

The path to the 2-amino-2-deoxyaldoses through the aminonitriles only became a generally acceptable and practical way after Wolfrom[30] succeeded in improving the synthesis of the aminonitriles, and after Kuhn and Kirschenlohr[31] showed that by catalytic hemihydrogenation of the amino-nitriles in dilute HCl, 2-amino-2-deoxyaldoses can be obtained in one step. The yield of amino sugar obtained by this method amounted in some in-stances to more than 70 %. The rather mild conditions also made it possible[32]

References p. 110

to synthesize lactosamine(4-β-D-galactopyranosyl-2-acetamido-2-deoxyglucose) from lactose by preserving the glycosidic bond. The syntheses took the following course: Wohl–Zemplén degradation of lactose to the 3-β-D-galactopyranosyl-D-arabinose, addition of aniline and HCN with subsequent hemihydrogenation. Besides NH_3, aliphatic and aromatic amines can be used for the synthesis of aminonitriles. For the hemihydrogenation of N-phenyl- and N-benzylaminonitriles 3 or 2 molecules H_2 are consumed with the forma-

TABLE I

THE 2-AMINO-2-DEOXYHEXOSES OF THE D-SERIES

1	*2*	*3*	*4*	*5*	*6*	*7*
		$[\alpha]_D$ in water				
Amino sugar or hexose	*Melting point (decomp.)*	*Beginning*	*End*	R_F	$R_{glucos-amine \cdot HCl}$	$R_{N-acetyl-glucosamine}$
β-D-Allosamine·HCl	145–148°	+ 1°	+16°	0.30	0.97	
β-N-Acetyl-D-allosamine	197°	− 74°	−53°			1.04
β-D-Allose	128°	0°	+14°	0.46		
D-Altrosamine·HCl	amorphous		−14°	0.33	1.10	
β-N-Acetyl-D-altros-amine	95–97°	− 4°	+ 5°			1.11
β-D-Altrose	103–105°	− 69°	+33°	0.53		
α-D-Glucosamine·HCl	190–210°	+100°	+72°	0.31	1.00	
α-N-Acetyl-D-glucos-amine	205°	+ 64°	+41°			1.00
α-D-Glucose	146°	+112°	+53°	0.44		
D-Mannosamine·HCl	178–180°	− 3°	− 3°	0.35	1.13	
β-N-Acetyl-D-mannos-amine·H$_2$O	105–108°	− 21°	+10°			1.04
β-D-Mannose	132°	− 17°	+14°	0.50		
α-D-Gulosamine·HCl	165–170°	+ 40°	−19°	0.32	1.04	
N-Acetyl-D-gulosamine	amorphous	− 54°	−59°			1.07
D-Gulose	sirup		−20°	0.48		
D-Idosamine·HCl	amorphous		+ 1°	0.41	1.29	
N-Acetyl-D-idosamine	amorphous		−45°			1.18
D-Idose	sirup		+15°	0.61		
α-D-Galactosamine·HCl	178–180°	+135°	+93°	0.29	0.91	
α-N-Acetyl-D-galactos-amine	172–173°	+115°	+86°			0.92
α-D-Galactose	167°	+150°	+80°	0.40		
α-D-Talosamine·HCl	151–153°	+ 3°	− 6°	0.33	1.08	
N-Acetyl-D-talosamine	amorphous		−11°			1.08
α-D-Talose	133–134°	+ 68°	+21°	0.57		

The R_F values given in column 5 were determined on Schleicher and Schüll 2043 mgl paper, ascending in pyridine–acetic ester–acetic acid–water = 5:5:1:3. The relative values $R_{glucosamine}$ or $R_{N-acetylglucosamine}$ in columns 6 and 7 were ascertained on the same paper by descending chromatography using pyridine–acetic ester–acetic acid–water = 5:5:1:3. For vapour saturation pyridine–acetic ester–water = 11:40:6 was put in the bottom of the vessel used[107].

TABLE II

THE 2-AMINO-2-DEOXYPENTOSES OF THE D-SERIES

Column 7 gives the R_{Gl} values ($R_{glucosamine}$) for the hydrochlorides and the $R_{N\text{-}Agl}$ values ($R_{N\text{-}acetylglucosamine}$) for the N acetyl compounds. The latter are italicized.

1	*2*	*3*	*4*	*5*	*6*	*7*
		\[α\]_D *in water*				
Aminopentose or pentose	*Melting point (decomp.)*	*Extrapolated*	*After 2 min*	*End*	R_F	R_{Gl} or $R_{N\text{-}Agl}$
α-D-Ribosamine·HCl	153–155°	+ 18.6°	+ 11.6°	— 5.8°	0.22	1.37
β-N-Acetyl-D-ribosamine	141–143°	— 82°	— 73.2°	— 39°	0.49	*1.43*
D-Ribose	86–87°	+ 20.3°		+ 23.9°	0.44	
β-D-Arabinosamine·HCl	154–157°	—174°	—158°	—124°	0.17	1.03
β-N-Acetyl-D-arabinos-amine	160–163°	—162°	—149°	— 97°	0.40	*1.18*
β-D-Arabinose	159–160°	—175°		—105°	0.33	
α-D-Xylosamine·HCl	168–170°	+ 82°	+ 76.9°	+ 44.9°	0.23	1.43
α-N-Acetyl-D-xylosamine	187–190°		+ 55°	+ 7.8°	0.46	*1.35*
α-D-Xylose	145°	+ 93.6°		+ 18.8°	0.38	
α-D-Lyxosamine·HCl	165–167°	+ 19°	+ 13.3°	— 4.6°	0.23	1.43
N-Acetyl-D-lyxosamine	sirup	—	—	+ 19°	0.45	*1.33*
α-D-Lyxose	106–107°	+ 5.6°		— 13.8°	0.39	
β-Methyl-2-amino-D-lyxo-furanoside·HCl	138–141°	— 95.8°		— 95.8°	0.40	
α-Methyl-2-amino-D-lyxo-furanoside·HCl	150–151°	+109.5°		+109.5°	0.56	

For the mirror image of D-arabinosamine·HCl (2-amino-2-deoxy-L-arabinose hydro-chloride), which was obtained in a different way, Wolfrom and Yosizawa[108] found: melting point 153–155° and $[\alpha]_D^{20} = +174°$ (for t = 0 extrapolated) → +115° (c = 0.5, water); for the N-acetyl compound; $[\alpha]_D^{20} = +147.5°$ (t = 0) → +94° (c = 1.0, water). The mirror image of D-ribosamine·HCl (2-amino-2-deoxy-L-ribose hydrochloride) shows, according to Wolfrom *et al.*[109], melting point 142–148° (decomp.) and $[\alpha]_D^{23} = +14.1°$ (t = 0) → —2.75° (c = 2, water).

Wolfrom *et al.*[110] have reported on the synthesis of D-ribosamine·HCl and D-lyxos-amine·HCl. The melting point 148–155° (decomp.) and rotatory power $[\alpha]_D^{25} = +54°$ → —36° (c = 2.3, water) stated for D-lyxosamine·HCl differs markedly from the cor-responding values found by Kuhn and Baschang[36] for preparations of melting point 164–167° (decomp.): $[\alpha]_D^{24} = +9°$ (c = 1.7, water).

tion of the corresponding 2-amino-2-deoxyaldoses and cyclohexanone or toluene.

In the synthesis of aminonitriles from aldose, primary amine and hydro-cyanic acid, the preponderant epimer produced is the one in which the amino group is in the *trans* position relative to neighbouring hydroxyl groups. The yields of mannosamine, allosamine, talosamine and gulosamine in the synthesis through the aminonitriles from the corresponding pentoses are therefore small. Nevertheless[33], in the instances of talosamine and allosamine it was possible, by a suitable choice of the amine (9-aminofluorene or diphenylmethylamine), according to the principle of Dimroth[34], to alter

TABLE III

COMPARISON OF $[\alpha]_D$- AND R_F-VALUES

(in Fischer–Nebel mixture)

1	2	3	4	5	6
Substance	Melting point	$[\alpha]_D$ Final value	$R_{glucos-amine \cdot HCl}$	$R_{N-acetyl-glucosamine}$	$R_{glucose}$
α-D-Erythrosamine·HCl	128°	$+ 5.3°$ (H_2O)	1.70		
N-Acetyl-D-erythros-amine	sirup	$- 7.6°$ (H_2O)		1.51	
D-Erythrose	amorphous	$-17°$ (H_2O)			1.80
D-Threosamine·HCl	amorphous	$-33°$ (CH_3OH)	1.98		
N-Acetyl-D-threos-amine	sirup	$-66°$ (CH_3OH)		1.75	
D-Threose		$-12°$ (H_2O)			

the synthesis in favour of the epimers desired. A suspension of the amino-nitrile obtained from pentose + amine + HCN is stirred in a small volume of hot alcohol, with the result that the solid phase is eventually completely rearranged into one of the epimers. One thus avoids the fractional crystalli-zation of the mixture of epimers which is always subject to losses. In this way, after hemihydrogenation, it was possible to obtain, without chromato-graphic separation, more than 50 % yields of pure D-talosamine and D-allosamine.

By catalytic hemihydrogenation of the aminonitriles in the D-series, all the eight 2-amino-deoxyhexoses[35], all the four 2-amino-2-deoxypentoses[36], and the two 2-amino-2-deoxytetroses[37] have been prepared (Tables I, II and III; for further data and derivatives see ref. 10).

Addition of HCN to the 2-acetamido-2-deoxyhexoses, after hemi-hydrogenation of the nitrile, leads to the 3-acetamido-3-deoxyheptoses[38]. Degradation of the methylpyranoside of 3-acetamido-3-deoxyheptoses with $NaIO_4$, together with reduction of the aldehyde group at the C-atom 6 with KBH_4 leads to the 3-acetamido-3-deoxyhexoses. In an analogous manner the corresponding aminopentoses can be prepared from the methyl-furanosides of the 2(or 3)-acetamido-2(or 3)-deoxyhexoses[39,40].

(e) The nitromethane method

In the field of the nitrogen-free sugars, syntheses with nitromethane are used for the lengthening of the carbohydrate chain and for the production of C-nitro-deoxyinositols[41], etc. Recently syntheses with nitromethane have also been carried out in the field of the amino sugars. Sowden and Fischer[43] had already succeeded in synthesizing 3,4,5,6-tetra-O-acetyl-

D-arabo-1-nitrohexene-1, by using the Schmidt and Rutz reaction[42] for the preparation of nitro-olefines from nitro-alcohols. Starting with this compound O'Neill[44] prepared N-acetyl-D-mannosamine by addition of NH_3 to the double bond and elimination of the nitro group by means of the Nef reaction[45].

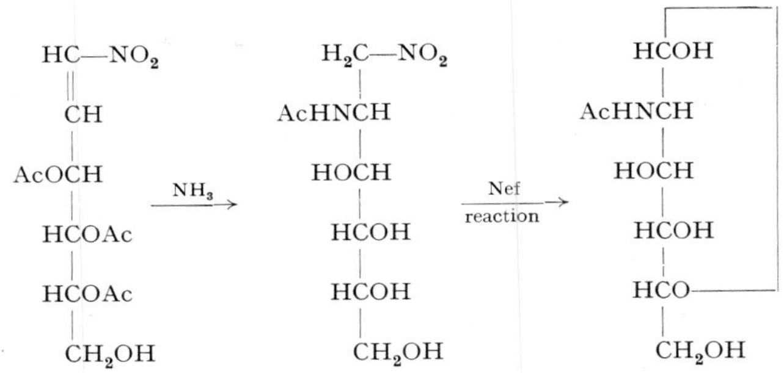

The addition of NH_3 to the double bond does not, however, as was originally supposed[44], proceed stereospecifically, but only stereoselectively. According to Sowden and Oftedahl[46], the D-manno and D-gluco epimers arise in the ratio of 6:1. The addition of NH_3 to 3,4,5,6-tetra-O-acetyl-D-arabo-1,1-bis(ethanesulfonyl)-hexene-1 yields, on the contrary, a preponderant amount of the D-gluco epimer.

An interesting path to the 3-amino-3-deoxyaldoses was found by Fischer and Baer[47,48]. Periodate cleavage of methylpentopyranosides or methyl-pentofuranosides, or of methylhexopyranosides, produces dialdehydes in which the acetal linkage is still maintained. Addition of nitromethane leads to renewed cyclization. After reduction of the nitro group, 3-amino-3-deoxy-aldoses are obtained. Taking methyl-β-D-ribofuranoside as an example, the formulas show the path of the reaction:

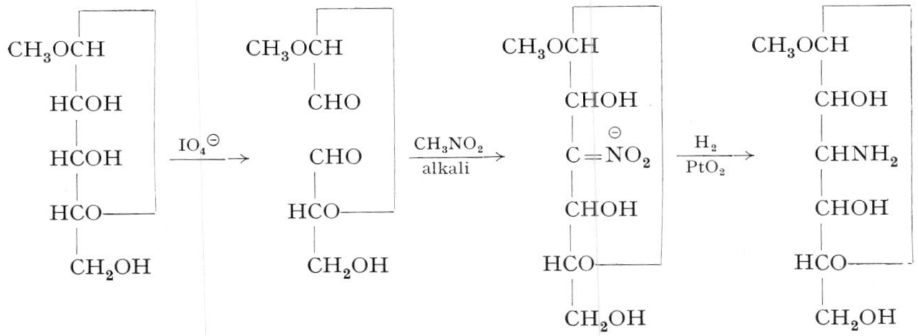

In the methylpyranosides the C-atom 3 is eliminated by IO_4^- as HCOOH. The synthesis proceeds largely stereoselectively, so that all the eight diastereoisomers theoretically expected never appear.

In this manner 3-amino-3-deoxy-D- and -L-ribose, 3-amino-3-deoxy-D-mannose and 3-amino-3-deoxy-D-glucose have been prepared. In an analogous way Richardson and Fischer[49], starting from laevoglucosan, obtained 3-amino-1,6-anhydro-3-deoxy-D-glucose, -D-altrose and -D-idose.

2. Derivatives

(a) Acyl derivatives

The peracetylation of amino sugars, which exist chiefly as hydrochlorides, can occur in pyridine[50], or in dimethylformamide[51] and pyridine with acetic anhydride. In general, mixtures of the α- and β-anomers are obtained. Treatment with methanolic NH_3 leads to the N-acyl derivatives[52]. The high stability of the acid–amide bond permits even reductive detosylization[53]. For selective N-acetylation a number of methods have been developed[36, 50, 54–57].

Crystallized N-acetylglucosamine is usually the α-anomer. The preparation of the β-anomer is achieved from the β-form of glucosamine·HCl in dimethylformamide[58] at lower temperatures, because the mutarotation in this solvent proceeds very slowly.

For the synthesis of the 6-phosphate of D-glucosamine, which is important for the biosynthesis of the mucopolysaccharides, several methods have recently been described[59, 60]. The N-acetyl compound is also known[61]. 2-Amino-2-deoxy-α-D-glucopyranosyl 1-phosphate has been prepared with Ag_3PO_4 as a Ca^{2+} salt from acetochlorglucosamine (2-acetamido-3,4,6-triacetyl-2-deoxy-α-glucosyl chloride[62]).

Sulfate esters of the amino sugars are widely distributed in nature in heparin, mucoitin sulfate and chondroitin sulfate. The interpretation of the structure of these compounds is difficult, but it may certainly be facilitated since the synthetic sulfate derivatives of the amino sugars permit the study of the alkali and acid stability[63].

(b) Glycosides

Direct glycosidation of the 2-amino-2-deoxyhexoses with alcohols and acids fails because of the protective effect of the NH_3^+ group. However, if the amino group is acylated, glycosidation occurs and is especially well done with cation exchangers[64–66]. With diazomethane in moist methanol–ether the β-methylglycoside of N-acetylglucosamine is obtained[67].

For the preparation of β-glycosides the acetobromine[68], acetochlorine[69–74] and, under certain conditions, the acetofluorine[75] compounds are suitable. For this 2-acetamido-3,4,6-tri-O-acetyl-2-deoxyglucosyl chloride and the corresponding galactosyl chloride are preferable, because the bromine com-

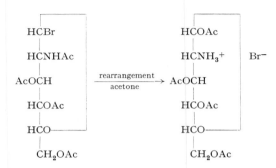

pounds rearrange very readily, especially in polar solvents[70,76,77]. By excluding humidity, the acetobromine compound of glucosamine can be obtained and yields with alcohols β-D-glucosaminides. After standing for some time, it becomes rearranged to form 1,3,4,6-tetra-O-acetyl-glucos-amine·HBr.

(c) Methyl ethers

In the field of the amino sugars the classical method for the elucidation of oligo- and poly-saccharide structure by permethylation, hydrolysis and identification of the cleavage products, has been applicable to a limited extent only. More recently Jeanloz, Stoffyn et al.[7,78] synthesized most of the still missing methyl ethers of D-glucosamine and D-galactosamine. The hydrochlorides of the methyl ethers often crystallize poorly and do not give sharp melting points. Therefore they are mostly converted to the cor-responding Schiff bases with 2-hydroxynaphthaldehyde, which crystallize readily.

Permethylation, which occurs in an alkaline medium, makes it necessary to shield the reducing end groups, in order to avoid decomposition reactions and rearrangements. This is done either by glycosidation with diazo-methane[67], or better by reduction with $NaBH_4$ [79], or, catalytically, with H_2. The methylation methods have been so much improved by Kuhn et al.[81–83] that it is often possible to obtain permethylated products in one step. Methylation is done in dimethylformamide with methyliodide and Ag_2O or $BaO + Ba(OH)_2·8H_2O$ or $SrO + Sr(OH)_2·8H_2O$. The amounts of the solvent (DMF) and base (Ag_2O, BaO, etc.), and also the water content, have a decisive influence on the course of the methylation[83].

3. Stability, oxidation and decomposition reactions

The 2-amino-2-deoxyhexoses are very stable in acids, even at 100°, as long as no other sugars or amino acids are present. The free bases are not stable and they decompose readily at room temperature in aqueous solution. Little is known about the reactions that occur subsequently.

The oxidation of D-glucosamine to the 2-amino-2-deoxyglucuronic acid with O_2 and PtO_2 is carried out successfully if the amino group is protected by the carbobenzoxy group[84]. D-Glucosamine can be oxidized to D-glucosaminic acid by atmospheric oxygen at 30° in the presence of PtO_2[85].

The oxidation of the 2-amino-2-deoxyhexoses and the 2-acetamido-2-deoxyhexoses with $NaIO_4$ does not always proceed in a well-defined manner, because overoxidation can readily occur[86-88]. The results obtained must therefore be interpreted with caution in the elucidation of structural problems.

Determination of the end groups is preferably done with hypoiodite according to the method of Macleod and Robison[89]. The reaction is quantitative if the precautionary measures prescribed are observed[79,80] and if alkali-labile 1,3-compounds are not present.

The deamination of the 2-amino-2-deoxyhexoses with ninhydrin seems to be a generally applicable reaction, which leads to the next lower pentoses[90,91].

Deamination with nitrous acid (HNO_2) needs further investigation before precise rules for it can be stated. Treatment of D-glucosamine with HNO_2 does not lead, as might be expected, to exchange of the NH_2- for an OH-group, but to 2,5-anhydro-D-mannose (chitose)[92,93]. In the reaction of the NH_2-group with HNO_2 a carbonium cation is formed as an intermediate at C-atom 2. The molecular environment of the carbonium cation will always determine the nature of the end product[94,95]. Thus 2-deoxyglucose arises from 2-amino-2-deoxysorbitol and 2,5-anhydro-D-glucuronic acid arises from D-glucosaminic acid after double Walden inversion at C-atom 2.

The Morgan–Elson reaction

The Elson–Morgan reaction[96] and Morgan–Elson reaction[97] are of great importance for the detection of 2-amino-2-deoxyhexoses and of the 2-acetamido-2-deoxyhexoses. With their help it is possible to detect these compounds in mixtures which contain nitrogen-free sugars, amino acids, etc.

If N-acetylglucosamine is heated with dilute alkali and then treated with p-dimethylaminobenzaldehyde in hydrochloric acid (Ehrlich's reagent), a reddish violet colour is obtained. The mechanism of this Morgan–Elson reaction, which was developed for quantitative estimation of N-acetylaminohexoses[98,99], has been the subject of many researches, especially since it has been used for the elucidation of structural problems.

Stanley[100] had shown that, when N-acetylglucosamine is heated with alkali, two chromogens arise. Kuhn and Krüger[101a,b] found that, when hot 0.05 N Na_2CO_3 solution acts on N-acetylglucosamine, three chromogens are formed of which chromogen I preponderates. Alkali is not decisive for the formation of the chromogen, but it works catalytically. Merely heating in water, collidine, benzyl alcohol, acetic anhydride, dimethylformamide or pyridine also leads to the formation of chromogens. When heating in

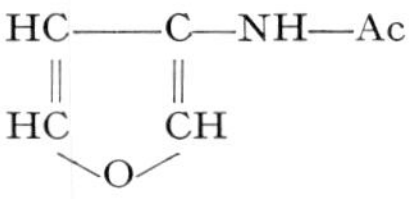

```
                                            HC——C—NH—Ac
  HC——C—NH—Ac                         H  ‖      ‖
     ‖       ‖              HOH2C—C—C       CH
  HC      CH                           |       \O/
     \O/                             OH
  3-Acetamino-furane              Chromogen III
```

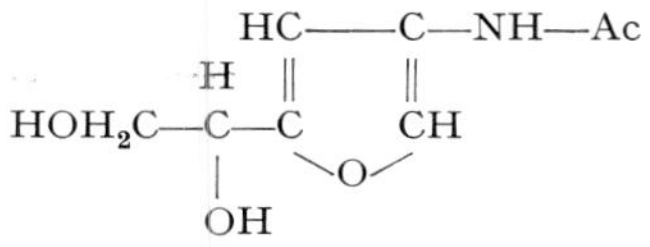

pyridine is used, chromogen III preponderates. All three chromogens, of which the chromogens II and III were obtained in a crystalline form, give an intense red colour with Ehrlich's reagent.

The formation of red pigments with Ehrlich's reagent in hydrochloric acid solution is a characteristic of several classes of substances. A series of α- and β-substituted pyrroles and some phenols (phloroglucin, resorcin, pyrogallol, etc.) give this reaction, either in the cold or after heating[1,6].

High vacuum distillation of the chromogen mixture obtained from N-acetylglucosamine yields 3-acetaminofurane[101a]. It was possible to identify chromogen III as 3-acetamino-5-[α,β-dihydroxyethyl]-furane[101b].

Because the C-atom 5 of N-acetylglucosamine is the only optically active C-atom still present in chromogen III, all the 2-acetamido-2-deoxyhexoses of the D-series should yield the same chromogen III. This has been proved for N-acetyl-D-galactosamine[101b].

For the chromogens I and II the following structures are under discussion (see formula 1–3, p. 108):

Chromogen I can be converted by heating into chromogen III, but apparently this does not occur through chromogen II.

It was concluded from these results that the chromogen formation takes place through the furanose form of the 2-acetamido-2-deoxyhexoses. According to this theory many observations are explained. The nature of the acyl group on the nitrogen is without decisive influence on the result of the reaction; on the other hand substituents on C-atom 4 of N-acetyl-glucosamine, which are not saponified, inhibit the chromogen formation. For example, 4-β-D-galactopyranosyl-N-acetyl-D-glucosamine, N,N-di-acetyl-

OH
H   H>C——C—NH—Ac
 | | ‖
HOH₂C—C——C   CH
         | ⟋⟍ ⟋
         H   O

OH

I

H   HC══C—NH—Ac   H   HC——C—NH—Ac (with H above right C)
 | | | | | ‖ |
HOH₂C—C——C   C—H   HOH₂C—C——C   C—H
 | ⟍ ⟋ ⟍ | ⟍ ⟋ ⟍
OH   H   O   OH   OH   O   OH

2   3

chitobiose, 4-O-methyl-N-acetyl-D-glucosamine, etc. all give negative Morgan–Elson reactions.

In contrast to this, substituents on C-atom 3 of N-acetylglucosamine facilitate chromogen formation. Thus 3-β-D-galactopyranosyl-N-acetyl-D-glucosamine yields chromogen I and galactose readily in the cold with 0.25 N Na₂CO₃ solution[102]. Under standard conditions[98] 3-O-methyl-N-acetyl-glucosamine gives 1.6 times and 3,6-di-O-methyl-N-acetylglucosamine 1.4 times the colour intensity given by N-acetylglucosamine[103]. All this supports the view that during chromogen formation water is split off primarily between C-atoms 3 and 4 (formula 3), or between C-atoms 2 and 3 (formula 2), which would also explain the fact that chromogen I still reduces Fehling's solution.

As may be expected, all the four N-acetylpentosamines[36] and the two N-acetyltetrosamines give the Morgan–Elson reaction. The readiness of the N-acetyltetrosamines to undergo this reaction is very much increased, because the furanose form is necessarily already present. Hence the reaction occurs even at room temperature[37]. Heating of N-acetyltetrosamines in pyridine gives a good yield of 3-acetaminofurane.

In the light of this knowledge one can also understand why some oligosaccharides, such as, for example, lacto-N-tetrose[104] (see also Table 7 in ref.8), which contain the N-acetylglucosamine bound glycosidically, give a positive Morgan–Elson reaction. They are decomposed stepwise by the hot alkali from the reducing end until the C-atom 1 of the amino sugar is set free and the chromogen formation can result. Reduction of the reducing end markedly lessens the readiness to undergo alkaline decomposition and therefore also the possibility of chromogen formation.

As exceptions to this, Wolfrom and Juliano[105] reported that 2-acetamido-2-deoxysorbitol and 3-O-β-D-glucopyranosyl-2-acetamido-2-deoxydulcite give a positive Morgan–Elson reaction, but these results need further confirmation.

The Elson–Morgan reaction[96] for the quantitative estimation of glucosamine and galactosamine, which are not acetylated to nitrogen, requires, during heating with alkali, the addition of acetylacetone. Here also several chromogens are formed[106], the absorption spectra of which differ markedly according to the conditions of the reaction. Nothing is yet known about the mechanism of this reaction.

REFERENCES

[1] P. W. KENT AND M. W. WHITEHOUSE, *Biochemistry of the Aminosugars*, Butterworths, London (1955).

[2] G. LEDDERHOSE, *Ber. deut. chem. Ges.*, B9 (1876) 1200.

[3] K. KUHN, *Angew. Chem.*, 69 (1957) 23.

[4] A. B. FOSTER AND A. J. HUGGARD, *Advances in Carbohydrate Chem.*, 10 (1955) 335.

[5] R. L. WHISTLER AND E. J. OLSON, *Advances in Carbohydrate Chem.*, 12 (1957) 299.

[6] F. ZILLIKEN AND M. W. WHITEHOUSE, *Advances in Carbohydrate Chem.*, 13 (1958) 237.

[7] R. W. JEANLOZ, *Advances in Carbohydrate Chem.*, 13 (1958) 189.

[8] H. H. BAER, *Fortschr. chem. Forsch.*, 3 (1958) 822.

[9] A. B. FOSTER AND D. HORTON, *Advances in Carbohydrate Chem.*, 14 (1959) 213.

[10] D. HORTON, *Advances in Carbohydrate Chem.*, 15 (1960) 159.

[11] R. KUHN, *Struktur und Stoffwechsel des Bindegewebes*, Thieme, Stuttgart, 1960, p. 1.

[12] S. ROSEMAN, *Ann. Rev. Biochem.*, 28 (1959) 545.

[13] A. FÜRST AND P. A. PLATTNER, *Intern. Congr. Pure and Appl. Chem.*, 13th Congr., 1951, p. 409; *J. Colloid Sci., Suppl.*, 1 (1954).

[14] W. N. HAWORTH, W. H. G. LAKE AND S. PEAT, *J. Chem. Soc.*, (1939) 271.

[15] S. P. JAMES, F. SMITH, M. STACEY AND L. F. WIGGINS, *J. Chem. Soc.*, (1946) 625.

[16] F. SHAFIZADEH, *Advances in Carbohydrate Chem.*, 13 (1958) 9.

[17] S. WINSTEIN AND R. BOSCHAN, *J. Am. Chem. Soc.*, 72 (1950) 4669.

[18] B. R. BAKER AND R. E. SCHAUB, *J. Org. Chem.*, 19 (1954) 646.

[19] B. R. BAKER, R. E. SCHAUB AND J. H. WILLIAMS, *J. Am. Chem. Soc.*, 77 (1955) 7.

[20] R. W. JEANLOZ, *J. Am. Chem. Soc.*, 79 (1957) 2591.

[21] Z. TARSIEJSKA AND R. W. JEANLOZ, *J. Am. Chem. Soc.*, 79 (1957) 2660.

[22] R. KUHN AND R. BROSSMER, *Ann. Chem., Liebigs*, 616 (1958) 221;
R. KUHN AND G. BASCHANG, *Ann. Chem., Liebigs*, 636 (1960) 164;
R. KUHN AND A. GAUHE, *Chem. Ber.*, 94 (1961) 842.

[23] G. BASCHANG, *Thesis*, Universität Heidelberg, 1960.

[24] J. E. HODGE, *Advances in Carbohydrate Chem.*, 10 (1955) 169.

[25] R. KUHN AND H. J. HAAS, *Ann. Chem., Liebigs*, 600 (1956) 148.

[26] K. HEYNS, H. PAULSEN, R. REICHSTEDT AND M. ROLLE, *Chem. Ber.*, 90 (1957) 2039.

[27] E. FISCHER AND H. LEUCHS, *Ber. deut. chem. Ges.*, B36 (1903) 24.

[28] P. A. LEVENE AND F. B. LA FORGE, *J. Biol. Chem.*, 20 (1915) 433.

[29] F. A. KUEHL JR., E. H. FLYNN, F. W. HOLLY, R. MOZINGO AND K. FOLKERS, *J. Am. Chem. Soc.*, 69 (1957) 1847.

[30] M. L. WOLFROM, A. THOMPSON AND I. R. HOOPER, *J. Am. Chem. Soc.*, 68 (1946) 2343.

[31] R. KUHN AND W. KIRSCHENLOHR, *Angew. Chem.*, 67 (1955) 786; *Ann. Chem., Liebigs*, 600 (1956) 115.

[32] R. KUHN AND W. KIRSCHENLOHR, *Ann. Chem., Liebigs*, 600 (1956) 135.

[33] R. KUHN AND J. C. JOCHIMS, *Ann. Chem., Liebigs*, 641 (1961) 143.

[34] O. DIMROTH, *Ann. Chem. Liebigs*, 377 (1910) 127.

[35] R. KUHN, W. BISTER AND H. FISCHER, *Ann. Chem., Liebigs*, 617 (1958) 109.

[36] R. KUHN AND G. BASCHANG, *Ann. Chem., Liebigs*, 628 (1959) 193.

[37] R. KUHN AND H. FISCHER, *Ann. Chem., Liebigs*, 641 (1961) 152.

[38] R. KUHN AND G. BASCHANG, *Ann. Chem., Liebigs*, 628 (1959) 206.

[39] R. KUHN AND G. BASCHANG, *Ann. Chem., Liebigs*, 636 (1960) 164.

[40] L. M. WOLFROM AND K. ANNO, *J. Am. Chem. Soc.*, 75 (1953) 1038.

[41] J. C. SOWDEN, *Advances in Carbohydrate Chem.*, 6 (1951) 291.

[42] E. SCHMIDT AND G. RUTZ, *Ber. deut. chem. Ges.*, B61 (1928) 2142.

[43] J. C. SOWDEN AND H. O. L. FISCHER, *J. Am. Chem. Soc.*, 69 (1947) 1048.

[44] A. N. O'NEILL, *Can. J. Chem.*, 37 (1959) 1747.

[45] J. N. NEF, *Ann. Chem., Liebigs*, 280 (1894) 263.

[46] J. C. SOWDEN AND M. L. OFTEDAHL, *J. Am. Chem. Soc.*, 82 (1960) 2303.

[47] H. H. BAER AND H. O. L. FISCHER, *J. Am. Chem. Soc.*, 81 (1959) 5184; 82 (1960) 3705.

[48] H. H. BAER, *Chem. Ber.*, 93 (1960) 2865.

[49] A. C. RICHARDSON AND H. O. L. FISCHER, *J. Am. Chem. Soc.*, 83 (1961) 1132.

[50] Y. INOUYE, K. ONODERA, S. KITAOKA AND S. HIRANO, *J. Am. Chem. Soc.*, 78 (1956) 4722.

[51] J. H. SCHLUBACH AND W. REPENNING, *Angew. Chem.*, 71 (1959) 193.

[52] R. KUHN AND W. KIRSCHENLOHR, *Chem. Ber.*, 87 (1954) 384.

[53] R. W. JEANLOZ, *J. Am. Chem. Soc.*, 76 (1954) 555.

[54] S. ROSEMAN AND J. LUDOWIEG, *J. Am. Chem. Soc.*, 76 (1954) 301.

[55] T. WHITE, *J. Chem. Soc.*, (1940) 428.

[56] G. QUADBECK, *Angew. Chem.*, 68 (1956) 361.

[57] A. NEUBERGER AND R. P. RIVERS, *J. Chem. Soc.*, (1939) 122.

[58] R. KUHN AND F. HABER, *Chem. Ber.*, 86 (1953) 722.

[59] J. M. ANDERSON AND E. E. PERCIVAL, *Chem. and Ind. (London)*, (1954) 1018; *J. Chem. Soc.*, (1956) 814.

[60] F. WALEY AND H. A. LARDY, *J. Am. Chem. Soc.*, 78 (1956) 1393.

[61] S. ROSEMAN, *Federation Proc.*, 13 (1954) 283; J. J. DISTLER, J. M. MERRICK AND S. ROSEMAN, *J. Biol. Chem.*, 230 (1958) 497.

[62] L. F. LELOIR AND C. E. CARDINI, *Biochim. et Biophys. Acta*, 20 (1956) 33.

[63] M. L. WOLFROM, R. A. GIBBONS AND A. J. HUGGARD, *J. Am. Chem. Soc.*, 79 (1957) 5043.

[64] J. E. CADOTTE, F. SMITH AND D. SPRIESTERSBACH, *J. Am. Chem. Soc.*, 74 (1952) 1501.

[65] R. KUHN, F. ZILLIKEN AND A. GAUHE, *Chem. Ber.*, 86 (1953) 466.

[66] F. ZILLIKEN, C. S. ROSE, G. A. BRAUN AND P. GYÖRGY, *Arch. Biochem. Biophys.*, 54 (1955) 392.

[67] R. KUHN AND H. H. BAER, *Chem. Ber.*, 86 (1953) 724.

[68] R. C. G. MOGGRIDGE AND A. NEUBERGER, *J. Chem. Soc.*, (1938) 745.

[69] F. MICHEEL, F. P. VAN DE KAMP AND H. PETERSEN, *Chem. Ber.*, 90 (1957) 521.

[70] Y. INOUYE, K. ONODERA, S. KITAOKA AND H. OCHAI, *J. Am. Chem. Soc.*, 79 (1957) 4218.

[71] D. H. LEABACK AND P. G. WALKER, *Chem. and Ind. (London)*, (1956) 1017.

[72] D. H. LEABACK AND P. G. WALKER, *J. Chem. Soc.*, (1957) 4754.

[73] C. J. MOREL, *Experientia*, 12 (1956) 419.

[74] Z. TARASIEJSKA AND R. W. JEANLOZ, *J. Am. Chem. Soc.*, 80 (1958) 6325.

[75] F. MICHEEL AND E. MICHAELIS, *Chem. Ber.*, 91 (1958) 188.

[76] G. FODOR AND L. ÖTVÖS, *Ann. Chem. Liebigs*, 604 (1957) 29.

[77] F. MICHEEL, F. P. VAN DE KAMP AND H. WULFF, *Chem. Ber.*, 88 (1955) 2011.

[78] See also Tables in refs. 8,10

[79] A. B. FOSTER AND D. HORTON, *J. Chem. Soc.*, (1958) 1890.

[80] R. KUHN AND H. H. BAER, *Chem. Ber.*, 89 (1956) 504.

[81] R. KUHN, H. TRISCHMANN AND I. LÖW, *Angew. Chem.*, 67 (1955) 32.

[82] R. KUHN, H. H. BAER AND A. SEELIGER, *Ann. Chem., Liebigs*, 611 (1958) 236.

[83] R. KUHN, H. EGGE, R. BROSSMER, A. GAUHE, P. KLESSE, W. LOCHINGER, E. RÖHM, H. TRISCHMANN AND D. TSCHAMPEL, *Angew. Chem.*, 72 (1960) 805.

[84] K. HEYNS AND H. PAULSEN, *Chem. Ber.*, 88 (1955) 188.

[85] K. HEYNS AND W. KOCH, *Chem. Ber.*, 86 (1953) 110.

[86] R. W. JEANLOZ AND E. FORCHIELLI, *J. Biol. Chem.*, 188 (1951) 361.

[87] A. NEUBERGER, *J. Chem. Soc.*, (1941) 47.

[88] D. AMINOFF AND W. T. J. MORGAN, *Biochem. J.*, 44 (1949) XXI.

[89] M. MACLEOD AND R. ROBISON, *Biochem. J.*, 23 (1929) 517.

[90] S. GARDELL, F. HEIJKENSKJÖLD AND A. ROCHNORLUND, *Acta Chem. Scand.*, 4 (1950) 970.

[91] P. J. STOFFYN AND R. W. JEANLOZ, *Arch. Biochem. Biophys.*, 52 (1954) 373.

[92] E. FISCHER AND E. ANDREAE, *Ber. deut. chem. Ges.*, B36 (1903) 2587.

[93] B. C. BERA, A. B. FOSTER AND M. STACEY, *J. Chem. Soc.*, (1956) 4531.

[94] A. B. FOSTER, *Chem. and Ind. (London)*, (1955) 627.

[95] F. SHAFIZADEH, *Advances in Carbohydrate Chem.*, 13 (1958) 43.

[96] L. A. ELSON AND W. T. J. MORGAN, *Biochem. J.*, 27 (1933) 1824.

[97] W. T. J. MORGAN AND L. A. ELSON, *Biochem. J.*, 28 (1934) 988.

[98] E. AMINOFF, W. T. J. MORGAN AND W. M. WATKINS, *Biochem. J.*, 51 (1952) 379.

[99] J. L. REISIG, J. L. STROMINGER AND L. F. LELOIR, *J. Biol. Chem.*, 217 (1955) 959.

[100] P. G. STANLEY, *Australian J. Exptl. Biol. Med. Sci.*, 31 (1953) 187.

[101a] R. KUHN AND G. KRÜGER, *Chem. Ber.*, 89 (1956) 1473.

[101b] R. KUHN AND G. KRÜGER, *Chem. Ber.*, 90 (1957) 264.

[102] R. KUHN, H. H. BAER AND A. GAUHE, *Chem. Ber.*, 87 (1954) 289.

[103] R. W. JEANLOZ AND M. TRÉMÈGE, *Federation Proc.*, 15 (1956) 282.

[104] R. KUHN AND H. H. BAER, *Chem. Ber.*, 89 (1956) 504.

[105] M. L. WOLFROM AND B. O. JULIANO, *J. Am. Chem. Soc.*, 82 (1960) 1673.

[106] B. SCHLOSS, *Anal. Chem.*, 23 (1951) 1321.

[107] F. G. FISCHER AND H. J. NEBEL, *Z. physiol. Chem., Hoppe-Seyler's*, 302 (1955) 10.

[108] M. L. WOLFROM AND Z. YOSIZAWA, *J. Am. Chem. Soc.*, 81 (1959) 3477.

[109] M. L. WOLFROM, F. SHAFIZADEH AND R. K. ARMSTRONG, *J. Am. Chem. Soc.*, 80 (1958) 4885.

[110] M. L. WOLFROM, F. SHAFIZADEH, R. K. ARMSTRONG AND T. M. SHENNAN, *J. Am. Chem. Soc.*, 81 (1959) 3716.

Chapter IV

Sugar Phosphates

LUIS F. LELOIR AND CARLOS E. CARDINI

Institute of Biochemical Investigations, "Fundación Campomar", and Faculty of Exact and Natural Sciences, University of Buenos Aires (Argentina)

1. Introduction

The studies on the chemistry and metabolic role of sugar phosphates were initiated by the work of Harden and Young[1] in 1906. They observed that phosphate esters accumulated during the fermentation of sugar by yeast juice and obtained fructose 1,6-diphosphate from the fermentation mixture. Subsequent work led to the isolation of several other esters. Studies by Embden, Meyerhof, Neuberg, Lohmann, Warburg, Cori, Lipmann and others with yeast, muscle or other extracts and the enzymes thereof led to the elucidation of many aspects of the enzymic interconversion of phosphate esters. Since then a large number of sugar phosphates have engrossed the list of known natural products and many have been obtained by synthesis.

A history of the discovery of phosphorus and of the first sugar esters was written by Schoen[2] in 1929 and continued by Courtois[3] until 1941. The monograph by Harden[4] describes the experiments which led to the isolation of hexose phosphates. A fairly complete review of knowledge on sugar phosphates was written by Leloir[5] in 1950 and supplemented up to 1957 by Foster and Overend[6]. Several other more restricted reviews are available: Fleury[7], Sowden[8], Albaum[9] and Umbreit[10]. Other reviews which can be mentioned are: Robison and McFarlane[11] on isolation and properties of hexose phosphates, Fischer[12] and Cramer[13] on chemical synthesis, Benson[14] on analytical methods, Jeanloz and Fletcher[15] on ribose derivatives, Overend and Stacey[16] on deoxy sugars, and Angyal and Andersen[17] on cyclitols. Information on sugar configuration has been published by Reeves[18,19], Ferrier and Overend[20], Bourne and Stephens[21].

2. Preparation of sugar phosphates*

(a) Enzymic methods

The procedure developed by Harden and Young in their pioneering studies is still used, with slight modifications, for the preparation of some sugar phosphates. Dried yeast or yeast juice can catalyze many of the reactions which occur in living yeast but the delicate adjustment between the different rates of reactions is lost. More organic phosphate is formed than used up, so that a considerable accumulation of sugar phosphates takes place. This complex mixture of esters, which was patiently fractionated by Robison and coworkers in their classical studies, contains fructose 1,6-diphosphate, fructose 6-phosphate, glucose 6-phosphate, glucose 1,6-diphosphate, trehalose phosphate, mannose phosphate and sedoheptulose phosphate. This starting material is still used for the preparation of fructose 1,6-diphosphate.

Many procedures have been described in which crude or purified enzymes are used. Thus glucose 1-phosphate can be prepared from starch and inorganic phosphate with phosphorylase and similar reactions can be used in the preparation of α-ribose 1-phosphate and of α-deoxyribose 1-phosphate from nucleosides with specific phosphorylases. The formation of β-glucose 1-phosphate from maltose with maltose phosphorylase may also be mentioned.

A type of reaction which is applicable in many cases is the phosphorylation with ATP using different kinases. In this manner many esters can be obtained from the free sugars such as glucose 6-phosphate, mannose 6-phosphate, fructose 1-phosphate, fructose 6-phosphate, fructose 1,6-diphosphate, galactose 1-phosphate, galactosamine 1-phosphate, gluconic acid 6-phosphate, ribose 5-phosphate and ribulose 5-phosphate. A special case of enzymic phosphorylation in which a pyrophosphate residue is transferred from ATP is the following reaction:

ATP + ribose 5-phosphate → 5-phosphoribosyl pyrophosphate + AMP

Other reactions which are used for the preparation of some esters are those catalyzed by isomerases. Thus fructose 6-phosphate may be converted to glucose 6-phosphate, ribose 5-phosphate to ribulose 5-phosphate. Specific epimerases which lead to inversion at positions 3 or 4 have been employed. For instance D-xylulose 5-phosphate can be converted to L-ribulose 5-phosphate by a 4-epimerase, or to D-ribulose 5-phosphate by a 3-epimerase.

The enzyme aldolase has found several uses, such as: the preparation of glyceraldehyde 3-phosphate from fructose 1,6-diphosphate and of fructose 1-phosphate from the 1,6-diphosphate plus glyceraldehyde.

---

* References are given in the descriptive section.

Gluconic acid 6-phosphate may be obtained from glucose 6-phosphate with a dehydrogenase and TPN. Glucosamine 6-phosphate can be prepared from glucose 6-phosphate and glutamine.

In some cases a series of reactions are used; for instance, sedoheptulose 1,7-diphosphate can be obtained from ribose 5-phosphate using four enzymes.

(b) Chemical methods applied to natural products

In many cases esters are prepared by simple procedures applied to natural products. Hydrolysis of nucleic acid or purine nucleotides may be used to prepare ribose 3-phosphate, ribose 5-phosphate or 2-deoxyribose 5-phosphate. Reaction with metal borohydrides leads to the formation of sugar alcohols from aldoses, for instance of ribitol 1-phosphate from ribose 5-phosphate. Aldoses may be converted to the onic acids by bromine oxidation, as in the preparation of gluconic acid 6-phosphate from glucose 6-phosphate. Uronic acids can be obtained from C-1 protected aldoses, thus glucose 1-phosphate is oxidized by oxygen with platinum catalyst to glucuronic acid 1-phosphate. Periodate oxidation of α-glycerophosphate and other esters leads to the formation of glycolaldehyde 2-phosphate.

Acid-catalyzed phosphate migration enables α-glycerophosphate to be converted to β-glycerophosphate. Similarly ribose 4-phosphate may be obtained from ribose 2-phosphate or ribose 3-phosphate.

(c) Chemical synthesis

(i) From sugar oxides

Bailly[22] obtained α-glycerophosphate by treating the 1:2-epoxide of glycerol

$$\overset{\displaystyle \overset{\text{O}}{\frown}}{\text{CH}_2\text{---CH---CH}_2\text{OH}}$$

with Na_2HPO_4 in aqueous solution at room temperature. Similar methods have been used for the preparation of β-hydroxyethyl and β-hydroxypropyl phosphate[23], glucose 3-phosphate and altrose 2-phosphate[24], and glucose 6-phosphate[25]. The method is somewhat restricted by the availability of the required epoxides but may be useful in the preparation of compounds labeled at the phosphate residue.

(ii) With polyphosphates

Glucose 6-phosphate has been prepared by heating glucose with polyphosphoric (mainly tetraphosphoric[26]) or with metaphosphoric acids[27]. A similar procedure applied to glucosamine yields glucosamine 6-phosphate.

Polyphosphoric acids can be prepared by heating phosphoric acid, and the conditions are given in a paper by Cherbuliez and Weniger[28]. Fructose 1-phosphate has been prepared by heating 2,3,4,5-diisopropylidene fructose with phosphoric anhydride.

(iii) With phosphorochloridic acids

Phosphoryl chloride (phosphorus oxychloride, $POCl_3$) was used by Neuberg and Pollak[29] in the preparation of some sugar phosphates. An aqueous solution of the sugar was used and $Ca(OH)_2$ or $CaCO_3$ was added in order to neutralize the HCl formed. E. Fischer[30] improved the method by using anhydrous pyridine. The reaction is as follows:

$$ROH + POCl_3 \xrightarrow[- HCl]{} RO-POCl_2 \xrightarrow[- 2HCl]{+ H_2O} RO-PO_3H_2$$

Several other compounds are formed in the reaction such as: diesters $(RO)_2PO_2H$, triesters $(RO)_3PO$ and cyclic esters. In order to avoid these side reactions, substituted compounds are now used, particularly diphenyl phosphorochloridate[31] $[(C_6H_5O)_2POCl]$, dibenzyl phosphorochloridate[23,32] $[(C_6H_5CH_2O)_2POCl]$ for monoesters, and phenyl phosphorodichloridate[31,33] $(C_6H_5O-POCl_2)$ for diesters.

After phosphorylation, the protecting group (phenyl or benzyl) may be removed under mild conditions by hydrogenolysis or by dilute NaOH or liquid ammonia.

Migration of the phosphate group may take place after phosphorylation, as in the preparation of D-xylose 3-phosphate[34]. The starting material was 1,2-isopropylidene xylose which on phosphorylation with diphenyl phosphorochloridate gave the 5-phenyl phosphate. Treatment of the latter with boiling alkali led to the formation of a 3,5-cyclic phosphate with elimination of one phenyl group. Hydrolysis of the latter gave a mixture of the 3- and 5-D-xylose phosphates.

(iv) Dicyclohexylcarbodiimide

A very useful reagent for the preparation of esters and particularly of nucleoside pyrophosphates is dicyclohexylcarbodiimide[35,36] (DCC). Its mechanism of action has been studied by Smith et al.[37] and is shown in Fig. 1. On reaction of DCC (I) with a monophosphate (II) an intermediate believed to have structure (III) is formed. With another molecule of monophosphate (II) a symmetrical pyrophosphate (IV) is formed together with dicyclohexyl urea (V). The reaction can be carried out in a partially aqueous solution because water is a poor nucleophilic agent as compared with the phosphate anion. If the reaction mixture contains excess of an alcohol (VI) then an asymmetrical diester (VII) is formed. This is the basis of a method for the preparation of monoesters with DCC which is carried out as follows[38] : benzyl phosphate or β-cyanoethyl phosphate is transformed, using DCC,

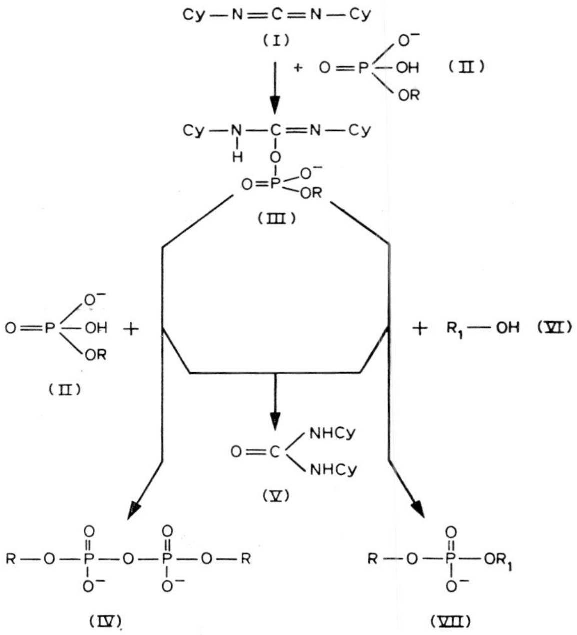

Cy=cyclohexyl

Fig. 1.

into the diester of the compound to be phosphorylated. The benzyl or β-cyanoethyl group is then removed by hydrogenolysis or with alkali respectively. For example the phosphorylation of ROH would be as follows:

$$CN—CH_2—CH_2—PO_3H_2 + ROH \xrightarrow{DCC} CN—CH_2—CH_2—O\underset{RO}{\overset{}{>}}P\underset{O}{\overset{O^-}{<}}$$

$$\xrightarrow{OH^-} CNCH_2CH_2OH + ROPO_3^{2-}$$

If the monophosphate (II) has an OH group in suitable position, a cyclic phosphate may be formed[39], as shown in Fig. 2.

(v) Protected sugars

The primary alcohol group of sugars is more easily phosphorylated than the others so that some sugar phosphates can be prepared directly. Thus

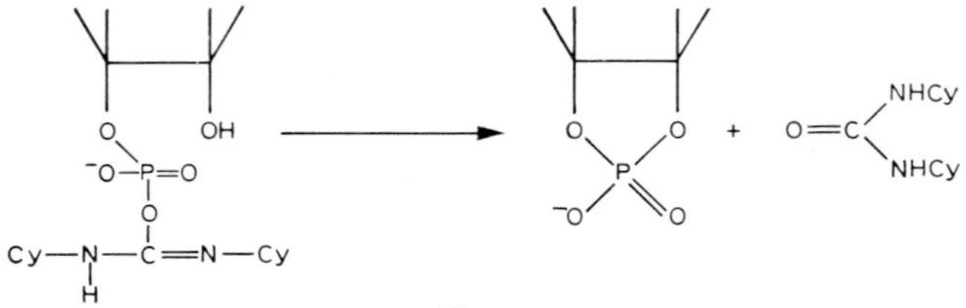

Fig. 2.

using one equivalent of diphenyl phosphorochloridate, 5-diphenyl phosphoro-
benzyl riboside can be obtained from benzyl riboside[40].

In general all the OH groups except the one to be phosphorylated are
protected with some easily removable substituent. As such acetyl, benzoyl,
isopropylidene and carbonate groups are frequently used.

(vi) Synthesis of aldose 1-phosphates

The synthesis of aldose 1-phosphates is generally carried out starting from
acetohalogen sugars[41]. The Br or Cl compounds are treated under anhydrous
conditions with the silver or other salts of inorganic phosphate or of substituted phosphates such as dibenzyl or diphenyl phosphate. Removal of
the protecting groups from the sugar and phosphate moieties yields the
sugar phosphate. Either the α- or the β-anomer may be formed according to
the conditions, and several factors are of importance in this respect. These
are: the nature of the phosphorylating agent, the action of neighbouring
groups and the type of treatment after phosphorylation which may lead to
preferential destruction of one of the anomers. In the synthesis of glucose
1-phosphate it has been found that results vary according to the nature of
the phosphate used. Thus α-glucose 1-phosphate has been prepared using
trisilver phosphate or silver diphenyl phosphate while the β-anomer was
obtained with silver dibenzyl phosphate or "monosilver phosphate". The
preparation usually called "monosilver phosphate" is actually a mixture of
disilver phosphate and phosphoric acid[42].

The influence of the neighbouring groups has been particularly studied
in the case of glycoside formation from acetohalogen sugars, and this point
has been competently reviewed[41,43,44]. The spatial relationship between
the 1-halide and the 2-acetoxyl group is important. When they are *cis*, as
in α-acetobromoglucose, the entering group replaces the halogen with
inversion so that the β-compounds are produced. When the halogen is *trans*
to the 2-acetoxyl group, orthoester formation may take place, so that the
final result is usually the conservation of anomeric configuration. The
synthesis of ribose 1-phosphates is a good example. When position 2 is
blocked with acetyl or benzoyl so that an orthoester can be formed, the
results are different from those obtained with carbonate. For instance,

starting with a ribose derivative with a benzoyl at position 2 (β-2,3,5-tri-O-benzoyl-β-D-ribofuranosyl bromide) phosphorylation gave the β-1-phosphate exclusively[45], that is, no inversion took place. However, starting with a ribose derivative with position 2 blocked by carbonate (β-5-O-acetyl-D-ribofuranosyl bromide 2,3-cyclic carbonate) phosphorylation gave the α-1-phosphate[46], that is, inversion took place. In both cases triethylammonium dibenzyl phosphate was used for the phosphorylation.

(vii) Cyclic esters

Cyclic phosphate esters with 5-, 6- and 7-membered rings have been prepared[39]. None has been isolated from natural sources but some are formed by the action of acid or alkali on natural compounds.

The first cyclic phosphate to be described was prepared by Fischer[30] by treating D-glucopyranosyl theophyllin with phosphoryl chloride in pyridine. It was presumably the 4:6-cyclic phosphate (5-membered ring). Better yields are obtained by using phenyl phosphorodichloridate as in the preparation of the 4:6-cyclic phosphate of phenyl β-D-glucoside[47]. Another method which has been used consists in treating monophosphates which have a free OH group conveniently located, with trifluoroacetic anhydride[48].

The formation of cyclic phosphates with DCC has been mentioned. The steric requirements of such processes have been studied by Khorana *et al.*[39]. Cyclization was found to take place both with α- and β-glucose 1-phosphates, in which the phosphate is *"cis"* and *"trans"* respectively to the OH at position 2. In the stable C1 conformation these groups are axial and equatorial in α-glucose 1-phosphate, and both equatorial in β-glucose 1-phosphate (Figs. 3 and 4). In these cases the five-membered cyclic phosphate can be

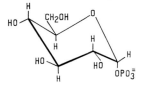

Fig. 3. α-Glucopyranose 1-phosphate (C1 conformation).

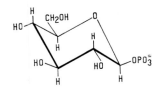

Fig. 4. β-Glucopyranose 1-phosphate (C1 conformation).

formed without strain. If the phosphate and OH at position 2 are *"trans"* and both axial as in α-mannose 1-phosphate in C1 conformation, no cyclic phosphate is formed (Fig. 5).

When the OH group next to the phosphate is free, a five-membered ring is formed. Thus xylose 3-phosphate gives the 3:4- or 2:3-cyclic phosphate. But if the OH next to the phosphate forms part of a furanose or pyranose ring then it is the next OH which reacts. Thus treatment with DCC leads to the formation of the 4:6-cyclic phosphate from glucose 6-phosphate and of the 3:5-cyclic phosphate from xylose 5-phosphate.

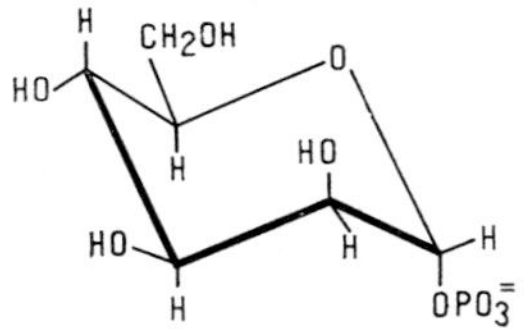

Fig. 5. α-Mannopyranose 1-phosphate (C1 conformation).

(d) Isolation of sugar phosphates

The classical methods for the separation of sugar phosphates were based on the different solubility of their salts[14,49,50].

The solubility of the barium salts depends on the number of acid groups and therefore on the pH of the solution. At neutral pH where the primary and secondary acid groups of phosphate are dissociated, inorganic phosphate and the sugar diphosphates form water-insoluble barium salts. At a pH of about 4 the secondary acid groups are not appreciably dissociated so that the salts become water-soluble.

The sugar monophosphates at neutral pH give water-soluble barium salts which can be precipitated by addition of two or three volumes of ethanol. However, some barium salts may be insoluble as in the case of the crystalline salt of glucose 6-phosphate. Other barium salts such as that of propanediol phosphate are soluble in ethanol.

The separation of inorganic phosphate from the esters can be achieved by forming the insoluble ammonium-magnesium salt but there often occurs considerable coprecipitation.

Other cations have found use besides barium. Thus, calcium, magnesium, mercury and lead have been employed. Several procedures for the separation of sugar phosphates have been described[14,49,50,51]. Salt precipitation is now mainly restricted to prepurification since finer separations can be achieved with anion exchange resins[14,49,52-55]. The resins may be used in the chloride or formate form but still better separations have been obtained with borate[56,57].

Some salts of sugar phosphates may be obtained in crystalline form, as in the case of barium glucose 6-phosphate and barium trehalose phosphate. Salts of organic bases usually tend to crystallize more easily. Those which have been found more useful are cyclohexylamine, brucine, strychnine and benzylamine.

3. Separation of the phosphate group

(a) Acid hydrolysis

(i) General mechanisms

Studies on the action of acids on phosphoric esters are important in the determination of structures and for analytical purposes. Measurements of the rate of acid hydrolysis were carried out by Lohmann[58] in studies of glucose and fructose phosphates and by Levene[59] in his investigations on nucleotides. Since then they have been used routinely.

The rate of acid hydrolysis is characteristic of each ester. Some esters hydrolyze very slowly in hot acid, for instance α- or β-glycerophosphate or glucose 6-phosphate, while others, like 2-deoxyribose 1-phosphate, hydrolyze at room temperature and at pH 4.

The main factors which affect the rate of hydrolysis are the temperature, the pH, the structure of the carbon chain, the position of the phosphate group and the presence of a second substituent on the phosphate.

Careful studies on the effect of hydrogen ion concentration have been carried out with only a few esters but the results seem to be fairly general[60,61]. After the first studies of Malengreau and Prigent[62], several workers[63-72] have investigated the pH dependence of the rate of hydrolysis. For mono-alkyl phosphates, for instance methyl phosphate, the rate of hydrolysis has a maximum at pH 4, a minimum at about pH 1 and rises again in strongly acid solutions (Fig. 6). As pointed out by Bailly[63] the maximum at pH 4 corresponds to the maximal concentration of the monoanion $(R-O-PO_3H^-)$. Both an OH and an O^- joined to the P atom are necessary

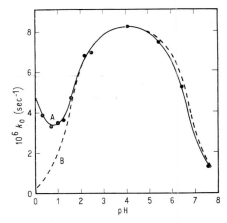

Fig. 6. Hydrolysis of monomethyl phosphate. A, experimental curve; B, calculated for decomposition of the monoanion[71].

for the reaction. Thus, diesters are much more stable; for instance, at pH 4 methyl phosphate hydrolyzes 5,000 times faster than dimethyl phosphate[66].

Furthermore it has been proved[71], using $H_2^{18}O$, that the linkage which breaks is that between O and P:

$$Me-O-\overset{\overset{\displaystyle O}{\|}}{\underset{\underset{\displaystyle OH}{|}}{P}}-O^- + H_2^{18}O \rightarrow MeOH + H-{}^{18}O-\overset{\overset{\displaystyle O}{\|}}{\underset{\underset{\displaystyle OH}{|}}{P}}-O^-$$

The hydrolysis of the monoanion species is probably a general reaction and should take place in every mono-substituted phosphate ester at pH 4 although it may not be detectable because other reactions such as a fission of the C–O bond may be faster[71].

Besides methyl phosphate several other esters have been studied and found to hydrolyze as a monoanion species. Thus as shown in Fig. 7, α-glucose

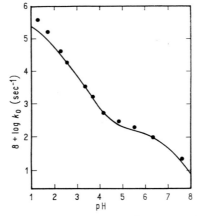

Fig. 7. Hydrolysis of α-glucose 1-phosphate. ● Experimental values; — calculated for decomposition of the monoanion plus that of neutral species[72].

1-phosphate hydrolyzes as the monoanion at about pH 4 and as the neutral species in more acid solution[72]. Other compounds which hydrolyze as the monoanion are β-glycerophosphate[73], inositol phosphate[74] and ribitol phosphate[75].

The mechanism of the hydrolysis occurring at about pH 1, where the undissociated form $R-O-PO(OH)_2$ is predominant, has been studied in several cases. Some esters such as methyl phosphate hydrolyze probably by a bimolecular nucleophilic substitution (S_N2) mechanism with rupture of the C–O bond[71]. This mechanism does not seem to operate on sugar phosphates and in general when the substituent is a more bulky group than methyl. In the special case of α-glucose 1-phosphate the hydrolysis at pH 1 is very rapid and similar to that of benzyl phosphate[70]. The fission has been inter- preted[72] as a monomolecular nucleophilic substitution process (S_N1) with slow heterolysis between C and O leading to the formation of a carbonium ion as shown in Fig. 8. This special type of reaction is believed to be due to

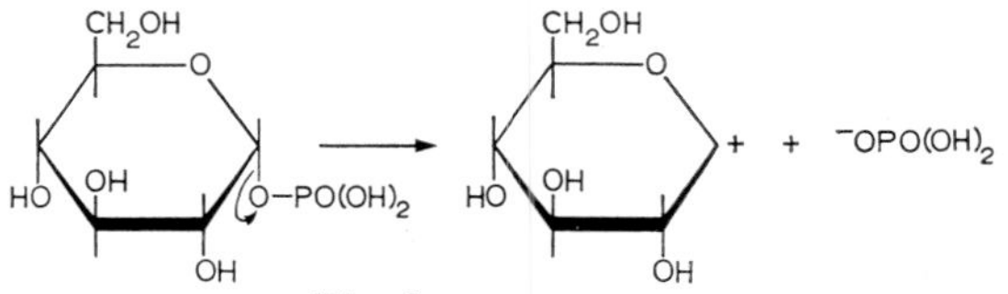

Fig. 8.

an acceleration of the S_N1 process by the oxygen atom of the pyranose ring.

In strongly acid solutions (5 N perchloric acid) the conjugate acid is formed. Methyl phosphate[71] hydrolyzes both by C–O and P–O rupture while only the C–O bond is affected in α-glucose 1-phosphate[72]. The reaction has been formulated as shown in Fig. 9, either with a ring-closed or a ring- opened ion as intermediate. The first step is the addition of a proton to α-glucose 1-phosphate followed by a slow reaction not involving water. Mechanism A in Fig. 9 is similar to that proposed for the hydrolysis of glycosides[20,21,76,77].

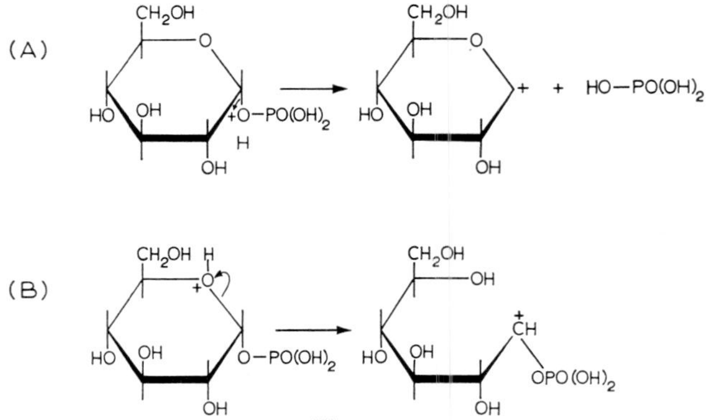

Fig. 9.

(ii) Acid hydrolysis of aldose 1-phosphates

The phosphate groups located at the hemiacetalic hydroxyl are more acid-labile than those which esterify alcoholic hydroxyl groups. Thus while mannose 1-phosphate or glucose 1-phosphate is hydrolyzed in a few minutes in $0.1\ N$ acid at $100°$, more than 100 hours are required for the 6-phosphates.

The knowledge acquired in the study of glycosides[20,21,76-79] is partly applicable to aldose 1-phosphates. The β-anomers are usually more acid-labile than the α, thus in N acid at $33°$ the K value is $5.0 \cdot 10^{-3}$ for α-glucose 1-phosphate and $15 \cdot 10^{-3}$ for the β-anomer. For glucose 1,6-diphosphate the K values are $0.78 \cdot 10^{-3}$ for the α and $3.15 \cdot 10^{-3}$ for the β[80]. The difference may be due to the fact that in the $C1$ conformation the phosphate group of the α-compound is axial and that of the β is equatorial (Figs. 3 and 4). In the latter position the group would be more prone to attack by acid than in the axial position which is more shielded. For methyl glycosides of D-sugars the α-anomer is more acid-stable than the β and the inverse is true for L-sugars (L-arabinose). In both cases the stable form has the methyl group in axial position.

The rate of acid hydrolysis is also influenced by the group at C-6. If the primary alcohol group in α-glucose 1-phosphate is esterified with phosphate as in α-glucose 1,6-diphosphate the hydrolysis constant becomes about 10 times smaller[81]. If the CH_2OH is replaced by COOH as in glucuronic acid 1-phosphate, K becomes 10–20 times smaller[82].

Similar effects have been observed in the hydrolysis of glycosides[78] and have been explained by assuming that the intermediate ion (Fig. 9A) is an oxonium with a half chair configuration (Fig. 10) and that its formation is

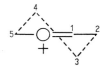

Fig. 10. Half chair intermediate cation.

rate controlling: bulky groups at C-6 would decrease the ease with which this half chair oxonium ion can be formed and thus would decrease the rate of hydrolysis. Inversely a decrease in bulk at C-6 would increase the ease of configurational change and therefore of hydrolysis. Thus α-D-xylopyranose 1-phosphate hydrolyzes 1.45 times faster than α-glucopyranose 1-phosphate. The stabilizing effect of charged groups at C-6 such as carboxyl does not appear to be wholly due to bulk and has been attributed to an inductive effect[83].

The substituents at position 2 influence the rate of hydrolysis. Substitution of an OH by H usually increases acid lability. An NH_2 group has the opposite effect. Thus the 1-phosphates of 2-deoxyamino sugars are more stable than the corresponding sugars. The effect is attributed to the formation of the NH_3^+ group which would prevent the attack by protons.

(iii) Acid hydrolysis of aldose 1-pyrophosphates

Compounds with a pyrophosphate group at the hemiacetalic hydroxyl group are very labile to acid. Thus 5-phosphoribosyl pyrophosphate hydrolyzes at pH 4.5 and 65° giving pyrophosphate and ribose 5-phosphate[84]. The nucleoside pyrophosphate sugars such as uridine diphosphate glucose[85] and guanosine diphosphate mannose[86] are more acid-labile than the corresponding sugar 1-phosphates. As in aldose 1-phosphates the group at C-6 influences the rate of hydrolysis and it seems that more bulky groups determine greater stability. Thus uridine diphosphoglucuronic acid is more stable than uridine diphosphate glucose[87] and uridine diphosphate acetylglucosamine 6-phosphate[88] may give by hydrolysis acetylglucosamine 1,6-diphosphate, while acetylglucosamine 1-phosphate has never been isolated as a product of acid hydrolysis of uridine diphosphate acetylglucosamine[89].

(iv) Acid hydrolysis of polyalcohol phosphates

When α- or β-glycerophosphate is heated at 100° in 1 N acid, a migration of the phosphate group takes place and an equilibrium mixture which contains 87% of α- and 13% of β-isomer is formed[63]. The migration of the phosphate occurs through the formation of a cyclic phosphate and is faster than hydrolysis. Similar events occur with other compounds such as myo-inositol-monophosphate[90-93] and ribitol phosphate[75].

During the hydrolysis of ribitol phosphate at pH 1 to 2 the migration of phosphate is slow in relation to the formation of anhydro 1,4-ribitol. The latter reaction mechanism is interpreted by Baddiley[75] as a protonization of the ester oxygen atom at position 1 with subsequent reaction with the OH at position 4 (Fig. 11) (cf. ref. 77).

In less acid solutions (pH 4) the changes are different and hydrolysis proceeds faster than migration. Under these conditions there is no interconversion of α- and β-glycerophosphate. The latter hydrolyzes twice as fast as the α-form[63]. Hydrolysis at pH 4 has been used for analytical purposes.

The acid lability of phosphate joined to inositol seems to be different for axial and equatorial groups. Thus after partial hydrolysis of inositol hexaphosphate (phytic acid) the isomer which remains unhydrolyzed is myo-inositol 2-phosphate which carries an axial phosphate group[17].

Sugar alcohols joined to a substituted pyrophosphate, such as in cytidine diphosphate glycerol, hydrolyze yielding a monoester (ribitol phosphate and glycerol phosphate respectively[94]). In this respect they differ from the sugar analogs such as uridine diphosphate glucose which hydrolyzes yielding the free sugar[85]. It may be pointed out that acid hydrolysis yields the same products which are transferred by enzyme action. Cytidine diphosphate glycerol yields glycerophosphate on acid hydrolysis and presumably transfers the same substance by enzyme action[94]. Uridine diphosphate glucose is hydrolyzed by acid to glucose and transfers glucose when acted upon by enzymes[95].

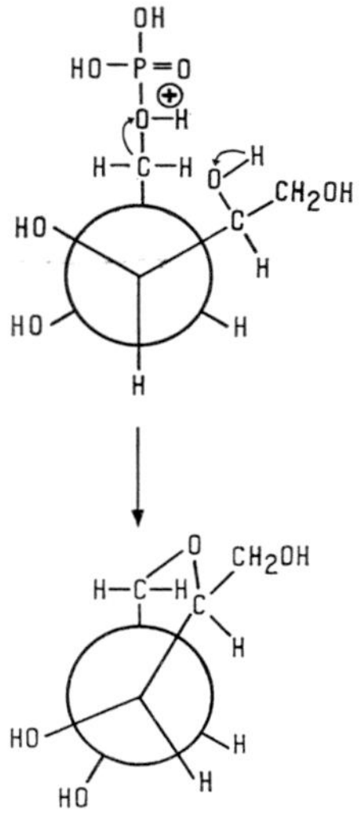

Fig. 11. Hydrolysis of ribitol 1-phosphate[77].

(v) Acid hydrolysis of sugar phosphates other than aldose 1-phosphates

The behavior of sugar phosphates towards acid depends on the vicinity of the carbonyl group. The hydrolysis constant of glucose 2-phosphate is about 20 times higher than that of glucose 6-phosphate[96]. Introduction of a carbonyl group in α-glycerophosphate gives triose phosphate and the hydrolysis constant increases from 0.09 to 37 (in 1 N acid at 100°). The process does not seem to be a simple hydrolysis because methylglyoxal is formed[97].

The pyranose or furanose structure of the esters appears to influence the rate of hydrolysis. Thus glucose 6-phosphate which can form a pyranose ring is more stable than fructose 6-phosphate which can only form a furanose ring. The acid lability of some compounds such as glycolaldehyde phosphate[98], erythrose 4-phosphate[99] and erythrulose phosphate[100] may be partly due to the fact that they cannot form ring structures. Furthermore ribose 5-phosphate is more stable than ribulose 5-phosphate[101] and in this case the difference is presumably due to the fact that the former can form a furanose ring while the latter can only exist in the linear form.

Other differences which have been observed are the following. Ribofuranoside 3-phosphate is more labile than ribofuranoside 2-phosphate[102]. A methylene group at position 2 labilizes the phosphorus at positions 3 or 6 of galactose[103]. Ribose 5-phosphate is considerably more stable than

2-deoxyribose 5-phosphate[104]. Glucosamine 6-phosphate is more stable than glucose 6-phosphate[105].

(b) Alkaline hydrolysis

(i) Phosphate monoesters

Monoalkyl phosphates are very stable to alkali. The dianion $R-O-PO_3^{2-}$ is predominant in alkaline solution and the stability appears to be due to electrostatic repulsion to attack by OH^-. The neutral triesters $(RO)_3 \equiv PO$ are readily hydrolyzed by alkali to the diesters $(RO)_2 = PO_2^-$. No inversion or migration has been detected during alkaline hydrolysis so that the affected bond is probably P–O. Neighboring groups such as OH (as in glycol phosphate or glycerolphosphate) increase stability while NH_2 (as in aminoethyl phosphate) decreases it[106,107].

Hydrolysis at pH 7–10 is increased by lanthanum, cerium and thorium[108,109] with P–O rupture[69] and this type of hydrolysis is believed to be similar to that occurring under enzyme action[61,108,109].

Sugar phosphates with a free aldehyde or keto group are rapidly degraded with alkali whereas substances in which the reducing group is blocked, such as aldose 1-phosphates, are stable to alkali. The latter is also true for the onic acid phosphates.

Studies on the action of alkali on substituted sugars in the absence of oxygen have yielded interesting results[110-112]. Phosphoric esters appear to behave like the methylated sugars which yield saccharinic acids. Glyceraldehyde 3-phosphate yields lactic acid[113] which may be considered as the simplest saccharinic acid. Glucose 3-phosphate is transformed into meta-saccharinic acid like 3-methyl glucose[114] (Fig. 12).

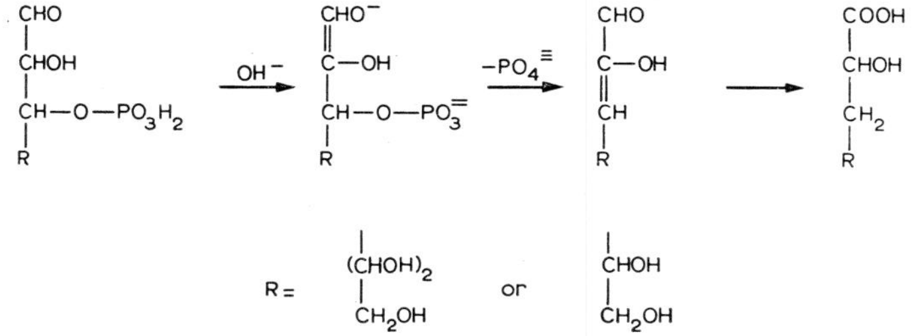

Fig. 12.

Similar results have been obtained with ribose 3-phosphate[114]. When the phosphate group is in position 2 a dienol-1,2 cannot be formed so that such compounds are more stable in alkali[57,115].

A study of the different sugar phosphates other than the 3-phosphates has not been carried out but it is likely that they are transformed by alkali by the same mechanism as the corresponding methyl derivatives[110,111]. Therefore alkaline degradation might be a good method for structural studies.

In the presence of oxygen alkali leads to a rapid degradation of sugars with formation of a complex mixture of products.

(ii) Phosphate diesters

It was observed by Bailly and Gaumé[116] that when the monomethyl ester of α- or β-glycerophosphate was heated in alkali, a mixture of methanol and α- and β-glycerophosphate was formed. Similarly, treatment of α-glycerophosphorylcholine with $1\ N$ alkali at $37°$ yields choline and α- and β-glycerophosphate. The process appears to be general for phosphate diesters which have a vicinal cis-hydroxyl group such as glycerophosphoryl inositol[90,92,93] and ribonucleic acids. Monoesters such as the phosphatidic acids[117,118] do not react in that way. The reaction presumably occurs by formation of a cyclic phosphate which then hydrolyzes to the two isomers (Fig. 13). When the vicinal hydroxyl group is absent, the diester is normally resistant to alkaline hydrolysis.

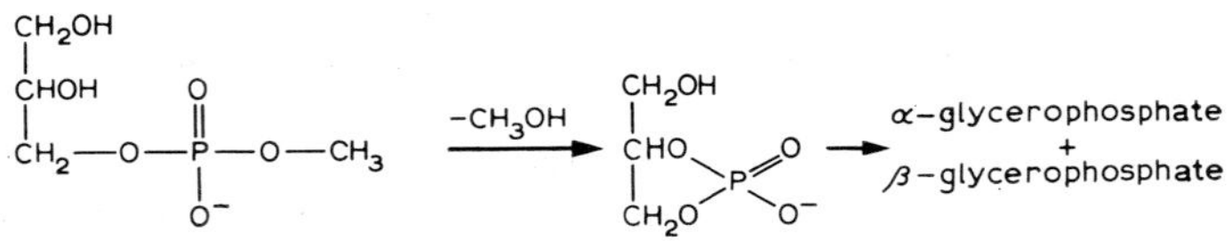

Fig. 13.

Mild alkaline degradation of nucleic acids leads to the formation of cyclic 2,3-nucleotides which on further treatment yield a mixture of the 2- and 3-nucleotides[119]. Cyclic inositol phosphate gives two isomers when hydrolyzed with alkali[120].

When the second substituent in the phosphate is another phosphate instead of an alkyl group, formation of the cyclic compound occurs under mild alkaline treatment. Thus, uridine diphosphate glucose yields uridine monophosphate and glucose cyclic $1:2$-phosphate[115] and 5-phosphoribosyl pyrophosphate gives ribose 5-phosphate cyclic $1:2$-phosphate and inorganic phosphate[121]. Similar changes occur with cytidine diphosphate ribitol and cytidine diphosphate glycerol[94].

(c) Phosphate removal by other procedures

(i) Phenylhydrazine

The formation of osazones by treatment with phenyl hydrazine leads to liberation of the phosphate group when it is near the carbonyl. This occurs with triose phosphate, glycolaldehyde phosphate, glucose 3-phosphate, fructose 1-phosphate, fructose 1,6-diphosphate and glucose 2-phosphate[115,122]. The procedure can be used for analytical purposes.

(ii) Periodate

Oxidation with periodate followed by acid hydrolysis leads to the liberation of phosphate in compounds which have at least two vicinal OH groups next to the phosphate. The method has been used for the estimation of α-glycerophosphate[123] and of inositol monophosphate[124].

4. Analytical methods[14, 50]

The rate of hydrolysis is typical for each ester and has found use in analysis. Some esters such as those with the phosphate at the primary alcohol group and the polyalcohol phosphates are not appreciably hydrolyzed in 1 N acid at 100° in 7–10 min. These are usually classed as stable esters. Other phosphates such as the aldose 1-phosphates are completely hydrolyzed under the above mentioned conditions. Ketose 1-phosphates are partially hydrolyzed. Some phosphates such as the ribose and deoxyribose 1-phosphates are so labile that their phosphate reacts as inorganic phosphate in the usual methods of estimation. A review on the subject is available[125].

Specific color reactions for the sugar moiety are important in distinguishing the different esters[14,126].

The estimation of sugar phosphates with enzymes offers many possibilities. For instance, fructose 1,6-diphosphate can be estimated using aldolase, glucose 6-phosphate with the corresponding dehydrogenase, etc. Methods for the analysis of glucose 1-phosphate, glucose 6-phosphate, fructose 1-phosphate and fructose 1,6-diphosphate have been described[51,127].

Separation by anion exchange resins is useful both for analytical and for preparative purposes[52–55]. The separation of diphosphates from monophosphates is easy and under certain conditions the monoesters can be separated from each other. Good results have been obtained by using borate[56,57,128], so that compounds as similar as ribose 2-phosphate and ribose 3-phosphate have been separated.

Several methods for paper chromatography have been described[129–134] as well as methods for separation by electrophoresis[135]. Both procedures have been combined for two-dimensional separations[134].

5. Acid strength

Sugar phosphates are stronger acids than orthophosphoric acid. Thus the pK values for the latter are pK_1 1.97, pK_2 6.82 and pK_3 12, while for sugar

References p. 140

phosphates pK_1 is 0.84 to 1.25 and pK_2 is 5.7 to 6.1 (Table I). The reasons for this enhancement in acidity on esterification have been discussed by several authors[57,136,137].

TABLE I

APPARENT IONIZATION CONSTANTS OF SOME ORTHOPHOSPHATE
DERIVATIVES[5,136,137,138]

Phosphoric esters	pK_1	pK_2	pK_3
Orthophosphoric acid	1.97	6.82	12
α-Glycerophosphoric acid	1.40	6.44	
β-Glycerophosphoric acid	1.37	6.34	
Glyceraldehyde phosphoric acid	2.10	6.75	
Dihydroxyacetone phosphoric acid	1.77	6.45	
Xylose 1-phosphate	1.25	6.15	
Glucose 1-phosphate	1.10	6.13	
Glucose 3-phosphate	0.84	5.67	
Glucose 4-phosphate	0.84	5.67	
Glucose 6-phosphate	0.94	6.11	
Galactose 1-phosphate	1.00	6.17	
Fructose 6-phosphate	0.97	6.11	
Fructose 1,6-diphosphate	1.48	6.32	
Phytic acid	1.84	6.3	9.7

These constants are not corrected for activities and hence are only apparent values

6. Descriptive

It has been considered that a list of the known sugar phosphates should be of interest even if it is only used as a guide to literature. The list which follows may not be quite complete and only mentions briefly the bio- and chemical syntheses. Aspects which were treated more in detail in previous reviews[5,6] have not been included. The preparations of many sugar esters are described in Colowick and Kaplan's book[139].

(a) Two-carbon compounds

Glycolaldehyde phosphate has been prepared by periodate oxidation of some phosphate esters such as α-glycerophosphate[64,140] or ribose 5-phosphate[141] and also by oxidation of the latter by lead tetraacetate[142]. No enzymes acting on glycolaldehyde have been described.

(b) Three-carbon compounds

Propanediol phosphate was isolated from sea-urchin eggs and cow brain and synthesized from propanediol and phosphoryl chloride[143].

L(−)α-Glycerophosphate[139] occurs in free and combined forms in nature. It can be formed enzymically by reduction of dihydroxyacetone phosphate or by phosphorylation of glycerol with ATP[144]. Chemical synthesis has been carried out by lead tetraacetate oxidation of diisopropylidene D-mannitol to isopropylidene D-glyceraldehyde, reduction of the latter to give isopropylidene D-glycerol which on treatment with phosphoryl chloride and hydrolysis gave L(−) α-glycerophosphate[145].

β-Glycerophosphate is formed by treating α-glycerophosphate with acid or by forming first the diester (with methyl sulfate) and then treating with alkali[116]. It may be prepared by phosphorylating the symmetrical glycerol dichlorohydrin with phosphoryl chloride[146].

Cyclic 1,2-glycerophosphate is formed from cytidine diphosphate glycerol in aqueous ammonia[147]. It has been synthesized from β-glycerophosphate with trifluoroacetic anhydride[148].

D-Glyceraldehyde 3-phosphate has been obtained by enzymic cleavage of fructose 1,6-diphosphate and trapping with hydrazine[11,149] or by phosphorylation of glyceraldehyde with ATP[150]. Chemical synthesis has been carried out from 1,3:4,6-di-O-methylene-D-mannitol. Treatment with benzoyl chloride and removal of methylene groups and periodate oxidation gave 2-O-benzoyl-D-glyceraldehyde. The latter was converted through the mercaptal to the dimethylacetal. Phosphorylation followed by hydrogenolysis gave the dimethyl acetal of D-glyceraldehyde 3-phosphate[151]. The D-L form has also been prepared[139,152].

Dihydroxyacetone phosphate is formed enzymically from fructose 1,6-diphosphate[11,153] or by phosphorylation of dihydroxyacetone with ATP[150]. Synthesis has been effected by phosphorylation of monoacetyldihydroxyacetonedimethyl acetal[154,155].

(c) Four-carbon compounds

D-Erythritol 4-phosphate has been obtained by the action of ATP on erythritol with a bacterial enzyme[156]. Chemical synthesis has been achieved by phosphorylation of 1,2,3-O-tribenzoyl erythritol with diphenyl phosphorochloridate[157] and also by borohydride reduction of D-erythrose 4-phosphate[99].

D-Erythrose 2-phosphate. Oxidation of ribose 3-phosphate with periodate yields D-erythrose 2-phosphate[158].

D-Erythrose 4-phosphate is a normal intermediate in plant and animal metabolism and is formed by the action of transaldolase and transketolase. An enzyme from acetobacter forms acetyl phosphate and D-erythrose phosphate from fructose 6-phosphate and inorganic phosphate[159]. Phosphorylation of D-erythrose with a bacterial enzyme and ATP[160] or with

diphenyl phosphorochloridate of a suitable substituted D-erythrose derivative[99] yields D-erythrose 4-phosphate. Oxidation of D-glucose 6-phosphate
with lead tetraacetate leads to the formation of D-erythrose 4-phosphate[142].

Erythrulose phosphate. An ester of erythrulose, presumably the 1-phos-
phate, has been obtained by enzymic condensation of triose phosphate and
formaldehyde[100].

(d) Five-carbon compounds

(i) Pentitols

D-Ribitol 1-phosphate has been obtained by reduction of ribose 5-phos-
phate[161] and by hydrolysis of cytidine diphosphate ribitol[162]. It is formed
enzymically from ribitol and ATP[163].

Cyclic 1,2-ribitol phosphate has been obtained by the action of aqueous
ammonia on cytidine diphosphate ribitol and was synthesized by treating
ribitol 1-phosphate with trifluoroacetic anhydride[162].

L-Arabitol phosphate has been obtained by the action of ATP and a
bacterial enzyme on L-arabitol[163].

(ii) Aldopentoses

Ribose derivatives. α-D-Ribofuranose 1-phosphate was first obtained by
the action of nucleoside phosphorylase on nucleosides[139,164]. It has been
prepared by treatment of 5-O-acetyl-D-ribofuranosyl 1-bromide 2,3-cyclic
carbonate with triethyl ammonium dibenzyl phosphate followed by removal
of the protecting groups[46].

β-D-Ribofuranose 1-phosphate has been obtained by phosphorylation of
2,3,5-tri-O-benzoyl-β-D-ribofuranosyl 1-bromide with triethyl ammonium
dibenzyl phosphate[45].

D-Ribopyranose 1-phosphate was prepared from 2,3,4-tri-O-acetyl-D-
ribopyranosyl 1-bromide and silver dibenzyl phosphate[45].

D-Ribose 2-phosphate has been obtained by hydrolysis of adenosine
2'-phosphate[57] or uridine 2'-phosphate[165].

D-Ribose 3-phosphate is formed from adenosine 3'-phosphate[57] or uridine
3'-phosphate[165] by hydrolysis.

D-Ribose 4-phosphate may be obtained by acid isomerization of ribose
2-phosphate or 3-phosphate[57].

D-Ribose 5-phosphate is a normal metabolite in plants and animals. It was
first prepared by acid hydrolysis of inosinic acid[166] or from adenosine
5'-phosphate[139,166]. It is formed enzymically from ribose and ATP[139,167].
Synthesis has been carried out by phosphorylating 2,3-isopropylidene-
methyl-D-ribofuranoside[102].

D-Ribose 5-pyrophosphate has been synthesized by treating D-ribose
5-phosphate with dicyclohexylcarbodiimide and inorganic phosphate[168].

α-D-Ribofuranose 1,5-diphosphate was obtained enzymically from glucose 1,6-diphosphate and ribose 5-phosphate[169] and from ATP and ribose 5-phosphate[170]. Synthesis has been carried out from benzyl 5-diphenylphosphoryl-β-D-ribofuranoside by conversion to the corresponding 1-halide followed by treatment with trimethylammonium dibenzyl phosphate[40].

α-D-Ribofuranose 1-pyrophosphate 5-phosphate (5-phosphoribosyl pyrophosphate) is an intermediate in the synthesis of purine- and pyrimidine-nucleotides[171]. It is formed by enzymic transfer of a pyrophosphate group from ATP to D-ribose 5-phosphate[84,121]. It has been synthesized starting from benzyl 5-diphenylphosphoryl-β-D-ribofuranoside 2,3-cyclic carbonate by transformation to the 1-halide and treatment with triethylammonium tribenzyl pyrophosphate[40].

Arabinose derivatives. α-L-Arabofuranose 1-phosphate has been synthesized from 2,3,5-tri-O-acetyl-β-D-arabinofuranosyl 1-bromide and trimethylammonium dibenzyl phosphate[172].

α-D-Arabofuranose 1-phosphate has been prepared from the acetobromo derivative and triethylammonium dibenzyl phosphate[172].

α-L-Arabopyranose 1-phosphate has been prepared by treatment of 2,3,4-acetyl-L-arabopyranosyl 1-bromide with monosilver phosphate[173] or triethylammonium dibenzyl phosphate[172].

β-L-Arabopyranose 1-phosphate is formed by a plant enzyme from L-arabinose and ATP[174] and has been synthesized from the acetobromo derivative and trisilver phosphate[173].

D-Arabinose 5-phosphate has been found to be formed by crude bacterial extracts from L-arabinose or D-ribose[175]. It was also prepared from 1,2-isopropylidene arabofuranose and phosphorylchloride[176]. A simpler procedure consists in treating glucosamine 6-phosphate with ninhydrin[177].

Xylose derivatives. α-D-Xylopyranone 1-phosphate was synthesized from the acetobromoxylose and trisilver phosphate[178] or with silver diphenyl phosphate[179].

β-D-Xylopyranose 1-phosphate has been prepared from the acetobromo xylose and monosilver phosphate[173] or silver dibenzyl phosphate[179].

D-Xylose 3-phosphate is formed from the 5-phenyl phosphate of 1,2-isopropylidene xylofuranose which by alkaline treatment gives a 3,5-cyclic phosphate. Hydrolysis of the latter yields a mixture of the 3- and 5-phosphates[34].

D-Xylofuranose 5-phosphate has been prepared by phosphorylation of 1,2-isopropylidene xylofuranose[180-182].

(iii) Ketopentoses

L-Ribulose 5-phosphate is formed by the action of an *Aerobacter aerogenes* enzyme, L-ribulose and ATP[163]. It is also formed from D-xylulose 5-phosphate by enzymic epimerization[183] at position 4 or from L-xylulose 5-phosphate by a bacterial 3-epimerase[184]. It is also formed from ribose 5-phosphate by the action of an isomerase[101].

D-Ribulose 5-phosphate has been prepared from 6-phosphogluconic acid with yeast[139,185] and E. coli[186] enzymes and separated by anion exchange[187].

D-Ribulose 1,5-diphosphate is a key intermediate in CO_2 fixation in plants. It is formed from D-ribose 5-phosphate by enzymic isomerization and phosphorylation[139,188,189].

D-Xylulose 5-phosphate is a substrate for transketolase. It is formed from ATP and D-xylulose with a liver enzyme[190] or a bacterial enzyme[191]. It has been prepared from D-ribose 5-phosphate by the combined action of an isomerase and a 3-epimerase with ribulose 5-phosphate as intermediate[139,192–195].

L-Xylulose 5-phosphate has been obtained by the action of ATP and a bacterial kinase on L-xylulose[184].

(iv) Deoxypentoses

α-2-Deoxy-D-ribofuranose 1-phosphate has been obtained by enzyme action on guanine deoxyriboside or thymine deoxyriboside[139,196,197]. Chemical preparation has been achieved from 3,5-di-O-toluoyl-2-deoxy-D-ribofuranosyl chloride and disilver phosphate[198].

2-Deoxy-D-ribose 5-phosphate has been obtained by the action of a nucleoside phosphorylase and a mutase on hypoxanthine[199], by enzymic condensation of triose phosphate and acetaldehyde[104,200] and by enzymic phosphorylation of D-2-deoxyribose[201]. Acid hydrolysis of deoxy-adenylic or deoxy-guanylic acid yields deoxyribose 5-phosphate[139]. A chemical synthesis is available[202].

2-Deoxy-D-ribofuranose 1,5-diphosphate has been prepared by enzymic transphosphorylation of deoxyribose 1-phosphate with ribose 1,5-diphosphate[203].

(e) Six-carbon compounds
(i) Hexitols

D-Sorbitol 5-phosphate is formed by reduction of D-fructose 6-phosphate with an enzyme system[204] or with borohydride[205].

1,5-Anhydroglucitol 6-phosphate has been obtained by the action of hexokinase and ATP on 1,5-anhydroglucitol[206].

D-Mannitol 1-phosphate has been isolated from Lactobacillus arabinosus[207] and is formed enzymically from fructose 6-phosphate[205]. It may be prepared by borohydride reduction of fructose 6-phosphate or mannose 6-phosphate[205].

(ii) Aldohexoses

Glucose derivatives. α-D-Glucose 1-phosphate can be prepared by the action of potato phosphorylase on starch[159,208] or synthesized from acetobromo glucose and trisilver phosphate[209] or silver diphenyl phosphate[139,210].

β-D-Glucose 1-phosphate was obtained by the action of maltose phosphorylase from *Neisseria meningitidis*[211]. Synthesis has been achieved with acetobromo glucose and silver dibenzyl phosphate[212] or monosilver phosphate[213].

L-Glucose 1-phosphate has been synthesized by treating acetobromo L-glucose with trisilver phosphate[214].

D-Glucose 2-phosphate is formed as decomposition product of uridine diphosphate glucose with cyclic 1,2-glucose phosphate as intermediate[115]. It has been prepared by phosphorylation of 1,3,4,6-tetraacetyl-β-D-glucose with diphenyl phosphorochloridate[96].

D-Glucose 3-phosphate has been prepared by phosphorylation of 1,2,5,6-diisopropylidene glucose with diphenyl phosphorochloridate[114].

D-Glucose 4-phosphate was prepared by treating 1,2,3,6-tetraacetyl-glucose with diphenyl phosphorochloridate[215].

D-Glucose 5-phosphate. A compound which might be glucose 5-phosphate has been prepared by phosphorylation of 1,2-isopropylidene-glucofuranose[216].

Glucose 6-phosphate was first isolated from yeast fermentation products as the crystalline brucine salt[217]. Several procedures have been described for the preparation of the amorphous[218] and crystalline barium salt[139,219,220]. Several methods are also available for chemical synthesis[25-27,221].

α-D-Glucopyranose 1,6-diphosphate was first isolated from yeast fermentation products[81,139,222]. It is formed enzymically from glucose 1-phosphate[223,224]. Synthesis has been carried out from 1-bromo-2,3,4-triacetyl 6-diphenylphosphoglucopyranose and trisilver phosphate[225] or silver diphenyl phosphate[80,139]. The β anomer was also prepared[80,139].

D-Glucose 4,6-cyclic phosphate has been prepared by treatment of α-methyl- or β-phenyl-D-glucoside with phenyl phosphorochloridate[30,47].

α-D-Glucopyranose 1,2-cyclic phosphate is formed by alkaline degradation of uridine diphosphate glucose[115] or by treatment of glucose 1-phosphate with dicyclohexylcarbodiimide[39].

Methyl-α-glucoside 6-phosphate has been obtained by treating glucose 6-phosphate with methanol and HCl[226].

Mannose derivatives. α-D-Mannose 1-phosphate has been synthesized by treating acetobromomannose with trisilver phosphate[227] or silver diphenyl phosphate[228].

D-Mannose 6-phosphate has been isolated from the products of yeast fermentation[229]. It is formed enzymically from mannose and ATP[139,230,231] and from mannose 1-phosphate[228]. Chemical synthesis has been carried out by treating 1,2,3,4-tetraacetyl-D-mannose with diphenyl phosphorochloridate[228].

α-D-Mannose 1,6-diphosphate is formed enzymically from glucose 1,6-diphosphate and mannose 1-phosphate[222]. It has been synthesized by treating α-1-bromo-2,3,4-triacetyl-6-diphenylphospho-D-mannose with silver diphenyl phosphate[228].

Galactose derivatives. α-D-Galactose 1-phosphate was first isolated from the liver of galactose-fed rabbits[232,233]. It is formed enzymically from galactose and ATP[174,234–236]. Synthesis has been carried out by treatment of α-acetobromogalactose with trisilver phosphate[227,237] or silver diphenyl phosphate[210].

β-D-Galactose 1-phosphate has been synthesized like the α anomer but using silver monophosphate[213] or silver dibenzyl phosphate[210].

D-Galactose 3-phosphate has been prepared from 1,2-isopropylidene-4,6-ethylidene-D-galactopyranose and diphenyl phosphorochloridate[103].

D-Galactose 6-phosphate is formed enzymically from α-galactose 1-phosphate[238] and chemically from 1,2,3,4-diisopropylidene galactopyranose[239].

(iii) Ketohexoses

D-Fructose 1-phosphate was first prepared by phosphatase action on fructose 1,6-diphosphate[240]. It is formed enzymically by condensation of dihydroxyacetonephosphate and D-glyceraldehyde[241] and from fructose and ATP[242–244]. Synthesis has been carried out by treating 2,3,4,5-diisopropylidene-D-fructopyranose with phosphoryl chloride[245], or P_2O_5[246], or diphenyl phosphorochloridate[139].

D-Fructose 6-phosphate has been isolated from the hexose monophosphate fraction of yeast[139,229]. It is formed enzymically from fructose and ATP[230,231].

D-Fructose 1,6-diphosphate is usually isolated from yeast fermentation products[139]. Purification procedures have been described[247,248].

D-Tagatose 6-phosphate is formed by liver phosphofructokinase acting on tagatose[249]. Synthesis has been carried out starting with 1,2,3,4-diisopropylidene tagatose[139,250].

L-Sorbose 1-phosphate has been obtained by enzymic condensation of L-glyceraldehyde with dihydroxyacetone phosphate[241,251] and by the action of liver fructokinase on L-sorbose[244]. Chemical synthesis has been effected starting with 2,3,4,6-diisopropylidene L-sorbose[139,251,252].

L-Sorbose 6-phosphate has been synthesized by phosphorylation of 2,3-isopropylidene L-sorbose[139,251,252].

(iv) Deoxyhexoses

2-Deoxy-D-galactose 3-phosphate was prepared from 4,6-benzylidene α-methyl-2-deoxy-D-galactoside and diphenyl phosphorochloridate[103].

2-Deoxy-D-galactose 6-phosphate was prepared by phosphorylation of 3,4-isopropylidene α-methyl-2-deoxy-D-galactoside[103].

L-Fucose 1-phosphate has been prepared by phosphorylating L-fucose with ATP and an enzyme from *E. coli*[253].

L-Rhamnulose 1-phosphate has been found to be formed by the action of bacteria on rhamnulose[254,255].

L-Fuculose 1-phosphate is formed from L-fuculose, ATP and an *E. coli* enzyme[253].

6-Deoxy-L-sorbose 1-phosphate is formed from L-fuculose 1-phosphate with a 3-epimerase from *Lactobacillus pentosus*[253].

(v) Cyclitols (see also Chapter VIII, p. 297)

myo-Inositol 1-phosphate has been obtained by alkaline hydrolysis of soybean phosphoinositide[256]. Synthesis has been carried out starting from 1-O-α-D-galactopyranosyl *myo*-inositide. Benzylation followed by methanolysis gave 2,3,4,5,6-pentabenzyl *myo*-inositol which was phosphorylated with diphenyl phosphorochloridate[257].

myo-Inositol 2-phosphate has been prepared by partial hydrolysis of inositol hexaphosphate (phytic acid[258]). Synthesis has been carried out by phosphorylating pentaacetyl myo-inositol with diphenyl phosphorochloridate[256,259].

(vi) Onic and uronic acids

6-Phospho-D-gluconic acid is formed from gluconic acid by yeast gluconokinase[260] and from glucose 6-phosphate by the corresponding dehydrogenase or by bromine oxidation[26,139].

α-D-Glucuronic acid 1-phosphate has been obtained by enzymic phosphorylation of glucuronic acid[261], by hydrolysis of uridine diphosphate glucuronic acid[87] and by oxidation of α-glucose 1-phosphate with oxygen and platinum catalyst[262].

β-D-Glucuronic acid 1-phosphate was prepared by catalytic oxidation of β-glucose 1-phosphate[262].

α-D-Galacturonic acid 1-phosphate has been prepared by catalytic oxidation of α-galactose 1-phosphate[263].

2-Keto-3-deoxy-6-phosphogluconic acid was first isolated as a product of the action of a bacterial enzyme (*Pseudomonas saccharophyla*) on 6-phosphogluconic acid[264]. It is also formed from ATP and 2-keto-3-deoxy-D-gluconic acid with an enzyme from *E. coli*[265].

References p. 140

(vii) Amino sugars

α-D-Glucosamine 1-phosphate is formed from glucosamine 6-phosphate with phosphoglucomutase[266]. It has been synthesized by treatment of α-1-bromo-3,4,6-tri-O-acetylglucosamine with the diethylammonium salt of diphenyl phosphate[267].

Glucosamine 6-phosphate is obtained enzymically from hexose phosphate and glutamine[268,269] and from glucosamine and ATP[139,270]. Synthesis has been carried out by phosphorylation of 1,3,4-tri-O-acetyl-N-acetyl-β-D-glucosamine[105] or N-anisylidene-D-glucosamine[271] and also by treating glucosamine with polyphosphoric acid[272].

α-N-acetylglucosamine 1-phosphate has been prepared from 1-chloro-tetraacetylglucosamine and trisilver phosphate[273] and from 1-bromo-3,4,6-tri-O-acetylglucosamine and triethylammonium diphenyl phosphate[267].

N-acetylglucosamine 6-phosphate has been obtained enzymically from acetylglucosamine and ATP[274] and from glucosamine 6-phosphate and an acetylating system[268]. It can be prepared by chemical acetylation of glucosamine 6-phosphate[272] and from N-anisylidene glucosamine in two steps[271].

N-acetylglucosamine 1,6-diphosphate is formed enzymically from glucose 1,6-diphosphate and acetylglucosamine 1-phosphate[275].

D-Galactosamine 1-phosphate was obtained from ATP and galactosamine with liver or yeast enzymes[276].

D-Galactosamine 6-phosphate has been synthesized by treatment of galactosamine with polyphosphoric acid[272].

N-Acetylgalactosamine 1-phosphate is formed by enzymic phosphorylation of acetylgalactosamine[274] and by chemical acetylation of galactosamine 1-phosphate[277].

N-Acetylgalactosamine 6-phosphate has been prepared by enzymic or chemical acetylation of acetylgalactosamine 6-phosphate[272].

(f) Seven-carbon compounds

Sedoheptulose 1-phosphate is formed by enzymic condensation of erythrose and dihydroxyacetone phosphate[278].

Sedoheptulose 7-phosphate was first detected in yeast fermentation products[8]. It is formed by transfer of "active glycolaldehyde" to ribulose 5-phosphate[139,278] and by the action of a specific phosphatase on heptulose 1,7-diphosphate[142].

Sedoheptulose 1,7-diphosphate has been prepared by enzymic condensation of D-erythrose 4-phosphate with dihydroxyacetone phosphate[99,139,142,279].

Mannoheptulose phosphate was isolated from avocado leaves[280].

3-Keto-D-araboheptose phosphate was obtained by incubation of glucose 6-phosphate with liver enzymes[281].

2-Keto-3-deoxy-D-araboheptonic acid 7-phosphate has been obtained by incubating a crude *E. coli* extract with ribose 5-phosphate[282] or a purified extract with D-erythrose 4-phosphate plus phosphoenolpyruvate[283].

(g) Eight-carbon compounds

2-Keto-octulose 8-phosphate has been obtained by enzyme action on ribose 5-phosphate and fructose 6-phosphate[284].

2-Keto-3-deoxy-8-phospho-octonic acid was found to be formed from D-arabinose 5-phosphate and phosphoenolpyruvate with an enzyme from *Pseudomonas aeruginosa*[285].

(h) Disaccharide phosphates

α,α'-Trehalose 6-phosphate was first isolated from yeast fermentation products[286]. It is formed enzymically from uridine diphosphate glucose and glucose 6-phosphate[287].

α-Maltose 1-phosphate has been obtained by treating bromoacetyl maltose with trisilver phosphate[178].

α-Lactose 1-phosphate was reported to be formed enzymically from uridine diphosphate glucose and glucose 1-phosphate[288]. It has been synthesized from acetobromolactose and silver diphenyl phosphate[289].

β-Lactose 1-phosphate was obtained from acetobromolactose and monosilver phosphate[289].

Sucrose phosphate is formed enzymically from uridine diphosphate and fructose 6-phosphate[290].

(k) Polysaccharide phosphates

Starch. A certain amount of phosphate is found in most starches[291]. The evidence indicates that the phosphate groups are joined to C-6 of the glucose residues.

Teichoic acid. A polyribitol phosphate has been extracted from gram-positive bacteria and named teichoic acid[292,293]. Similar compounds extracted from *Lactobacillus arabinosus* and *Bacillus subtilis* have side chains containing alanine and glucose.

Polyribose phosphate. A polymer containing ribose and phosphate has been isolated from *Haemophilus influenzae*[294].

Polymannose phosphate. A polysaccharide containing mannose and phosphate in the ratio 5 to 1 has been isolated from cultures of the yeast *Hansenula holstii* grown on glucose[295].

REFERENCES

[1] A. HARDEN AND W. J. YOUNG, *Proc. Roy. Soc. (London) B*, 77 (1906) 405.
[2] M. M. SCHOEN, *Bull. soc. chim. biol.*, 11 (1929) 819.
[3] J. COURTOIS, *Bull. soc. chim. biol.*, 23 (1941) 133.
[4] A. HARDEN (Ed.), *Alcoholic Fermentation*, Longmans, Green and Co., London, 1923.
[5] L. F. LELOIR in L. ZECHMEISTER (Ed.), *Fortschr. chem. org. Naturstoffe*, Vol. 8, Springer, Vienna, 1951, p. 47.
[6] A. B. FOSTER AND W. G. OVEREND, *Quart. Rev.*, 11 (1957) 61.
[7] P. FLEURY in M. POLONOVSKI (Ed.), *Exposés ann. biochim. méd.*, Vol. II, Masson, Paris, 1939, p. 161.
[8] J. SOWDEN, *Ann. Rev. Biochem.*, 26 (1957) 650.
[9] H. G. ALBAUM in W. RUHLAND (Ed.), *Handbuch d. Pflanzenphysiol.*, Vol. IX, Springer, Berlin, 1958, p. 155.
[10] W. W. UMBREIT in W. RUHLAND (Ed.), *Handbuch d. Pflanzenphysiol.*, Vol. IX, Springer, Berlin, 1958, p. 152.
[11] R. ROBISON AND M. G. MCFARLANE in E. BAMANN AND K. MYRBÄCK (Eds.), *Die Methoden d. Fermentforschung*, Vol. I, Georg Thieme, Leipzig, 1941, p. 296.
[12] H. O. L. FISCHER, *Angew. Chem.*, 69 (1957) 405.
[13] F. CRAMER, *Angew. Chem.*, 72 (1960) 236.
[14] A. A. BENSON in K. PEACH AND M. V. TRACEY (Eds.), *Moderne Methoden der Pflanzenanalyse*, Vol. 2, Springer, Berlin, 1955, p. 113.
[15] R. W. JEANLOZ AND H. G. FLETCHER, *Adv. in Carbohydrate Chem.*, 6 (1951) 135.
[16] W. G. OVEREND AND M. STACEY, *Adv. in Carbohydrate Chem.*, 8 (1953) 45.
[17] S. J. ANGYAL AND L. ANDERSON, *Adv. in Carbohydrate Chem.*, 14 (1959) 135.
[18] R. E. REEVES, *J. Am. Chem. Soc.*, 72 (1950) 1499.
[19] R. E. REEVES, *Adv. in Carbohydrate Chem.*, 6 (1951) 123.
[20] R. J. FERRIER AND W. G. OVEREND, *Quart. Rev.*, 13 (1959) 265.
[21] E. J. BOURNE AND R. STEPHENS, *Ann. Rev. Biochem.*, 25 (1956) 89.
[22] O. BAILLY, *Ann. chim. (Paris)*, 6 (1916) 133.
[23] F. R. ATHERTON, H. T. OPENSHAW AND A. R. TODD, *J. Chem. Soc.*, (1945) 385.
[24] W. E. HARVEY, J. J. MICHALSKI AND A. R. TODD, *J. Chem. Soc.*, (1951) 2271.
[25] G. P. LAMPSON AND H. A. LARDY, *J. Biol. Chem.*, 181 (1949) 693.
[26] J. E. SEEGMILLER AND B. L. HORECKER, *J. Biol. Chem.*, 192 (1951) 175.
[27] M. VISCONTINI AND C. OLIVIER, *Helv. Chim. Acta*, 36 (1953) 446.
[28] E. CHERBULIEZ AND H. WENIGER, *Helv. Chim. Acta*, 29 (1946) 2006.
[29] C. NEUBERG AND H. POLLAK, *Biochem. Z.*, 23 (1910) 515; 26 (1910) 514.
[30] E. FISCHER, *Ber.*, 47 (1914) 3193.
[31] P. BRIGL AND H. MÜLLER, *Ber.*, 72 (1939) 2121.
[32] J. BADDILEY, V. M. CLARK, J. J. MICHALSKI AND A. R. TODD, *J. Chem. Soc.*, (1949) 815.
[33] E. BAER AND H. C. STANIER, *J. Am. Chem. Soc.*, 75 (1953) 4510.
[34] J. G. MOFFAT AND H. G. KHORANA, *J. Am. Chem. Soc.*, 79 (1957) 1194.
[35] H. G. KHORANA, *Chem. Rev.*, 53 (1953) 145.
[36] H. G. KHORANA AND A. R. TODD, *J. Chem. Soc.*, (1953) 2257.
[37] M. SMITH, J. G. MOFFAT AND H. G. KHORANA, *J. Am. Chem. Soc.*, 80 (1958) 6204.
[38] P. T. GILHAM AND G. M. TENER, *Chem. and Ind. (London)*, (1959) 542.
[39] H. G. KHORANA, G. M. TENER, R. S. WRIGHT AND J. G. MOFFAT, *J. Am. Chem. Soc.*, 79 (1957) 430.
[40] G. M. TENER AND H. G. KHORANA, *J. Am. chem. Soc.*, 80 (1958) 1999.
[41] L. J. HAYNES AND F. H. NEWTH, *Adv. in Carbohydrate Chem.*, 10 (1955) 207.
[42] R. FLATT AND G. BRUNISHOLZ, *Helv. Chim. Acta*, 34 (1951) 692.
[43] E. PACSU, *Adv. in Carbohydrate Chem.*, 1 (1945) 78.
[44] R. U. LEMIEUX, *Adv. in Carbohydrate Chem.*, 9 (1954) 1.
[45] R. S. WRIGHT AND H. G. KHORANA, *J. Am. Chem. Soc.*, 78 (1956) 811.
[46] G. M. TENER, R. S. WRIGHT AND H. G. KHORANA, *J. Am. Chem. Soc.*, 79 (1957) 441.
[47] J. BADDILEY, J. G. BUCHANAN AND L. SZABÓ, *J. Chem. Soc.*, (1954) 3826.
[48] D. M. BROWN, D. I. MAGRATH AND A. R. TODD, *J. Chem. Soc.*, (1952) 2708.

49 C. E. CARDINI AND L. F. LELOIR in S. P. COLOWICK AND N. O. KAPLAN (Eds.), *Methods in Enzymology*, Vol. III, Ademic Press, New York, 1957, p. 835.

50 W. W. UMBREIT, R. H. BURRIS AND J. F. STAUFFER (Eds.), *Manometric Techniques*, Burgess, Minnesota, USA, 1957.

51 H. G. HERS, H. BEAUFAYS AND C. DE DUVE, *Biochim. et Biophys. Acta*, 11 (1953) 416.

52 A. A. BENSON, J. A. BASSHAM, M. CALVIN, T. C. GOODALE, V. A. HAAS AND W. STEPKA, *J. Am. Chem. Soc.*, 72 (1950) 1710.

53 A. A. BENSON in S. P. COLOWICK AND N. O. KAPLAN (Eds.), *Methods in Enzymology*, Vol. III, Academic Press, New York, 1957, p. 110.

54 H. SCHMITZ AND G. WALFURGER, *Angew. Chem.*, 71 (1959) 549.

55 J. DULBERG, W. G. ROESSLER, T. H. SANDERS AND C. R. BREWER, *J. Biol. Chem.*, 194 (1952) 199.

56 J. X. KHYM AND W. E. COHN, *J. Am. Chem. Soc.*, 75 (1953) 1153.

57 J. X. KHYM, D. G. DOBERTY AND W. E. COHN, *J. Am. Chem. Soc.*, 76 (1954) 5523.

58 K. LOHMANN, *Biochem. Z.*, 194 (1928) 306.

59 P. A. LEVENE AND L. W. BASS (Eds.), *Nucleic Acids*, The Chemical Catalog Co., New York, 1931, p. 208.

60 C. A. VERNON, *Phosphoric Esters and Related Compounds*, The Chemical Society, London, Special Publ., No. 8 (1957) 17.

61 M. COHN, *J. Cellular Comp. Physiol.*, 54 suppl. 1 (1959) 17.

62 F. MALENGREAU AND G. PRIGENT, *Z. physiol. Chem., Hoppe-Seyler's*, 73 (1911) 68.

63 M. C. BAILLY, *Bull. soc. chim. (France)*, 9 (1942) 314, 340, 405, 421.

64 P. FLEURY AND J. COURTOIS, *Bull. soc. chim. (France)*, 8 (1941) 69.

65 P. FLEURY AND J. COURTOIS, *Bull. soc. chim. (France)*, 9 (1942) 570.

66 M. COHN, *J. Biol. Chem.*, 180 (1949) 771.

67 A. DESJOBERT, *Bull. soc. chim. (France)*, 14 (1947) 809; *Compt. rend.*, 224 (1947) 575.

68 A. DESJOBERT, *Bull. soc. chim. biol.*, 33 (1951) 42.

69 W. W. BUTCHER AND F. H. WESTHEIMER, *J. Am. Chem. Soc.*, 77 (1955) 2420.

70 J. KUMAMOTO AND F. H. WESTHEIMER, *J. Am. chem. Soc.*, 77 (1955) 2515.

71 C. A. BUNTON, D. R. LLEWELLYN, K. G. OLDHAM AND C. A. VERNON, *J. Chem. Soc.*, (1958) 3574.

72 C. A. BUNTON, D. R. LLEWELLYN, K. G. OLDHAM AND C. A. VERNON, *J. Chem. Soc.*, (1958) 3588.

73 P. A. T. SWOBODA AND E. M. CROOK, *Biochem. J.*, 59P (1955) XXIV.

74 A. DESJOBERT AND P. FLEURY, *Bull. soc. chim. biol.*, 36 (1954) 475.

75 J. BADDILEY, *Phosphoric Esters and Related Compounds*, The Chemical Society, London, Special publ., No. 8 (1957) 119.

76 C. A. BUNTON, T. A. LEWIS, D. R. LLEWELLYN AND C. A. VERNON, *J. Chem. Soc.*, (1955) 4419.

77 F. SHAFIZADEH, *Adv. in Carbohydrate Chem.*, 13 (1958) 9.

78 J. T. EDWARD, *Chem. and Ind. (London)*, (1955) 1102.

79 A. B. FOSTER AND W. G. OVEREND, *Chem. and Ind. (London)*, (1955) 566.

80 T. POSTERNAK, *J. Biol. Chem.*, 180 (1949) 1269.

81 C. E. CARDINI, A. C. PALADINI, R. CAPUTTO, L. F. LELOIR AND R. E. TRUCCO, *Arch. Biochem. Biophys.*, 22 (1949) 87.

82 S. A. BARKER, E. J. BOURNE, J. G. FLEETWOOD AND M. STACEY, *J. Chem. Soc.*, (1958) 4128.

83 R. L. WHISTLER AND G. N. RICHARDS, *J. Am. Chem. Soc.*, 80 (1958) 4889.

84 C. N. REMY, W. T. REMY AND J. M. BUCHANAN, *J. Biol. Chem.*, 217 (1955) 885.

85 R. CAPUTTO, L. F. LELOIR, C. E. CARDINI AND A. C. PALADINI, *J. Biol. Chem.*, 184 (1950) 333.

86 E. CABIB AND L. F. LELOIR, *J. Biol. Chem.*, 206 (1954) 779.

87 I. D. E. STOREY AND G. J. DUTTON, *Biochem. J.*, 59 (1955) 279.

88 J. L. STROMINGER, *Biochim. et Biophys. Acta*, 17 (1955) 283.

89 E. CABIB, L. F. LELOIR AND C. E. CARDINI, *J. Biol. Chem.*, 203 (1953) 1055.

90 D. M. BROWN, G. E. HALL AND H. M. HIGSON, *J. Chem. Soc.*, (1958) 1360.

91 T. POSTERNAK, *Helv. Chim. Acta*, 41 (1958) 1890.

92 J. N. HAWTHORNE, P. KEMP AND R. B. ELLIS, *Biochem. J.*, 75 (1960) 501.

[93] J. N. HAWTHORNE, Biochem. J., 75 (1960) 495.
[94] J. BADDILEY AND J. G. BUCHANAN, Quart. Rev., 12 (1958) 152.
[95] L. F. LELOIR AND C. E. CARDINI in P. D. BOYER, H. LARDY AND K. MYRBÄCK (Eds.), The Enzymes, Vol. 2, Academic Press, New York, 1960, p. 39.
[96] K. R. FARRAR, J. Chem. Soc., (1949) 3131.
[97] E. BAER AND C. S. McARTHUR, J. Biol. Chem., 154 (1944) 451.
[98] P. FLEURY AND J. COURTOIS, Bull. soc. chim. (France), 8 (1941) 75; 9 (1942) 570.
[99] C. E. BALLOU, H. O. L. FISCHER AND D. L. MacDONALD, J. Am. Chem. Soc., 77 (1955) 5967.
[100] F. C. CHARALAMPOUS AND G. C. MUELLER, J. Biol. Chem., 201 (1953) 161.
[101] B. AXELROD AND R. JANG, J. Biol. Chem., 209 (1954) 847.
[102] A. M. MICHELSON AND A. R. TODD, J. Chem. Soc., (1949) 2476.
[103] A. B. FOSTER, W. G. OVEREND AND M. STACEY, J. Chem. Soc., (1951) 980.
[104] E. RACKER, J. Biol. Chem., 196 (1952) 347.
[105] J. M. ANDERSON AND E. PERCIVAL, J. Chem. Soc., (1956) 814.
[106] E. CHERBULIEZ AND M. BOUVIER, Helv. Chim. Acta, 36 (1953) 1200.
[107] E. CHERBULIEZ AND J. RABINOWITZ, Helv. Chim. Acta, 39 (1956) 1844.
[108] E. BAMANN AND M. MEISENHEIMER, Ber., 71 (1938) 1711.
[109] E. BAMANN, F. FISCHLER AND H. TRAPMANN, Biochem. Z., 325 (1954) 413.
[110] J. C. SOWDEN, Adv. in Carbohydrate Chem., 12 (1957) 35.
[111] R. L. WHISLTER AND J. N. BeMILLER, Adv. in Carbohydrate Chem., 13 (1958) 289.
[112] G. MACHELL AND G. N. RICHARDS, J. Chem. Soc., (1960) 1924, 1932, 1938.
[113] O. MEYERHOF AND K. LOHMANN, Biochem. Z., 271 (1934) 89.
[114] D. BROWN, F. HAYES AND A. TODD, Ber., 90 (1957) 936.
[115] A. C. PALADINI AND L. F. LELOIR, Biochem. J., 51 (1952) 426.
[116] O. BAILLY AND J. GAUMÉ, Bull. soc. chim. (France), 2 (1935) 354.
[117] E. BAER AND M. KATES, J. Biol. Chem., 175 (1948) 79.
[118] E. BAER AND M. KATES, J. Biol. Chem., 185 (1950) 615.
[119] R. MARKHAM AND J. D. SMITH, Biochem. J., 52 (1952) 552.
[120] T. POSTERNAK, Helv. Chim. Acta, 42 (1959) 390.
[121] H. G. KHORANA, J. F. FERNANDES AND A. KORNBERG, J. Biol. Chem., 230 (1958) 941.
[122] H. J. DEUTICKE AND S. HOLLMANN, Z. physiol. Chem., Hoppe-Seyler's, 258 (1939) 160.
[123] C. F. BURMASTER, J. Biol. Chem., 164 (1946) 233.
[124] H. PAULUS AND E. P. KENNEDY, J. Biol. Chem., 235 (1960) 1303.
[125] L. F. LELOIR AND C. E. CARDINI in S. P. COLOWICK AND N. O. KAPLAN (Eds.), Methods in Enzymology, Vol. III, Academic Press, New York, 1957, p. 840.
[126] G. ASHWELL in S. P. COLOWICK AND N. O. KAPLAN (Eds.), Methods in Enzymology, Vol. III, Academic Press, New York, 1957, p. 73.
[127] E. C. SLATER, Biochem. J., 53 (1953) 157.
[128] B. L. HORECKER AND P. Z. SMYRNIOTIS, Arch. Biochem., 29 (1950) 232.
[129] S. S. COHEN AND D. B. McNAIR SCOTT, Science, 111 (1950) 543.
[130] G. N. KOWKABANY, Adv. in Carbohydrate Chem., 9 (1954) 303.
[131] C. S. HANES AND F. A. ISHERWOOD, Nature, 164 (1949) 1107.
[132] R. S. BANDURSKY AND B. AXELROD, J. Biol. Chem., 193 (1951) 405.
[133] D. C. MORTIMER, Can. J. Chem., 30 (1952) 653.
[134] V. C. RUNECKLES AND G. KROTKOV, Arch. Biochem. Biophys., 70 (1957) 442.
[135] A. B. FOSTER, Adv. in Carbohydrate Chem., 12 (1957) 81.
[136] W. D. KUMLER AND J. J. EILER, J. Am. Chem. Soc., 65 (1943) 2355.
[137] R. BARRE, J. E. COURTOIS AND G. WORMSER, Bull. soc. chim. biol., 36 (1954) 454.
[138] J. R. VAN WAZER (Ed.), Phosphorus and its compounds, Vol. I, Interscience, New York, 1958.
[139] S. P. COLOWICK AND N. O. KAPLAN (Eds.), Methods in Enzymology, Vol. III, Academic Press, New York, 1957.
[140] P. FLEURY, J. COURTOIS AND A. DESJOBERT, Bull. soc. chim. (France), 19 (1952) 458.
[141] H. S. LORING, L. W. LEVY, L. K. MOSS AND J. M. PLOESER, J. Am. Chem. Soc., 78 (1956) 3724.
[142] V. KLYBAS, M. SCHRAMM AND E. RACKER, Arch. Biochem. Biophys., 80 (1959) 229.
[143] O. LINDBERG, Arkiv Kemi, Mineral. Geol., 23A (1946) 1.

[144] C. BUBLITZ AND E. P. KENNEDY, *J. Biol. Chem.*, 211 (1954) 951.
[145] E. BAER, *Biochem. Preparations*, 2 (1952) 31.
[146] H. KING AND L. PYMAN, *J. Chem. Soc.*, (1914) 1238.
[147] J. BADDILEY, J. G. BUCHANAN, A. P. MATHIAS AND A. R. SANDERS, *J. Chem. Soc.*, (1956) 4186.
[148] T. UKITA, N. A. BATES AND H. E. CARTER, *J. Biol. Chem.*, 216 (1955) 867.
[149] O. MEYERHOF, *Bull. soc. chim. biol.*, 20 (1938) 1033; 21 (1939) 965.
[150] H. G. HERS AND T. KUSAKA, *Biochim. et Biophys. Acta*, 11 (1953) 427.
[151] C. E. BALLOU AND H. O. L. FISCHER, *J. Am. Chem. Soc.*, 77 (1955) 3329.
[152] E. BAER, *Biochem. Preparations*, 1 (1949) 50.
[153] O. MEYERHOF AND W. KIESSLING, *Biochem. Z.*, 273 (1934) 413.
[154] C. E. BALLOU AND H. O. L. FISCHER, *J. Am. Chem. Soc.*, 78 (1956) 1659.
[155] C. E. BALLOU, *Biochem. Preparations*, 7 (1960) 45.
[156] J. K. SHETTER, *J. Am. Chem. Soc.*, 78 (1956) 3722.
[157] D. L. McDONALD, H. O. L. FISCHER, C. E. BALLOU, *J. Am. Chem. Soc.*, 78 (1956) 3720.
[158] H. S. LORING, L. K. MOSS, L. W. LEVY AND W. F. HAIN, *Arch. Biochem. Biophys.*, 65 (1956) 578.
[159] M. SCHRAMM AND E. RACKER, *Nature*, 179 (1957) 1349.
[160] H. H. HIATT AND B. L. HORECKER, *J. Bacteriol.*, 71 (1956) 649.
[161] J. BADDILEY, J. G. BUCHANAN AND B. CARSS, *J. Chem. Soc.*, (1957) 1869.
[162] J. BADDILEY, J. G. BUCHANAN, B. CARSS AND A. P. MATHIAS, *J. Chem. Soc.*, (1956) 4583.
[163] F. J. SIMPSON AND W. A. WOOD, *J. Biol. Chem.*, 230 (1958) 473.
[164] H. M. KALCKAR, *J. Biol. Chem.*, 167 (1947) 477.
[165] W. E. COHN AND D. G. DOBERTY, *J. Am. Chem. Soc.*, 78 (1956) 2863.
[166] P. A. LEVENE AND W. A. JACOBS, *Ber.*, 44 (1911) 746.
[167] B. L. HORECKER, M. GIBBS, H. KLENOW AND P. Z. SMYRNIOTIS, *J. Biol. Chem.*, 207 (1954) 393.
[168] B. L. HORECKER, J. HURWITZ AND L. A. HEPPEL, *J. Am. Chem. Soc.*, 79 (1957) 701.
[169] H. KLENOW, *Arch. Biochem. Biophys.*, 46 (1953) 186.
[170] E. SCARANO, *Nature*, 172 (1953) 951.
[171] A. KORNBERG, I. LIEBERMAN AND E. S. SIMMS, *J. Biol. Chem.*, 215 (1955) 389.
[172] R. S. WRIGHT AND H. G. KHORANA, *J. Am. Chem. Soc.*, 80 (1958) 1994.
[173] E. W. PUTMAN AND W. Z. HASSID, *J. Am. Chem. Soc.*, 79 (1957) 5057.
[174] E. F. NEUFELD, D. S. FEINGOLD AND W. Z. HASSID, *J. Biol. Chem.*, 235 (1960) 906.
[175] W. A. VOLK, *J. Biol. Chem.*, 234 (1959) 1931.
[176] P. A. LEVENE AND C. C. CHRISTMAN, *J. Biol. Chem.*, 123 (1938) 607.
[177] W. A. VOLK, *Biochim. et Biophys. Acta*, 37 (1960) 365.
[178] W. R. MEAGHER AND W. Z. HASSID, *J. Am. Chem. Soc.*, 68 (1946) 2135.
[179] N. J. ANTIA AND R. W. WATSON, *J. Am. Chem. Soc.*, 80 (1958) 6134.
[180] P. A. LEVENE AND A. L. RAYMOND, *J. Biol. Chem.*, 102 (1933) 347.
[181] P. A. J. GORIN, L. HOUGH AND J. K. N. JONES, *J. Chem. Soc.*, (1955) 582.
[182] J. L. BARNWELL, W. A. SAUNDERS AND R. W. WATSON, *Chem. and Ind. (London)*, (1955) 173; *Can. J. Chem.*, 33 (1955) 711.
[183] D. P. BURMA AND B. L. HORECKER, *J. Biol. Chem.*, 231 (1958) 1039.
[184] R. L. ANDERSON AND W. A. WOOD, *Biochim. et Biophys. Acta*, 42 (1960) 374.
[185] B. L. HORECKER, P. Z. SMYRNIOTIS AND J. S. SEEGMILLER, *J. Biol. Chem.*, 193 (1951) 383.
[186] D. B. McNAIR SCOTT AND S. S. COHEN, *Biochem. J.*, 65 (1957) 686.
[187] B. L. HORECKER AND P. Z. SMYRNIOTIS, *J. Am. Chem. Soc.*, 74 (1952) 2123.
[188] J. HURWITZ, A. WEISSBACH, B. L. HORECKER AND P. Z. SMYRNIOTIS, *J. Biol. Chem.*, 218 (1956) 769.
[189] B. L. HORECKER, J. HURWITZ AND A. WEISSBACH, *Biochem. Preparations*, 6 (1958) 83.
[190] J. HICKMAN AND G. ASHWELL, *J. Biol. Chem.*, 232 (1958) 737.
[191] P. K. STUMPF AND B. L. HORECKER, *J. Biol. Chem.*, 218 (1956) 753.
[192] J. HURWITZ AND B. L. HORECKER, *J. Biol. Chem.*, 223 (1956) 993.
[193] E. C. HEATH, J. HURWITZ, B. L. HORECKER AND A. GINSBURG, *J. Biol. Chem.*, 231 (1958) 1009.
[194] M. J. WOLIN, F. J. SIMPSON, W. A. WOOD, *Biochim. et Biophys. Acta*, 24 (1957) 635.

[195] D. P. BURMA AND B. L. HORECKER, *J. Biol. Chem.*, 231 (1958) 1053.

[196] M. FRIEDKIN, *J. Biol. Chem.*, 184 (1950) 449.

[197] M. FRIEDKIN AND D. W. ROBERTS, *J. Biol. Chem.*, 207 (1954) 257.

[198] D. L. McDONALD AND H. G. FLETCHER, *J. Am. Chem. Soc.*, 82 (1960) 1832.

[199] L. A. MANSON AND J. O. LAMPEN, *J. Biol. Chem.*, 191 (1951) 95.

[200] G. F. DOMAGK AND B. L. HORECKER, *J. Biol. Chem.*, 233 (1958) 283.

[201] A. GINSBURG, *J. Biol. Chem.*, 234 (1959) 481.

[202] D. L. McDONALD AND H. G. FLETCHER, *J. Am. Chem. Soc.*, 81 (1959) 3719.

[203] H. L. A. TARR, *Chem. and Ind. (London)*, (1957) 562.

[204] T. E. SHOCKLEY AND H. S. PRIDE, *J. Bacteriol.*, 77 (1959) 695.

[205] J. B. WOLFF AND N. O. KAPLAN, *J. Biol. Chem.*, 218 (1956) 849.

[206] R. A. FERRARI, P. MANDELSTAM AND R. K. CRANE, *Arch. Biochem. Biophys.*, 80 (1959) 372.

[207] J. BADDILEY, J. G. BUCHANAN, B. CARSS, A. P. MATHIAS and A. R. SANDERSON, *Biochem. J.*, 64 (1956) 599.

[208] R. M. McCREADY, *Biochem. Preparations*, 4 (1955) 63.

[209] M. E. KRAHL AND C. F. CORI, *Biochem. Preparations*, 1 (1949) 33.

[210] T. POSTERNAK, *J. Am. Chem. Soc.*, 72 (1950) 4824.

[211] C. FITTING AND M. DOUDOROFF, *J. Biol. Chem.*, 199 (1952) 153.

[212] M. L. WOLFROM, C. S. SMITH, D. E. PLETCHER AND A. E. BROWN, *J. Am. Chem. Soc.*, 64 (1942) 23.

[213] F. J. REITHEL, *J. Am. Chem. Soc.*, 67 (1945) 1056.

[214] A. L. POTTER, J. C. SOWDEN, W. Z. HASSID AND M. DOUDOROFF, *J. Am. Chem. Soc.*, 70 (1948) 1751.

[215] F. J. REITHEL AND C. K. CLAYCOMB, *J. Am. Chem. Soc.*, 71 (1949) 3669.

[216] K. JOSEPHSON AND S. PROFFE, *Biochem. Z.*, 258 (1933) 147.

[217] R. ROBISON AND E. J. KING, *Biochem. J.*, 25 (1931) 323.

[218] M. A. SWANSON, *J. Biol. Chem.*, 184 (1950) 647.

[219] W. A. WOOD AND B. L. HORECKER, *Biochem. Preparations*, 3 (1953) 71.

[220] M. ORLOWSKI, *J. Biol. Chem.*, 234 (1959) 1651.

[221] H. A. LARDY AND H. O. L. FISCHER, *Biochem. Preparations*, 2 (1952) 39.

[222] L. F. LELOIR in W. D. McELROY AND B. GLASS (Eds.), *Phosphorus Metabolism*, Vol. I, Johns Hopkins Press, Baltimore, 1951, p. 72.

[223] A. C. PALADINI, R. CAPUTTO, L. F. LELOIR, R. E. TRUCCO AND C. E. CARDINI, *Arch. Biochem.*, 23 (1949) 55.

[224] L. F. LELOIR, R. E. TRUCCO, C. E. CARDINI, A. C. PALADINI AND R. CAPUTTO, *Arch. Biochem.*, 24 (1949) 65.

[225] L. F. LELOIR, O. M. REPETTO, C. E. CARDINI, A. C. PALADINI AND R. CAPUTTO, *Anales asoc. quim. arg.*, 37 (1949) 187.

[226] E. J. KING, R. R. McLAUGHLIN AND W. T. J. MORGAN, *Biochem. J.*, 25 (1931) 310.

[227] S. P. COLOWICK, *J. Biol. Chem.*, 124 (1938) 557.

[228] T. POSTERNAK AND J. P. ROSSELET, *Helv. Chim. Acta*, 36 (1953) 1614.

[229] R. ROBISON, *Biochem. J.*, 26 (1932) 2191.

[230] L. BERGER, M. W. SLEIN, S. P. COLOWICK AND C. F. CORI, *J. Gen. Physiol.*, 29 (1945) 379.

[231] M. KUNITZ AND M. R. McDONALD, *J. Gen. Physiol.*, 29 (1946) 393.

[232] H. W. KOSTERLITZ, *Biochem. J.*, 31 (1937) 2217.

[233] H. W. KOSTERLITZ, *Biochem. J.*, 37 (1943) 318.

[234] R. E. TRUCCO, R. CAPUTTO, L. F. LELOIR AND N. MITTELMAN, *Arch. Biochem.*, 18 (1948) 137.

[235] J. F. WILKINSON, *Biochem. J.*, 44 (1949) 460.

[236] C. E. CARDINI AND L. F. LELOIR, *Arch. Biochem. Biophys.*, 45 (1953) 55.

[237] R. G. HANSEN, W. J. RUTTER AND P. KRICHESKY, *Biochem. Preparations*, 4 (1955) 1.

[238] T. POSTERNAK AND J. P. ROSSELET, *Helv. Chim. Acta*, 37 (1954) 246.

[239] P. A. LEVENE AND A. L. RAYMOND, *J. Biol. Chem.*, 92 (1931) 765.

[240] M. MacLEOD AND R. ROBISON, *Biochem. J.*, 27 (1933) 286.

[241] O. MEYERHOF, K. LOHMANN AND P. SCHUSTER, *Biochem. Z.*, 286 (1936) 319.

[242] A. STAUB AND C. S. VESTLING, *J. Biol. Chem.*, 191 (1951) 395.

[243] F. Leuthardt and E. Testa, *Helv. Chim. Acta*, 34 (1951) 931.
[244] H. G. Hers, *Biochim. et Biophys. Acta*, 8 (1952) 416, 424.
[245] B. M. Pogell, *J. Biol. Chem.*, 201 (1953) 645.
[246] A. L. Raymond and P. A. Levene, *J. Biol. Chem.*, 83 (1929) 619.
[247] H. Z. Sable, *Biochem. Preparations*, 2 (1952) 52.
[248] R. W. McGilvery, *J. Biol. Chem.*, 200 (1953) 835.
[249] F. Leuthardt and E. Testa, *Helv. Physiol. et Pharmacol. Acta*, 8 (1950) 67.
[250] E. L. Totton and H. A. Lardy, *J. Biol. Chem.*, 181 (1949) 701.
[251] K. M. Mann and H. A. Lardy, *J. Biol. Chem.*, 187 (1950) 339.
[252] H. A. Lardy, V. D. Wiebelhaus and K. M. Mann, *J. Biol. Chem.*, 187 (1950) 325.
[253] P. C. Huang and O. Neal Miller, *J. Biol. Chem.*, 231 (1958) 201.
[254] E. Englesberg, *Arch. Biochem. Biophys.*, 71 (1957) 179.
[255] D. M. Wilson and S. Ajl, *J. Bacteriol.*, 73 (1957) 415.
[256] F. L. Pizer and C. E. Ballou, *J. Am. Chem. Soc.*, 81 (1959) 915.
[257] C. E. Ballou and L. I. Pizer, *J. Am. Chem. Soc.*, 81 (1959) 4745.
[258] M. A. MacCormick and H. E. Carter, *Biochem. Preparations*, 2 (1952) 65.
[259] B. M. Iselin, *J. Am. Chem. Soc.*, 71 (1949) 3822.
[260] H. Z. Sable and A. J. Guarino, *J. Biol. Chem.*, 196 (1952) 395.
[261] E. F. Neufeld, D. S. Feingold, W. Z. Hassid, *Arch. Biochem. Biophys.*, 83 (1959) 96.
[262] C. A. Marsh, *J. Chem. Soc.*, (1952) 1578.
[263] D. S. Feingold, E. F. Neufeld and W. Z. Hassid, *Arch. Biochem. Biophys.*, 78 (1958) 401.
[264] J. MacGee and M. Doudoroff, *J. Biol. Chem.*, 210 (1954) 617.
[265] M. A. Cynkin and G. Ashwell, *J. Biol. Chem.*, 235 (1960) 1576.
[266] D. H. Brown, *J. Biol. Chem.*, 204 (1953) 877.
[267] F. Maley, F. M. Maley and H. A. Lardy, *J. Am. Chem. Soc.*, 78 (1956) 5303.
[268] L. F. Leloir and C. E. Cardini, *Biochim. et Biophys. Acta*, 12 (1953) 15.
[269] B. M. Pogell and R. M. Gryder, *J. Biol. Chem.*, 228 (1957) 701.
[270] D. H. Brown, *Biochim. et Biophys. Acta*, 7 (1951) 487.
[271] F. Maley and H. A. Lardy, *J. Am. Chem. Soc.*, 78 (1956) 1393.
[272] J. J. Distler, J. M. Merrick and S. Roseman, *J. Biol. Chem.*, 230 (1958) 497.
[273] L. F. Leloir and C. E. Cardini, *Biochim. et Biophys. Acta*, 20 (1956) 33.
[274] L. F. Leloir, C. E. Cardini, J. M. Olavarría, *Arch. Biochem. Biophys.*, 74 (1958) 84.
[275] L. Reissig, *J. Biol. Chem.*, 219 (1956) 753.
[276] C. E. Cardini and L. F. Leloir, *Arch. Biochem. Biophys.*, 45 (1953) 55.
[277] C. E. Cardini and L. F. Leloir, *J. Biol. Chem.*, 225 (1957) 317.
[278] B. L. Horecker, P. Z. Smyrniotis and H. Klenow, *J. Biol. Chem.*, 205 (1953) 661.
[279] B. L. Horecker, P. Z. Smyrniotis, H. H. Hiatt and P. A. Marks, *J. Biol. Chem.*, 212 (1955) 827.
[280] A. Nordal and A. A. Benson, *J. Am. Chem. Soc.*, 76 (1954) 5054.
[281] V. N. Nigam, H. G. Sie and W. H. Fishman, *J. Am. Chem. Soc.*, 82 (1960) 1007.
[282] P. R. Srinivasan and D. B. Sprinson, *J. Biol. Chem.*, 234 (1959) 717.
[283] A. Weissbach and J. Hurwitz, *J. Biol. Chem.*, 234 (1959) 705.
[284] E. Racker and E. Schroeder, *Arch. Biochem. Biophys.*, 66 (1957) 241.
[285] D. H. Levin and E. Racker, *J. Biol. Chem.*, 234 (1959) 2532.
[286] D. Robison and W. T. J. Morgan, *Biochem. J.*, 22 (1928) 1277.
[287] E. Cabib and L. F. Leloir, *J. Biol. Chem.*, 231 (1958) 275.
[288] J. E. Gander, W. E. Petersen and P. D. Boyer, *Arch. Biochem. Biophys.*, 69 (1957) 85.
[289] F. J. Reithel and R. G. Young, *J. Am. Chem. Soc.*, 74 (1952) 4210.
[290] C. E. Cardini and L. F. Leloir, *J. Biol. Chem.*, 214 (1955) 157.
[291] T. Posternak, *J. Biol. Chem.*, 188 (1951) 317.
[292] J. J. Armstrong, J. Baddiley, J. G. Buchanan, B. Carss and G. R. Greenberg, *J. Chem. Soc.*, (1958) 4344.
[293] J. Baddiley, *Proc. Chem. Soc.*, (1959) 177.
[294] S. Zamenhoff, G. Leidy, P. L. Fitzgerald, H. E. Alexander and E. Chargaff, *J. Biol. Chem.*, 203 (1953) 695.
[295] E. Jeanes, J. E. Pittsley, P. R. Watson and R. J. Dimler, *Arch. Biochem. Biophys.*, 92 (1961) 343.

Chapter V

Glycosides

J. CONCHIE AND G. A. LEVVY

Rowett Research Institute, Bucksburn, Aberdeen (Great Britain)

1. Introduction

There are three general reactions for the synthesis of glycosides, the Fischer[1], the Helferich[2] and the Koenigs–Knorr[3]. The first of these, the Fischer reaction, is by far the simplest, the sugar and the aglycone merely being heated together in the presence of an acid catalyst, but is only applicable to the lower aliphatic alcohols. It is often difficult, if not impossible, to obtain any one desired anomer by this reaction, and it cannot be applied to disaccharides because of alcoholysis. The Helferich reaction is restricted to the preparation of phenolic glycosides, and requires the fully acetylated sugar which is fused with the phenol in presence of a catalyst. The choice of catalyst determines the anomer of the glycoside that is obtained. On the other hand, the Koenigs–Knorr reaction is applicable to all classes of aglycone. It requires the acetylglycosyl halide as starting-material, and usually yields the β-anomer of the glycoside. In both the Helferich and the Koenigs–Knorr reactions it is necessary to deacetylate the product, and very simple methods are available for this purpose. In a few instances it has been found necessary or convenient to develop special methods of glycoside synthesis. The most generally interesting of these is the preparation of glycosiduronic acids by the catalytic oxidation of the glycosides. The subject of glycoside synthesis is dealt with in greater detail in a more extensive review[4].

2. The Fischer reaction

When a sugar is refluxed with an alcohol in the presence of an acid catalyst, a mixture of the anomeric glycopyranosides results. Although this reaction is so simple, its usefulness is limited. One or other anomer may predominate and there is no easy way of controlling the $\alpha:\beta$ ratio in the equilibrium mixture. To take the best-known example, the reaction between methyl

D-glucose   methyl-α-D-glucopyranoside

alcohol and glucose gives methyl α-D-glucopyranoside in 40–50% yield. Crystallization of the β-anomer from the mother liquor is a matter of considerable difficulty. To obtain even one anomer from the reaction product by fractional crystallization is not always possible. Thus, preparation of methyl N-acetyl-D-glucosaminide[5] by the Fischer reaction always yields a mixture of 85% of the α- and 15% of the β-anomer, which cannot be separated by fractional crystallization. The α-anomer can be obtained pure after conversion of the mixture into the more readily fractionated poly-O-acetates. Both anomers can be isolated by chromatography of the original product on a charcoal–Celite column. To prepare the β-anomer, however, it is more profitable to resort to the Koenigs–Knorr reaction, and this is often necessary when a specific anomer is required.

When the reaction is carried out at a lower temperature, the isomeric glycofuranosides can sometimes be obtained. Treatment of L-fucose with 0.8% methanolic hydrogen chloride for 3 days at 15°, followed by chromatography of the product on a cellulose column, yielded 44% of the β-L-furanoside, 20.6% of the α-L-furanoside, 15.4% of the α-L-pyranoside and 20% of the β-L-pyranoside[6].

If hydrogen chloride is employed as catalyst, it must be removed with silver carbonate before working up the product. The whole procedure has been considerably simplified by the introduction of cation-exchange resins as catalysts that can simply be filtered off at the end of the reaction[7]. This method was shown to be suitable for the preparation of the methyl glycosides of α-D-glucopyranose, α-D-mannopyranose, α-D-galactopyranose, β-D-xylopyranose, α-L-rhamnopyranose, and β-D- and β-L-arabinopyranose, as well as the methyl glycosides of α- and β-D-glucofuranosiduurono-6,3-lactone and α-D-galactopyranosiduronic acid methyl ester. It has since been applied to the preparation of a wide variety of other glycosides.

3. The Helferich reaction

The other two general reactions for the synthesis of glycosides require the fully acetylated sugar as starting-material. In the Koenigs–Knorr reaction, this is next converted into the acetylglycosyl halide, whilst in the Helferich reaction it is used directly.

References p. 152

CH$_2$OH

D-glucose

$\xrightarrow{\text{Ac}_2\text{O} \atop \text{ZnCl}_2}$

CH$_2$OAc

penta-O-acetyl-
α-D-glucopyranose

$\xrightarrow{\text{C}_6\text{H}_5\text{OH} \atop \text{ZnCl}_2}$

CH$_2$OAc

phenyl tetra-O-acetyl-
α-D-glucopyranoside

Poly-O-acetylated sugars are prepared by treatment with acetic anhydride in the presence of a catalyst, the choice of which determines the anomer that is obtained. Whilst a directional catalyst can behave variably with different sugars, the same anomer is always obtained from the D- or L-enantiomorph of a single sugar. This is also true of the next stage in the Helferich reaction.

The most widely-used catalysts for acetylation are sodium acetate and zinc chloride. With sodium acetate, the product is predominantly in the β-form, except in the case of D- and L-arabinose, where the α-anomer is obtained. (By definition of the terms α and β, α-D- and α-L-arabinose are enantiomorphs.) Zinc chloride usually gives the α-acetyl derivative of the sugar, but D-glucosamine and D-galactosamine yield the β-form with this catalyst. Of the other catalysts commonly employed, perchloric acid behaves like zinc chloride, whereas pyridine tends to give a mixture of the α- and β-poly-O-acetates.

At the next stage in the Helferich reaction, the sugar acetate is fused with the aglycone in the presence of a directional catalyst, and the glycoside acetate produced is subsequently deacetylated as described below. Either anomer of the poly-O-acetylated sugar may be employed, the configuration of the glycoside being determined by the catalyst used in the condensation with the phenol. Sometimes, however, the yield may be improved by using the poly-O-acetate with the same anomeric configuration as the glycoside. Zinc chloride is the only commonly employed catalyst that gives the α-anomer, but quite often it yields the β-anomer. In one such instance, mercuric cyanide has been successfully employed to obtain the glycoside α-acetate[8]. All the other catalysts employed in this condensation, notably p-toluenesulphonic acid, are alike in giving the β-anomer, but there are occasional exceptions. In the preparation of p-nitrophenyl D- and L-fucopyranosides, for instance, both zinc chloride and p-toluenesulphonic acid give the α-glycoside acetate.

4. The Koenigs–Knorr reaction

In the Koenigs–Knorr reaction acylglycosyl halides are condensed with alcohols or phenols. The acylglycosyl halide most often employed is the acetylglycosyl bromide, but sometimes it is so unstable that the chloride

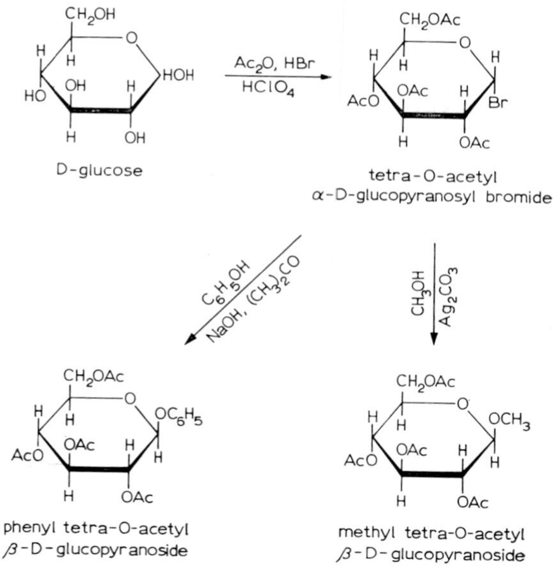

CH2OH
HOH
HO
OH
D-glucose
Ac2O, HBr
HClO4
CH2OAc
AcO
OAc
Br
tetra-O-acetyl
α-D-glucopyranosyl bromide
C6H5OH
NaOH, (CH3)2CO
CH3OH
Ag2CO3
OC6H5
phenyl tetra-O-acetyl
β-D-glucopyranoside
OCH3
methyl tetra-O-acetyl
β-D-glucopyranoside

is preferred. The halide is usually prepared from the poly-*O*-acetate of the sugar by treatment with hydrogen bromide or hydrogen chloride[9]. Whichever anomer of the poly-*O*-acetate is employed, the acetylglycosyl halide takes up its more stable configuration. Subsequent condensation of the halide with the aglycone is most often accompanied by Walden inversion at C-1. With most sugars, the stable acetylglycosyl halide has the α-configuration and the Koenigs–Knorr reaction then results in the formation of β-glycosides. There are, however, exceptions, for instance D- and L-arabinose, in which the halide has the β-configuration, resulting in the production of the α-glycoside. The product of the Koenigs–Knorr reaction requires deacetylation as described below.

It is often possible to prepare the acylglycosyl bromide from the sugar without isolation of the intermediary poly-*O*-acetate. In one such method[10], the sugar is acetylated with acetic anhydride and perchloric acid, and when reaction is complete, hydrogen bromide is generated *in situ* from phosphorus tribromide, itself prepared by adding phosphorus and bromine to the reaction mixture.

Silver oxide or silver carbonate is the catalyst most commonly used for the condensation of acetylglycosyl halides with alcohols or phenols. Except in the case of the lower aliphatic alcohols, the aglycone is dissolved in a dry solvent, which is often an organic base to promote the forward reaction. With phenols, but not alcohols, the use of sodium or potassium hydroxide

References p. 152

in aqueous acetone is just as widely applicable. These catalysts cause Walden inversion at C-1. The use of an organic base, in absence of silver oxide or silver carbonate, results in a mixture of α- and β-glycoside acetates which can often be separated by fractional crystallization. Mercuric salts are also frequently employed as catalysts, and lead to the formation of one or the other anomer of the glycoside acetate, depending on the conditions.

Benzoylglycosyl bromides have sometimes been employed instead of the acetylglycosyl bromides. When a silver catalyst is added, Walden inversion occurs in the usual way. Benzoylglycosyl bromides have now, however, been shown to react rapidly with simple alcohols in absence of any catalyst. Under these conditions, the configuration of the product is determined by steric hindrance. As a general rule[11], "in the absence of an acid acceptor all the benzoylated glycopyranosyl halides... which have a benzoyloxy group at C-2 *trans* to the halogen, react with methanol without the Walden inversion while those halides having a *cis* relationship between the groups on C-1 and C-2 react with inversion at C-1". Thus, since the aglycone always takes up a *trans* position with respect to the benzoyl group at C-2, this reaction yields β-D-glucosides, β-D-ribosides and β-D-xylosides, but α-D-mannosides and α-D-arabinosides.

Reaction of acetylglycosyl bromides with silver phosphates yields aldose 1-phosphates. According to the procedure employed there may or may not be Walden inversion[12] at C-1.

5. Deacetylation of glycoside acetates

phenyl tetra-*O*-acetyl-β-D-   phenyl β-D-glucopyranoside
glucopyranoside

Deacetylation of the glycoside acetates is necessary after the Helferich and Koenigs–Knorr reactions. Aqueous alkali is no longer used for this purpose. The reagent most commonly employed is sodium methoxide in very small, catalytic quantities, and the acetate is dissolved in anhydrous methanol or a mixture of methanol and chloroform. Reaction is usually very rapid. Alternative reagents often used for deacetylation are barium and ammonium methoxides; the former is particularly useful for debenzoylation.

6. Preparation of glycosyluronic acids

The methods of glycoside synthesis already described can be applied to a limited extent to the preparation of glycosyluronic acids. In the Koenigs–

Knorr and Helferich reactions, the intermediates are prepared from the methyl ester of the uronic acid. β-Glycosides of D-glucuronic acid have been prepared by both reactions. Decomposition of the methyl ester occurs during the deacetylation. No great success has attended attempts to prepare the α-glycosides of D-glucuronic acid by the Helferich reaction.

D-Glucuronic acid normally exists as the 6,3-lactone, D-glucurone, which is a furanose, whereas salts and esters of the acid are in the pyranose form. The naturally-occurring β-D-glucosiduronic acids also have the pyranose configuration. If D-glucurone is used instead of methyl glucuronate as starting-material in the Koenigs–Knorr or Helferich reaction, the product will be a furanoside, and will retain the lactone ring. As noted above, the Fischer reaction can be employed to prepare the methyl α- and β-glycosides of D-glucurone directly. It is not feasible to prepare β-D-glucofuranosiduronic acids from their lactones, since the lactone ring cannot be opened without decomposing the whole molecule.

phenyl β-D-glucopyranoside   phenyl β-D-glucopyranosiduronic acid

A general method for the preparation of glycosyluronic acids is the selective oxidation of the primary alcohol group in the glycoside of the corresponding sugar. In the most successful procedure, oxidation is carried out with gaseous oxygen in presence of a platinum catalyst, in neutral or mildly alkaline solution[13]. Both alkyl and aryl glycosyluronic acids can be prepared in this way, and the oxidation appears to be generally applicable to the glycosides of different sugars. α-Glucuronic acid 1-phosphate is obtained by oxidation of α-glucose 1-phosphate. The usefulness of this reaction depends upon the ease with which the appropriate compound for oxidation can be prepared.

The synthesis of some β-D-glucopyranosiduronic acids of biochemical interest has not yet been achieved, and one must rely upon biosynthetic methods of preparation.

REFERENCES

[1] E. FISCHER, *Ber. deut. chem. Ges.*, 26 (1893) 2400.
[2] B. HELFERICH AND E. SCHMITZ-HILLEBRECHT, *Ber. deut. chem. Ges.*, 66 (1933) 378.
[3] W. KOENIGS AND E. KNORR, *Ber. deut. chem. Ges.*, 34 (1901) 957.
[4] J. CONCHIE, G. A. LEVVY AND C. A. MARSH, *Advances in Carbohydrate Chem.*, 12 (1957) 157.
[5] F. ZILLIKEN, C. S. ROSE, G. A. BRAUN AND P. GYÖRGY, *Arch. Biochem. Biophys.*, 54 (1955) 392.
[6] J. G. GARDINER AND E. PERCIVAL, *J. Chem. Soc.*, (1958) 1414.
[7] J. E. CADOTTE, F. SMITH AND D. SPRIESTERSBACH, *J. Am. Chem. Soc.*, 74 (1952) 1501.
[8] H. FEIER AND O. WESTPHAL, *Chem. Ber.*, 89 (1956) 589.
[9] L. J. HAYNES AND F. H. NEWTH, *Advances in Carbohydrate Chem.*, 10 (1955) 207.
[10] M. BÁRCZAI-MARTOS AND F. KÖRÖSY, *Nature*, 165 (1950) 369.
[11] H. G. FLETCHER JR. AND C. S. HUDSON, *J. Am. Chem. Soc.*, 72 (1950) 4173.
[12] E. W. PUTMAN AND W. Z. HASSID, *J. Am. Chem. Soc.*, 79 (1957) 5057.
[13] C. A. MARSH, *J. Chem. Soc.*, (1952) 1578.

Chapter VI

The Oligosaccharides*

SHIGERU TSUIKI**, YOHICHI HASHIMOTO AND WARD PIGMAN

*University of Alabama, Medical Center, Department of Medicine,
Birmingham, Ala. and the New York Medical College,
Biochemistry Department, New York, N.Y. (U.S.A.)*

1. Introduction

The oligosaccharides[1] comprise a large group of polymeric carbohydrates, each member consisting of relatively few monosaccharide units (Greek *"oligo"*, a few), which, on complete acid hydrolysis, yield only simple sugars or derivatives. They are composed of monosaccharide residues connected through glycosidic linkages with the loss of $n - 1$ molecules of water ($n =$ number of monosaccharide residues $=$ degree of polymerization). On the basis of the number of monosaccharide residues per mole, the oligosaccharides are classified as disaccharides, trisaccharides, tetrasaccharides, penta-saccharides, etc.

$$C_6H_{12}O_6 + C_6H_{12}O_6 - H_2O = C_{12}H_{22}O_{11} \qquad \text{(disaccharides)}$$

$$3\,C_6H_{12}O_6 - 2\,H_2O = C_{18}H_{32}O_{16} \qquad \text{(trisaccharides)}$$

No sharp distinction can be drawn between the oligosaccharides and the polysaccharides. The structures are similar and the oligosaccharides become polysaccharides as the number of combined sugar units increase. In the present discussion oligosaccharides will be limited arbitrarily to carbohydrates with ten or less monosaccharide residues in the molecule. Generally, the poly-

* Prepared with support from the National Institute of Arthritis and Metabolic Diseases (USPHS A-3555) and the U.S. Army, Medical Research and Development Board (ASG MD-773).
** Present address: Department of Medical Chemistry, Tohoku University, School of Medicine, Sendai (Japan).

saccharides have a much greater degree of polymerization, in some cases values of several thousand.

Most of the known oligosaccharides are naturally occurring substances or are products of the partial acid, or enzymatic hydrolysis of polysaccharides or of transglycosylation reactions. Transglycosylations, discussed in detail at the end of this chapter, differ from hydrolyses in that another sugar acts as the acceptor instead of water.

Hydrolysis: Sucrose + water $\xrightarrow{\text{acids or enzyme}}$ glucose + fructose

Transglycosylation: Sucrose + sucrose $\xrightarrow{\text{enzyme}}$ fructosyl-sucrose + glucose

In a disaccharide, one monosaccharide residue is combined by an oxygen bridge between its hemiacetal hydroxyl and the hydroxyl of another residue. If the second hydroxyl is an alcoholic hydroxyl, as in lactose, one reducing group remains in the disaccharide. If hemiacetal hydroxyls of both monosaccharide residues are utilized for the glycosidic linkage, as in trehalose, the resulting disaccharide has no reducing group. According to the presence or absence of a reducing group, disaccharides (and also higher oligosaccharides) are classified as reducing and nonreducing. The reducing oligosaccharides are named as glycosylaldoses (glycosylketoses), and the nonreducing oligosaccharides as glycosyl aldosides (or glycosyl ketosides). Thus, lactose is 4-O-β-D-galactopyranosyl-D-glucose and α,α-trehalose is α-D-glucopyranosyl α-D-glucopyranoside.

α-Lactose   α,α-Trehalose

Reducing oligosaccharides show many of the properties of simple sugars such as mutarotation, reduction of alkaline solutions of salts of heavy metals, existence of α,β and pyranose and furanose isomers, and ready oxidation and reduction. Nonreducing sugars behave as alcohols unless the linkages are hydrolyzed by acids. The linkages are usually stable to the action of alkalies, but a few (e.g., turanose) are alkali-labile.

The constituent monosaccharide units of an oligosaccharide may be different, as in lactose, which on hydrolysis gives one molecule each of D-glucose and D-galactose, or alike, as in trehalose, which consists of two molecules of D-glucose. Most of the theoretically possible glucose disaccharides containing the pyranoid ring are known. Table I lists and shows some of the properties of such disaccharides.

TABLE I

PROPERTIES OF D-GLUCOPYRANOSYL-D-GLUCOSES

Common name	Linkage	M.P. (°C)	$[\alpha]_D$ (H_2O)	M_G*
α,α-Trehalose[2]	α,α	Dihydrate 97	+ 178.3	—
α,β-Trehalose[3]	α,β	145	+ 95	—
β,β-Trehalose[3]	β,β	130–135	— 41.5	—
Kojibiose[4]	2-α	—	+ 140	—
Sophorose[2]	2-β	180	+ 35 → + 20	—
Nigerose[5]	3-α	204–206	+ 136	0.69
Laminaribiose[6]	3-β	α 204–206 β 188–192	+ 25 → + 18.6 + 7 → + 20.8	0.69
Maltose[2,3]	4-α	α 108 β Monohydrate 102–103	+ 173 + 112 → + 130	0.32
Cellobiose[2]	4-β	225	+ 14 → + 35	0.28
(None)[7]	5-β	—	— 22.3	—
Isomaltose[8]	6-α	—	+ 103	0.69
Gentiobiose[2,9]	6-β	α 85–86 β 190	+ 21.4 → + 8.7 — 3.0 → + 10.5	0.75

* Mobility during paper electrophoresis, relative to D-glucose (see text).

The present text will describe only general concepts of oligosaccharides. For the individual oligosaccharides the recent review by Hassid and Ballou in Pigman's book[2] is recommended.

2. Preparation

Most of the methods of preparation of oligosaccharides, whether from natural products or by chemical synthesis, involve separation from complex mixtures. The introduction of displacement chromatography has greatly facilitated the separation of these mixtures[11]. A particularly useful adsorbent is activated carbon[12]; diatomaceous earth ("Celite") is added to the adsorbent as a support and to increase the rate of solvent flow. A mixture of sugars is adsorbed to a column of activated carbon and Celite (1:1), and monosaccharides are displaced by water. Gradual elution with increasing concentrations of aqueous ethanol enables the separation of di-, tri-, and higher oligosaccharides[12-14]. An example of these separations is illustrated in Fig. 1. Separation of different disaccharides also can be achieved by chromatographing the acetates through a hydrated magnesium silicate ("Magnesol")-Celite column[15,16]. This method is extremely useful for the preparation and separation of oligosaccharides since acetylated sugars often can be easily prepared and crystallized.

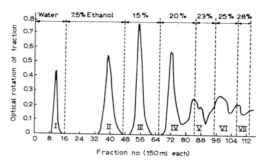

Fig. 1. Chromatographic separation of maltodextrins on activated carbon[14].

For the rapid separation of the components of a mixture of oligo-saccharides, paper chromatography has been employed[17]. A linear relation-ship was obtained between $R_F/(1 - R_F)$ and the degree of polymerization for a number of series of homologous oligosaccharides (Fig. 2)[18,19]. The migration of oligosaccharides during paper chromatography with the customary solvent systems is very slow. To overcome this difficulty, special techniques such as multiple development have been employed[20]. Another method is to form derivatives which have high R_F values. The oligosaccha-rides, for example, are reacted with benzylamine and development of the N-benzylglycosylamines is then carried out[21].

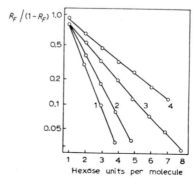

Fig. 2. Relation between movement in a paper chromatogram and structure of oligo-saccharides. 1 = Galactan series (reducing); 2 = Dextran series; 3 = Amylose series; 4 = Inulin series[18].

Paper electrophoresis has been especially useful for the separation of oligosaccharides[22]. Electric charges can be created in neutral oligosaccharides by running the electrophoresis in borate buffer or converting the sugars to the corresponding N-benzylglycosylamines. Comparison of the electrophoretic mobilities of various reducing disaccharides of D-glucose in borate buffer indicates a relationship of the mobilities to the structure; $(1 \to 2)$ and $(1 \to 4)$ linked disaccharides have much lower mobilities than those containing $(1 \to 3)$ or $(1 \to 6)$ linkages[10]. M_G values, which are the ratio of the distance travelled by the substance to the distance travelled by D-glucose, are shown in Table I for several disaccharides composed of D-glucose. On the other hand, the mobility of N-benzylglycosylamine derivatives seems to depend solely on the molecular size of the original oligosaccharides, and this property may permit the determination of the molecular size of oligosaccharides, at least up to a hexasaccharide[23].

3. Disaccharides

(a) General properties

The general properties of reducing disaccharides are similar to those of monosaccharides. Such disaccharides reduce solutions of alkaline copper salts (Fehling solution, etc.), mutarotate, and form glycosides. Except 2-substituted ones such as sophorose, reducing disaccharides form osazones. One significant difference from monosaccharides is that the disaccharides do not reduce copper acetate in neutral or slightly acidic solution (Barfoed test) in short time periods. Nonreducing disaccharides behave as alcohols except after acid hydrolysis which liberates reducing groups.

The identification of disaccharides is usually made through derivatives such as phenylosazones, phenylosotriazoles or octaacetates. Some general properties of phenylosazones and octaacetates of several disaccharides are shown in Table II.

Disaccharides are cleaved into two molecules of monosaccharide by acid or enzymatic hydrolysis. The progress of hydrolysis can be followed quantitatively by measuring the increase in reducing power. Considerable difference in the ease of hydrolysis is shown by disaccharides; sucrose, with its fructofuranose ring, is particularly labile to acids. The process of hydrolysis of sucrose to a mixture of equal amounts of fructose and glucose is called "inversion", because the optical rotation changes from *dextro* to *levo* as a result of the high levorotation of fructose[37]. The final mixture is called invert sugar. Octa-O-methylsucrose, obtained by the methylation of sucrose, does not undergo inversion of rotation on hydrolysis, and two dextrorotatory tetra-O-methyl-D-hexoses are obtained. The evidence indicates that the

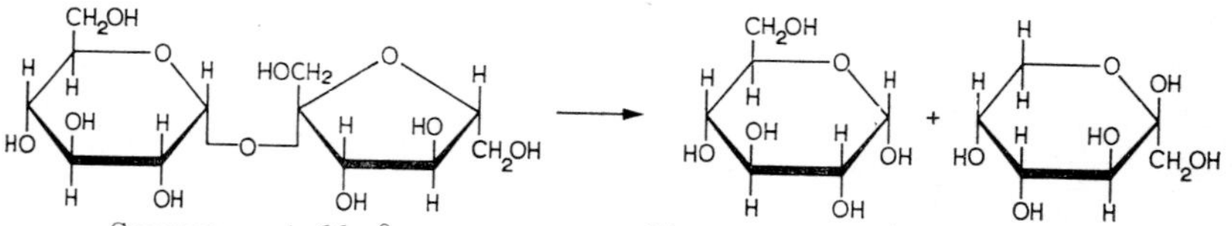

Sucrose = + 66.5° → D-Glucose = + 52°, D-Fructose = − 92°
Invert sugar = − 20°

inversion of unsubstituted sucrose, either by acids or by invertase, involves a ring shift of the D-fructose unit from the unstable furanose to the normal pyranose form (see formulas).

TABLE II

PHENYLOSAZONES AND OCTAACETATES OF SOME DISACCHARIDES

Substance	Phenylosazone		Octaacetate	
	M.P. (°C)	$[\alpha]_D$	M.P. (°C)	$[\alpha]_D$ (Chloroform)
α,α-Trehalose[3, 27]	—	—	100–102	+ 162
α,β-Trehalose[28]	—	—	140–141	+ 82
β,β-Trehalose[29]	—	—	181	− 18.6
Kojibiose[4]	—	—	α 166 / β 118	+ 150 / + 112
Sophorose[30, 31]	—	—	β 192	− 8, / − 2.8
Nigerose[32]	204–206	—	β 147–148	+ 86.6
Laminaribiose[5, 6]	199–201	− 76.0 (ethanol)	α 77– 78 / β 160–161	+ 20 / − 28.8
Maltose[3]	206	+ 1.33 (pyridine + ether)	α 125 / β 159–160	+ 122.8 / + 62.6
Cellobiose[3, 33]	198–200	− 6.5 (pyridine–ether 2 : 3)	α 229.5 / β 202	+ 41 / − 14.6
Isomaltose[24, 34]	177–179	+ 32.6 → + 46 (methylcellosolve)	β 143–144	+ 97
Gentiobiose[3, 16, 25]	179–181	− 70.8 → − 48.2 (pyridine–ethanol 4 : 6)	α 188–189 / β 191–192	+ 52.4 / − 5.5
Lactose[3]	210–214	− 25.4 → − 7.9	α 152 / β 90	+ 53.6 / − 4.7
Melibiose[3, 35]	176–178	+ 43.2 (pyridine)	β 177	+ 102.5
Sucrose[3]	—	—	69– 70	+ 59.6
Turanose[3]	215–220	—	α 158 / β 216–217	+ 107 / + 20.5
Primeverose[3]	220	− 109.7 (pyridine)	216–217[*]	− 26.2
Xylobiose[26, 36]	195–196	− 22.3 → − 77.0 (pyridine–ethanol 7 : 3)	155.5–156[*]	− 75

[*] Heptaacetate

(b) Determination of structure

The first step in the determination of the structure of an oligosaccharide is the identification of constituent monosaccharide units and the nature of the reducing unit if present. This can be done by applying appropriate tests to the hydrolysis products. If lactose is first oxidized with bromine to lactobionic acid and then hydrolyzed, D-gluconic acid and D-galactose are the products obtained. This evidence establishes lactose as being a D-galactosyl-D-glucose.

For nonreducing disaccharides such as sucrose or trehalose, the position of the hemiacetal hydroxyl of each unit involved in the linkage is evident. For reducing disaccharides, the position of substitution of the nonreducing unit in the reducing unit must be determined. For this purpose the methylation method has been the most valuable means.

Methylation of maltose by dimethyl sulfate and sodium hydroxide leads to a methyl hepta-O-methylmaltoside which after acid hydrolysis is con-

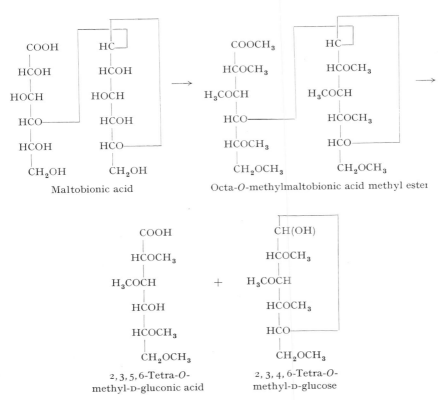

Maltobionic acid   Octa-O-methylmaltobionic acid methyl ester

2,3,5,6-Tetra-O-methyl-D-gluconic acid   2,3,4,6-Tetra-O-methyl-D-glucose

verted to 2,3,4,6-tetra-O-methyl-D-glucose and 2,3,6-tri-O-methyl-D-glu-cose[38]. The tetra-O-methyl-D-glucose must originate from the nonreducing D-glucopyranose residue. The preparation of the tri-O-methyl-D-glucose from maltose, however, still leaves two possibilities for the structure of maltose, since the disaccharide bridge may be connected to carbon 4 or 5. The position of the linkage is shown by the bromine oxidation of maltose to maltobionic acid which on methylation and hydrolysis yields, in addition to tetra-O-methyl-D-glucose, 2,3,5,6-tetra-O-methyl-D-gluconic acid; the unsubstituted hydroxyl at carbon 4 represents the position of the disaccharide linkage[39]. The methylation method works well for disaccharides when the necessary reference compounds (methylated monosaccharides) are known.

Introduction of chromatographic techniques has made it easy to separate and identify the resulting methylated monosaccharides, thus requiring comparatively small amounts of the original materials. Paper partition chromatography is usually preferred for this purpose[40]. Paper electrophoresis in borate buffer is also employed[40]. Special care must be taken for the methylation of oligosaccharides unstable to acids or alkalies. To overcome these difficulties, for example, the alkali-labile "Lacto-N-tetraose" was reduced to "Lacto-N-tetraitol" before methylation[41], (see below).

Lacto-N-tetraose: O-β-D-Galactopyranosyl-$(1 \rightarrow 3)$-2-acetamido-2-deoxy-O-β-D-glucopyranosyl-$(1 \rightarrow 3)$-O-β-D-galactopyranosyl-$(1 \rightarrow 4)$-α-D-glucopyranose.

Reliable methods for the elucidation of the configuration of the glycosidic linkage are based on enzymic hydrolyses. Maltose is hydrolyzed by the same yeast enzyme (α-D-glucosidase) as that which hydrolyses methyl α-D-glucoside. The β-D-glucosidase of almond emulsin produces no significant cleavage. Cellobiose, however, is hydrolyzed by the same enzyme (β-D-glucosidase) as that acting on β-D-glucosides. From this evidence together with the results from methylation studies, maltose is given the formula of 4-O-α-D-glucopyranosyl-D-glucose. Cellobiose is given the formula of 4-O-β-D-glucopyranosyl-D-glucose, since this disaccharide gives the same final products as for maltose by methylation studies.

The Isorotation Rules of Hudson are applicable to disaccharides. As shown in Table I, all α-D-glucopyranosyl-D-glucoses show high *dextro* optical rotations, whereas β-D-glucopyranosyl-D-glucoses have far smaller rotations. Likewise, consideration of the optical rotatory relationships of three isomers indicates that both anomeric carbons of naturally-occurring trehalose

$([\alpha]_\text{D} + 178.3°)$ have the α-configuration. A mutarotation of the disaccharides during enzymic or acid hydrolysis also gives an indication of the linkage involved. If downward mutarotation is obtained, the glycosidic linkage is considered to be of the α-D-type, since such mutarotation indicates conversion of the α-D-anomer of the liberated monosaccharide into β; upward mutarotation indicates a β-D-type. These considerations are correct only if ring changes or Walden inversions are not involved.

Periodate oxidation is also valuable for structural studies of nonreducing disaccharides. A nonreducing disaccharide consisting of glucopyranose and fructofuranose should consume three moles of periodate and form one mole of formic acid. If the D-fructose residue were to exist in the disaccharide as the pyranoid form, it would consume four moles of periodate and form two moles of formic acid per mole of disaccharide. Consumption of three moles of periodate and formation of one mole of formic acid by actual oxidation of sucrose confirmed the furanose structure of the D-fructose residue in sucrose[42].

The same results can be obtained by the methylation of sucrose followed by hydrolysis. Two dextrorotatory tetra-O-methyl-D-hexoses are formed. The tetra-O-methyl-D-glucose $([\alpha]_\text{D} + 81.3°)$ is the well known 2,3,4,6-tetra-O-methyl-D-glucopyranose. The tetra-O-methyl-D-fructose $([\alpha]_\text{D} + 31.3°)$ is not the same as the levorotatory crystalline 1,3,4,5-tetra-O-methyl-D-fructopyranose of $[\alpha]_\text{D} - 85.6°$. The structure of this compound is shown by the following evidence. Oxidation with nitric acid gives a liquid tri-O-methyl-2-keto-D-gluconic acid, which in turn is oxidized by acid permanganate to a crystalline tri-O-methyl-D-arabonic 1,4-lactone. This lactone is identical, except for the sign of the rotation, with the product obtained by the oxidation of tri-O-methyl-L-arabinose. Inasmuch as the tri-O-methyl-D-arabonic lactone from sucrose yields di-O-methyl-D-threaric acid (I) on further treatment with nitric acid, it must have the methyl groups at positions 2, 3, and 5; hence, the original methylated D-fructose from sucrose is the 1,3,4,6-tetra-O-methyl-D-fructofuranose[43,44].

$$\begin{array}{ccc}
\text{H} & & \text{OCH}_3 \\
| & & | \\
\text{HOOC} - \text{C} & \text{---------} & \text{C} - \text{COOH (I)} \\
| & & | \\
\text{OCH}_3 & & \text{H}
\end{array}$$

(I)

Application of the periodate oxidation method to the reducing disaccharides does not give definite results, because the intermediate products are unstable and tend to become completely degraded. Lactose, for example, on complete oxdiation gives nine moles of formic acid, two moles of formaldehyde, and one mole of carbon dioxide[45]. The whole reaction should be carried out at a low temperature (0–5°) in the dark. To avoid complications, the sugars may be reduced to the alcohols before applying periodate oxidation. The reducing group may be stabilized by forming a glycoside, phenylosotriazole[46] or phenylosazone[47,48]. One advantage of using the phenylosazone is that only $(1 \rightarrow 5)$ or $(1 \rightarrow 6)$ disaccharides can give a crystalline aldehyde (phenylosazone of mesoxalaldehyde) (II) after reaction with periodate. Oxidation with lead tetraacetate has also been used for the structural determination of reducing disaccharides[49,50].

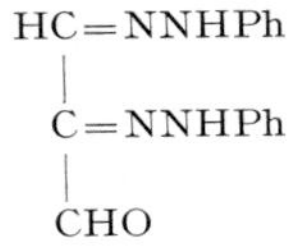

$$
\begin{array}{l}
HC=NNHPh \\
\quad | \\
C=NNHPh \quad (II) \\
\quad | \\
CHO
\end{array}
$$

Finally, the structure of disaccharides can be determined by synthesis. The fact that condensation of 1,2,3,4-tetra-O-acetyl-β-D-glucopyranose with tetra-O-acetylglucosyl bromide gives rise to octa-O-acetylgentiobiose establishes the $(1 \rightarrow 6)$ linkage in gentiobiose since the only linkage which can be formed is between these two carbon atoms[51 52].

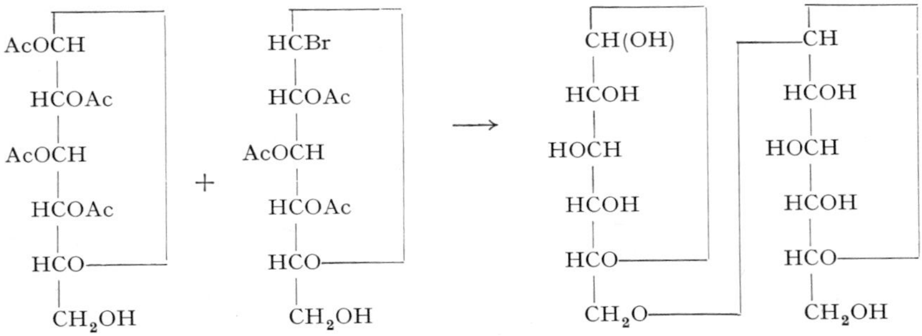

1,2,3,4-Tetra-O-acetyl-β-D-gluco-pyranose   Tetra-O-acetyl-D-glycosyl bromide   Gentiobiose

(c) Individual disaccharides

A few disaccharides are found free in the natural state. Lactose is found in the milk of all mammals to the extent of approximately 5%. Sucrose occurs almost universally throughout the plant kingdom in the juices, seeds, leaves, fruits, flowers, and roots of plants. The industrial sources of sucrose are usually sugar cane and sugar beet. Trehalose(α,α) is contained in large amounts in rye ergot, fungi, young mushrooms, yeast, and the "resurrection plant" *Selaginella lepidophylla*. The disaccharide has been shown to be a major blood sugar in some insects[53] and is found also in a highly toxic lipid isolated from *Mycobacterium tuberculosis*[54,55]. Its α,β- and β,β-isomers are known only as synthetic products[28,56].

Many of the known disaccharides are obtained through controlled acid or enzymatic hydrolysis of higher oligo- or polysaccharides. Cellobiose is not known to exist in free state but is the basic repeating unit of cellulose. Maltose is prepared from starch by the action of β-amylase. Isomaltose exists as a unit of amylopectin, glycogen, and especially certain bacterial dextrans. Nigerose is found in the partial hydrolyzates of starch[32] and of glycogen[57] in amounts which indicate that the α-($1 \rightarrow 3$) linkage may be an integral part of these structures. Melibiose occurs mainly as a constituent of the trisaccharide raffinose. Gentiobiose is the sugar constituent of a number of glycosides of which the most important are amygdalin and crocin. It is also prepared by the partial hydrolysis of the trisaccharide gentianose, and is found as a "reversion" product in starch hydrolysates. Partial hydrolysis of natural gums and mucilages provides the most common source of many disaccharides[58].

Some disaccharides and their properties are shown in Table III (see also Table I).

TABLE III

PROPERTIES OF DISACCHARIDES

Compound	Common name	M.P. (°C)	$[\alpha]_D$ (H₂O)
O-β-L-Arabopyranosyl-L-arabinose[58]	—	—	+ 220
O-α-L-Arabopyranosyl-L-arabinose[59]	—	—	— 14
O-α-L-Arabopyranosyl-D-glucose[2,3]	Vicianose	$\begin{cases} \alpha & — \\ \beta & 210 \end{cases}$	$\begin{cases} + \;56.6 \rightarrow + \;40.5 \\ + \;15.8 \rightarrow + \;39.7 \end{cases}$
O-α-D-Galactopyranosyl-L-arabinose[2]	—	amorphous	+ 152
O-β-D-Galactopyranosyl-D-arabinose[60]	—	—	—
O-β-D-Galactopyranosyl-L-arabinose[61]	—	amorphous	— 13
O-β-D-Galactopyranosyl-D-galactose[62]	—	159–160.5	+ 62
O-α-D-Galactopyranosyl-D-galactose[2]	—	210–211	+ 177
O-β-D-Galactopyranosyl-D-galactose[63]	—	—	+ 30
O-β-D-Galactopyranosyl-3,6-anhydro-D-galactose[64]	—	—	—
O-β-D-Galactopyranosyl-3,6-anhydro-L-galactose[2]	Agarobiose	amorphous	— 5.8
O-β-D-Galactopyranosyl-D-glucose[2,3]	Lactose · H₂O	$\begin{cases} \alpha & 202 \\ \beta & 252 \end{cases}$	$\begin{cases} + \;83.5 \rightarrow + \;52.3 \\ + \;34.2 \rightarrow + \;53.6 \end{cases}$
O-α-D-Galactopyranosyl-D-glucose[2,3]	Melibiose · H₂O	β 85	+ 110.5 $\rightarrow$ + 126.5

(continued on p. 164)

TABLE III (continued)

Compound	Common name	M.P. (°C)	$[\alpha]_D$ (H₂O)
6-O-β-D-Galactopyranosyl-D-glucose[3]	—	174–176	+ 54.2 → + 30
6-O-α-D-Galactopyranosyl-D-fructose[2]	Planteobiose	amorphous	+ 125
4-O-β-D-Galactopyranosyl-D-mannose[3]	—	α 150–160 / β 195–196	+ 38 → + 27 / + 11 → + 27
6-O-α-D-Galactopyranosyl-D-mannose[65]	Epimelibiose	201	+ 120.9 → + 124
4-O-β-D-Galactopyranosyl-D-xylose[66]	—	210–211	− 1 → + 15
3-O-α-D-Glucopyranosyl-D-arabinose[3]	—	172	+ 16.5
α-D-Glucopyranosyl β-D-fructofuranoside[2]	Sucrose	160–186	+ 66.5
3-O-α-D-Glucopyranosyl-D-fructose[2]	Turanose	157	+ 27.3 → + 75
4-O-α-D-Glucopyranosyl-D-galactose[67]	—	—	
4-O-β-D-Glucopyranosyl-D-galactose[68]	Lycobiose	246–247	+ 41.5
6-O-β-D-Glucopyranosyl-D-galactose[3]	—	crystalline	+ 1.6 → + 13
4-O-α-D-Glucopyranosyl-D-mannose[3]	Epimaltose	215–216	+ 97 → + 115
4-O-β-D-Glucopyranosyl-D-mannose[3]	Epicellobiose	α 139 / β 205	+ 14.6 → + 5 / − 6.5 → + 6
6-O-β-D-Glucopyranosyl-D-mannose[3]	Epigentiobiose	167.5–168	− 5.1 → − 11
1-O-β-D-Glucopyranosyl-D-mannitol[69]	—	140–141	− 18
6-O-β-D-Mannopyranosyl-D-galactose[3]	—	crystalline	+ 144 → + 134
4-O-β-D-Mannopyranosyl-D-glucose[70]	—	202–203	+ 30 → + 19
4-O-β-D-Mannopyranosyl-D-mannose[65]	Mannobiose	193.5–194	− 7.7 → − 2
6-O-β-L-Rhamnopyranosyl-D-glucose[3]	Rutinose	189–192	+ 3.2 → − 0
2-O-β-D-Xylopyranosyl-L-arabinose[72]	—	167–168	+ 32.9
5-O-β-D-Xylopyranosyl-L-arabinose[71]	—	—	− 34
3-O-α-D-Xylopyranosyl-L-arabinose[13]	—	117–119	+ 175 → + 183
6-O-β-D-Xylopyranosyl-D-glucose[2]	Primeverose	209	+ 23 → − 3
4-O-β-D-Xylopyranosyl-D-xylose[26]	Xylobiose	185–186	− 32 → + 25

4. Higher oligosaccharides

The methods described for the determination of the structure of disaccharides are applicable for the higher oligosaccharides. An additional especially useful method is to convert them to disaccharides of known structure by controlled acid or enzymic hydrolysis. Thus, although complete acid hydrolysis of raffinose gives one mole each of D-glucose, D-fructose, and D-galactose, mild acid hydrolysis or treatment with yeast invertase gives one mole of D-fructose and the disaccharide melibiose[74,75]. The α-D-galactopyranosidase of almond emulsin decomposes raffinose to sucrose and D-galactose[76]. Since the structures of melibiose and of sucrose are known, the order of the monosaccharide units and the nature of the linkages in raffinose are fixed by this procedure.

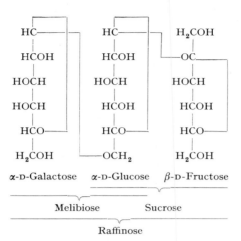

As shown in Table IV, many of known tri-, tetra- or pentasaccharides can be considered as a substituted sucrose. The bonds of non-terminal β-D-fructofuranosyl residues, which resist the action of invertase, can be cleaved selectively by carefully controlled acid hydrolysis, although the ease of hydrolysis seems to decrease with an increase in the number of monosaccharide units[77]. The trisaccharide melezitose is cleaved by dilute acid at the same rate as for sucrose to produce the resistant disaccharide turanose[78].

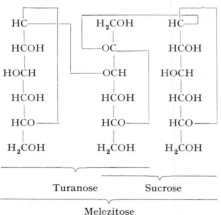

Next to sucrose, raffinose is probably the most abundant oligosaccharide in the plant kingdom. It exists free in small amounts (0.05%) in sugar beets but accumulates in the mother liquors during the preparation of sucrose.

TABLE IV

STRUCTURAL RELATIONSHIP OF SEVERAL TRI-,
TETRA-, AND PENTA-OLIGOSACCHARIDES TO SUCROSE

Sucrose	α-D-Gp-(1 → 2)-β-D-Fruf
Gentianose	β-D-Gp-(1 → 6)-β-D-Fruf-(2 → 1)-α-D-Gp
Melezitose	α-D-Gp-(1 → 3)-β-D-Fruf-(2 → 1)-α-D-Gp
Planteose	α-D-Galp-(1 → 6)-β-D-Fruf-(2 → 1)-α-D-Gp
Raffinose	α-D-Galp-(1 → 6)-α-D-Gp-(1 → 2)-β-D-Fruf

Stachyose

┌─────── Galactobiose ───────┐
α-D-Galp-(1 → 6)-α-D-Galp-(1 → 6)-α-D-Gp-(1 → 2)-β-D-Fruf
└──────── Manninotriose ────────┘

Verbascose α-D-Galp-(1 → 6)-α-D-Galp-(1 → 6)-α-D-Galp-(1 → 6)-α-D-Gp-(1 → 2)-β-D-Fruf
└──────── Galactotriose ────────┘

Lychnose   α-D-Galp-(1 → 6)-α-D-Gp-(1 → 2)-β-D-Fruf-(1 → 1)-Gal

Gp = Glucopyranosyl,   Galp = Galactopyranosyl,   Fruf = Fructofuranosyl.

Additional oligosaccharides are found in the juices of many plants. The melting points and optical rotations of some of these products are given in Table V.

Although all the higher oligosaccharides mentioned above are nonreducing, several reducing higher oligosaccharides have also been obtained. They are not usually found naturally but are obtained as the cleavage products of polysaccharides. By the acetolysis of cellulose and resolution by chromatography, a series of crystalline acetates have been obtained ranging in degree of polymerization[33,82] from 1 to 7. The corresponding deacetylated sugars have also been isolated. The properties of these cellulose oligosaccharides are shown in Table VI. As for cellulose, partial hydrolysis of amylose leads to a mixture of linear polymers which may be separated into fractions with degrees of polymerization[14] from 1 to 7 (Table VII). Maltotetra-, -penta-, and -hexaose have also been obtained from corn starch hydrolyzates by a

TABLE V

PROPERTIES OF NONREDUCING HIGHER OLIGOSACCHARIDES

	M.P. (°C)	$[\alpha]_D$ (H_2O)
Gentianose[2]	209–211	+ 31.5
Melezitose[2]	153–154	+ 88.2
Planteose[79]	123–124	+ 125.5
Raffinose ($\cdot 5H_2O$)[35]	78	+ 105.2
Stachyose[80]	101–105	+ 131.3
Verbascose[81]	253	+ 170.2
Lychnose[77]	—	+ 153–154

TABLE VI

PROPERTIES OF CELLULOSE OLIGOSACCHARIDES[33]

	Oligosaccharides		α-D-Acetate	
	M.P. (°C)	$[\alpha]_D$ (H_2O)	M.P. (°C)	$[\alpha]_D$ (CHCl$_3$)
Cellobiose	225	+ 14 → + 34.6	229.5	+ 41
Cellotriose	206–209 dec.	+ 35 → + 21.6	223–224	+ 22.6
Cellotetraose	252–253 dec.	+ 8.4 → + 16.5	230–234	+ 13.4
Cellopentaose	265–268 dec.	+ 10	252–255	− 0.2
Celloheptaose	283–286 dec.	+ 7 ± 3	263–266	− 4.4

combination of charcoal column and cellulose chromatography. The results of periodate oxidation and of hydrolysis with β-amylase are consistent with a (1 → 4) linkage between glucose units[83–85].

 The structure of maltotriose has been established rigorously. Hydrolysis of the methylated trisaccharide gives two moles of 2,3,6-tri-O-methyl-D-glucose and one mole of 2,3,4,6-tetra-O-methyl-D-glucose[86]. Thus, there are two (1 → 4)-D-glucosidic linkages per molecule. Further confirmation of the structure is obtained by reducing the monosaccharide unit containing the reducing group by hydrogenation to the corresponding alcohol; after partial hydrolysis and acetylation, the products are separated and identified by chromatography on silicates[87]. Hydrolysis of maltotriitol hendecaacetate leads to β-D-glucose pentaacetate, D-glucitol hexaacetate, β-maltose octaacetate and maltitol nonaacetate. The only trisaccharide which can produce these hydrolytic products is O-α-D-glucopyranosyl-(1 → 4)-O-α-D-glucopyranosyl-(1 → 4)-D-glucose. The anomeric configurations are confirmed by the hydrolysis of the sugar by yeast α-glucosidase but not by almond β-glucosidase. The optical rotations of the maltooligosaccharides are given in Table VII. Another amorphous oligosaccharide series consists of the di- to hexasaccharides obtained from the hydrolyzate of dextran, the structures of which are assigned as α-(1 → 6)-linked glucoses[19] (Table VIII).

TABLE VII

OPTICAL ROTATIONS OF THE MALTOSE OLIGOSACCHARIDES

	$[\alpha]_D$
Maltotriose[11]	+ 160
Maltotetraose[14,84]	+ 177, + 176
Maltopentaose[14,84]	+ 180
Maltohexaose[14,85]	+ 185, + 182
Maltoheptaose[14]	+ 186

TABLE VIII

ISOMALTOSE SERIES[19]

| | $[\alpha]_D (H_2O)$ | Benzoate | |
		M.P. (°C)	$[\alpha]_D (CHCl_3)$
Isomaltotriose	+ 142	226–227	+ 131
Isomaltotetraose	+ 153	176–179	+ 166
Isomaltopentaose	+ 160	—	—
Isomaltohexaose	+ 163	—	—

A series of crystalline oligosaccharides has been isolated by the partial hydrolysis of corn cob xylan[26,88,89,91]. The members of the series are linear polymers of α-$(1 \rightarrow 4)$-linked xylose (Table IX). The degree of polymerization of these oligosaccharides was determined by iodometric titration of the reducing groups before and after hydrolysis or by applying the Rast method to the acetates. The molecular weights obtained by the Rast method agree with the iodometric value, although the accuracy of the determination decreases as the molecular weight increases[90].

TABLE IX

PROPERTIES OF XYLAN OLIGOSACCHARIDES

| | Oligosaccharides | | β-D-Acetate | |
	M.P. (°C)	$[\alpha]_D (H_2O)$	M.P. (°C)	$[\alpha]_D(CHCl_3)$
Xylobiose[26,90,91]	185–186	— 32.0 → — 25.5	154–155	— 74.5
Xylotriose[26,90,91]	205–206	— 39.4 → — 47.0	109–110	— 84.3
Xylotetraose[26,90]	219–220	— 48.8 → — 60.0	201–202	— 93.7
Xylopentaose·1/2H$_2$O[26,90]	231–232	— 66.0	248–249	— 97.5
Xylohexaose·2H$_2$O[26,90]	236–237	— 72.8	260–261	— 102.0
Xyloheptaose[89]	240–242	— 74	—	—

As indicated in Tables VI to IX, a relationship exists between the degree of polymerization and the melting point or the optical rotation in each series of polymeric homologous polysaccharides. The plot of M_n/n vs. $(n-1)/n$, where M_n is the molecular rotation and n is the degree of polymerization yields a straight line for the α- and β-acetates of the cellulose oligosaccharides (Fig. 3) and for the β-acetates of the xylan oligosaccharides[33,90]. This relationship indicates that the type of linkage in each homologous series is uniform. The molecular rotation of raffinose and its related oligosaccharides shows a linear relationship with the degree of polymerization[35] (Fig. 4). This result indicates that the regularity between optical rotation and the

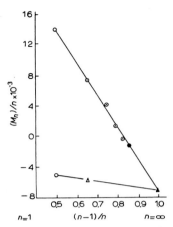

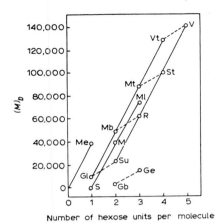

Fig. 3. Relation between degree of polymerization, n, and molecular rotation, M_n (D line of sodium), for the sugar acetates from cellulose. Upper line, α-D-acetates; lower line, β-D-acetates. Data from: O, Hudson and Johnson; ⊙, Dickey and Wolfrom; ●, Wolfrom and Dacons[33]; △, Hess and Dziengel; ▲, extrapolated limiting value for cellulose triacetate.

Fig. 4. Molecular-rotation relationships of several raffinose-type oligosaccharides. Me, methyl α-D-galactopyranoside; Gl, D-glucose; Mb, melibiose; Mt, manninotriose; Vt, verbascotetraose; S, D-glucitol; M, melibiitol; Ml, manninotriitol; Su, sucrose; R, raffinose; St, stachyose; V, verbascose; Gb, gentiobiose; Ge, gentianose.

degree of polymerization is not limited to oligosaccharides which contain a single type of monosaccharide residue, or which are necessarily derived from a single polysaccharide. A relationship between the degree of polymerization and the chromatographic or electrophoretic properties was indicated earlier (Fig. 2).

5. Oligosaccharides of animal origin

(a) Naturally occurring oligosaccharides of human milk

Although the principal oligosaccharide of milk is lactose, this disaccharide is accompanied by smaller amounts of other oligosaccharides, which can be separated from lactose by adsorption on activated carbon and elution with dilute acetic acid. The amounts vary somewhat with the mammalian species. In human milk, the concentration, exclusive of lactose, is about 3 g per liter. Preparative chromatography on carbon-Celite and cellulose columns has led to the isolation of five oligosaccharides in pure form[92-95] (see Table X).

Lacto-N-tetraose can be easily crystallized. Evidence for its structure is obtained by complete acid hydrolysis of the methylated lacto-N-tetraitol followed by a comparison of the resulting methylated monosaccharides with known derivatives[41] (see above) and also by a study of the products of partial acid hydrolysis[93]. Its structure is O-β-D-galactopyranosyl-$(1 \to 3)$-2-acetamido-2-deoxy-O-β-D-glucopyranosyl-$(1 \to 3)$-O-β-D-galactopyranosyl-$(1 \to 4)$-α-D-glucose.

TABLE X

Common name	$[\alpha]_D$ (H_2O)	$R_{lactose}$	% of oligo-saccharide fraction
Fucosyl-lactose	— 57.5	0.73	10
Lacto-N-tetraose	+ 25.5	0.36	15
Lacto-N-fucopentaose-I	— 16	0.27	8
Lacto-N-fucopentaose-II	— 28	0.19	4
Lacto-N-difucohexaose		0.11	7

Higher saccharides are also present[96,97].

Lacto-N-fucopentaose-I is related to lacto-N-tetraose by substitution of a 2-O-α-L-fucopyranosyl residue in the terminal galactosyl unit[95]. For another pentaose (lacto-N-pentaose-II), the α-L-fucose is substituted at C-4 of the 2-acetamido-2-deoxy-D-glucose instead of at C-2 of the terminal D-galactose to give a branched chain[98]. Lacto-N-difucohexaose consists of one glucosyl, one 2-acetamido-2-deoxy-D-glucopyranosyl, and two fucosyl residues.

Fucosyl-lactose was shown to be O-α-L-fucopyranosyl-$(1 \to 2)$-O-β-D-galactopyranosyl-$(1 \to 4)$-O-α-D-glucose[94,99]. A crystalline tetrasaccharide, comprised of L-fucose (two molecular residues per molecule), D-glucose, and 2-acetamido-2-deoxy-D-glucose, was obtained by partial hydrolysis of a capsular polysaccharide from *Pseudomonas fluorescens*[100].

Lactose is also found bound to N,O-diacetylneuraminic acid, which is removed by weak acids or by neuraminidase[101]. The concentration of this trisaccharide, neuraminosyl-lactose (O-acetyl-lactaminic acid-lactose) in human milk, based on the colorimetric determination[101], is 50–60 mg %. This amount, however, probably includes other oligosaccharides which contain neuraminic acid. The reducing group of the lactose moiety is free. A study

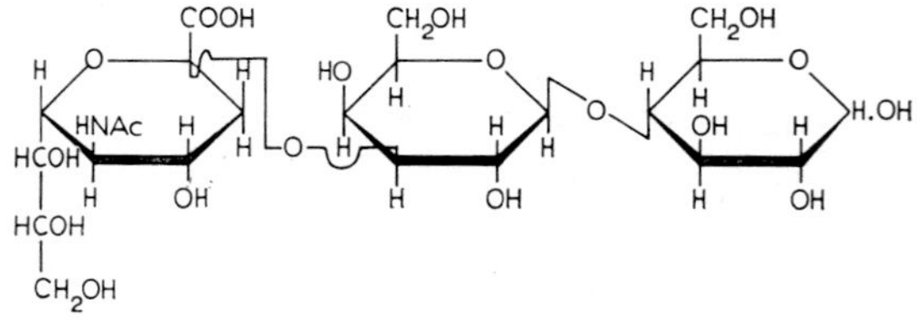

N-Acetyl-neuraminosyl-lactose

of the hydrolysis products of the methylated trisaccharide indicated that the linkage between the two components involves the reducing group of neuraminic acid and the hydroxyl at C-3 of the galactose residue of lactose. The dextrorotation of the trisaccharide ($[\alpha]_D^{21°} = +16°$) indicated an α-configuration[102].

(b) Oligosaccharides derived from animal polysaccharides

In recent years, a marked advance has been made in the knowledge of the animal polysaccharides (mucopolysaccharides). Acid or enzymic hydrolysis of these has led to the isolation of a number of new oligosaccharides, although only a few have been well characterized[103].

Hyalobiouronic acid, 3-O-(β-D-glucopyranosyl uronic acid)-2-amino-2-deoxy-D-glucose, can be obtained by the acid hydrolysis of hyaluronic acid in a yield of about 60%. This result indicates that the disaccharide is a repeating unit of the polysaccharide[104]. The structure of the disaccharide (I) was established as follows. The methyl ester of the disaccharide (II) was oxidized by mercuric oxide to the 2-amino-2-deoxy-gluconic acid derivative (III) which was reduced to the 3-O-glucosyl-2-amino-2-deoxy-gluconic acid (IV). Ninhydrin-oxidation of IV followed by acetylation yielded crystalline hepta-O-acetyl-2-O-β-D-glucopyranosyl-D-arabinose (V) which was also obtained by the Zemplén degradation of the known laminaribiose[105] (VI). The corresponding disaccharide obtained from chondroitin sulfuric acid (of hyaline cartilage) is chondrosine, 3-O-(β-D-glucopyranosyl uronic acid)-2-amino-2-deoxy-D-galactose. The structure was first indicated on the basis of periodate oxidation and a positive Morgan–Elson reaction of N-acetylated chondrosine[106]. Later it was verified by a method in which a derived glucosylpentitol was examined by periodate oxidation[107]. The β-configuration was established by its susceptibility to a β-glycosidase. These products are animal analogs of the so-called "aldobiouronic acids" obtained frequently by the acid hydrolysis of many plant materials. The glycosidic linkage of uronic acids resists hydrolysis much more than that of simple sugars and of amino sugars.

Blood group substances from various sources upon mild acid hydrolysis yield a disaccharide active as a growth promoting factor for Lactobacillus bifidus[108,110]. The disaccharide N-acetyllactosamine, 4-O-β-D-galactopyranosyl-2-acetamido-2-deoxy-D-glucose, has also been prepared by degradation of the oligosaccharide fraction of human milk[111]. The structure was indicated by periodate oxidation[108] and by reaction of the compound with phenylhydrazine to yield lactose phenylosazone with the elimination of an acetamido group[109,112]. Later it was established by chemical[113] and enzymic synthesis[114].

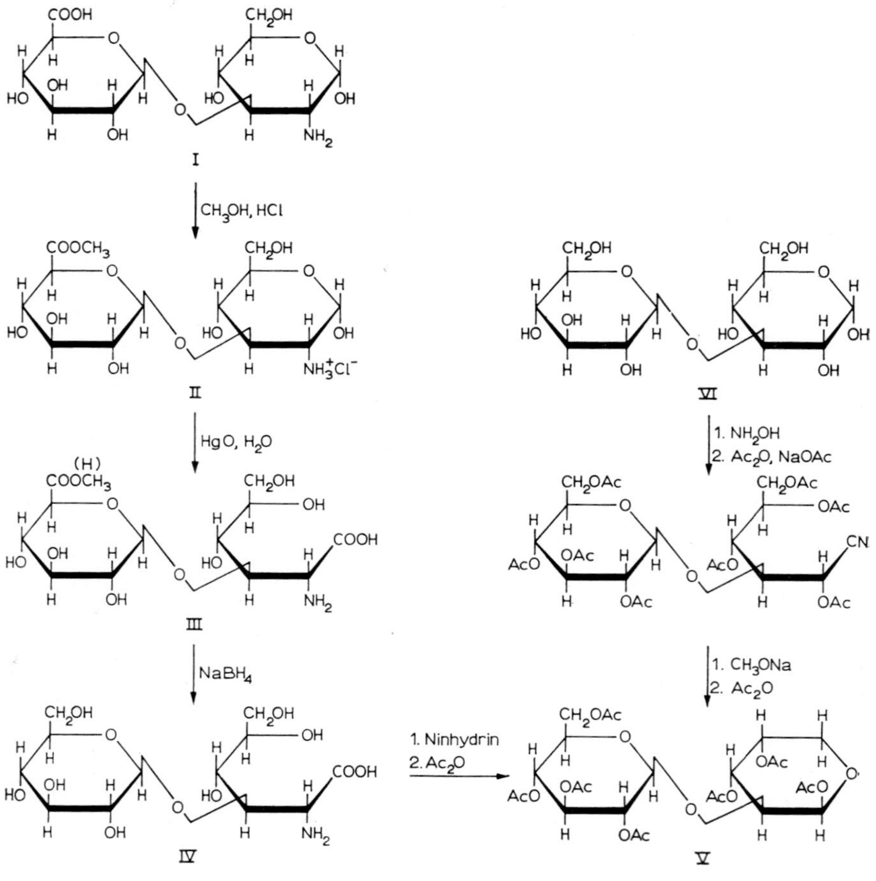

6. Enzymic synthesis of oligosaccharides by transglycosylation

(a) General discussion

Until recent years the carbohydrases have been considered to be entirely hydrolytic in their action on glycosides and oligosaccharides. More recently, many have been found to be able to catalyze the transfer of specific sugar residues from the glycosides (the donor) to another sugar (the acceptor), resulting in the formation of oligosaccharides. This particular reaction was first called transglycosylation by Hehre[f15] in 1951. Since this phenomenon occurs with highly purified enzyme preparations, it can be assumed that often both hydrolytic and transferring activities are dependent on the action of a single enzyme[116-119]. Glycosidic hydrolysis appears to be a special case of transglycosylation in which water acts as the acceptor. A hypothetical mechanism for transglycosylation has been suggested involving the intermediate formation of a glycosyl–enzyme complex[120-121].

$$\text{Glycosyl-O-R} + \text{enzyme} \rightleftarrows \text{glycosyl-enzyme} + \text{HOR}$$

$$\text{Glycosyl-enzyme} + \text{HOR}' \rightleftarrows \text{glycosyl-O-R}' + \text{enzyme}$$

When R' is H, the reaction results in hydrolysis, whereas when R'OH is a sugar the reaction involves the synthesis of a new oligosaccharide. Such transglycosylation reactions are usually classified by the nature of the glycosyl residue which can be transferred by a specific enzyme[120].

(b) α-Glucosyl transfer

One of the first reports of α-glucosyl transfer was the observation that unfermentable sugars are produced during the action of mold enzymes on maltose or starch[122]. Pan et al.[123-125] isolated an unfermentable trisaccharide from the digests of maltose by an enzyme from A. niger NNRL 337. This reducing trisaccharide, sometimes called panose, was identified as O-α-D-glucopyranosyl-(1→6)-O-α-D-glucopyranosyl-(1→4)-D-glucose[126,127]. French, Pazur and Giri and coworkers[128-132] found that enzyme preparations from molds produce at least four oligosaccharides during the hydrolysis of maltose. These are the disaccharide isomaltose, the trisaccharides panose and dextrantriose [O-α-D-glucopyranosyl-(1 → 6)-O-α-D-glucopyranosyl-(1 → 6)-D-glucose] and a tetrasaccharide [6-O-α-dextrantriosyl-D-glucose].

These results suggest that the glucosyl residues are transferred preferentially to the primary alcohol groups of glucose, maltose, isomaltose, and other higher oligosaccharides to give oligosaccharides with α-(1–6)-glucosidic

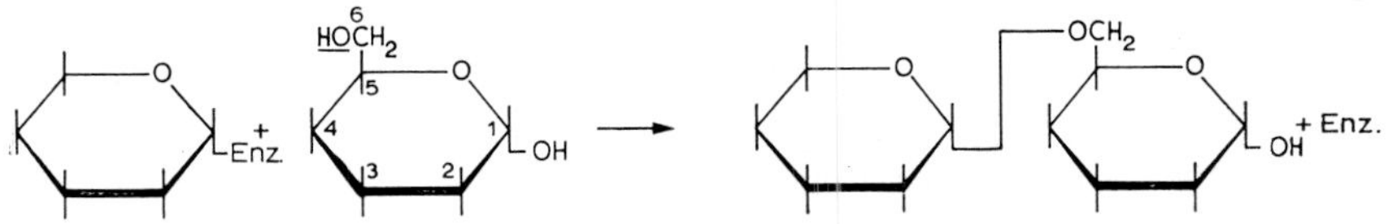

Glucosyl-enzyme + glucose   ——→ isomaltose
(Glucosyl-enzyme + maltose   ——→ panose)
(Glucosyl-enzyme + isomaltose ——→ dextrantriose)

linkages. Tsujisaka and Fukumoto[118] confirmed this preference by using a crystalline enzyme from A. niger.

However, two other disaccharides have been enzymically synthesized by mold enzymes. One is kojibiose [O-α-D-glucopyranosyl-(1 → 2)-D-glucose] and the other is nigerose [O-α-D-glucopyranosyl-(1 → 3)-D-glucose][133,134]. Nigerose is of special interest because of the existence of an intracellular glucan in *A. niger* having alternate α-(1–3) and α-(1–4) linkages.

Amylomaltase preparations from different strains of *E. coli* produce oligosaccharides having average chain lengths of 4 to 6, and some higher dextrins as intermediate products[135]. For this enzyme, D-xylose and D-mannose also can act as acceptors, and new disaccharides analogous to maltose have been detected. Miller and Miller and Copeland have purified a trans-α-glucosylase from a bovine prothrombin fraction by ion-exchange column chromatography and have demonstrated that this enzyme is a part of the α_1-globulin of the serum[136]. This enzyme is also capable of using maltose to synthesize α-(1–4)-linked oligosaccharides similar to amylomaltase[137].

White and Mahler[138,139], working with honey invertase, reported the transient formation of six oligosaccharides during the hydrolysis of sucrose, five of which differ distinctly from those obtained from the hydrolysates of sucrose with yeast invertase. This comparison was based on mobilities on a paper chromatogram, and on the reducing power and the ketose content. One of the two oligosaccharides which was isolated in appreciable amounts has been identified as α-maltosyl β-D-fructoside [O-α-D-glucopyranosyl-(1 → 4)-α-D-glucopyranosyl β-D-fructofuranoside] and the other was maltose. Since this enzyme acts upon maltose to give a series of maltodextrins, honey invertase can be regarded as a trans-α-glucosylase. Zimmermann[140] showed

α-Maltosyl β-D-fructofuranoside

the occurrence of a similar activity in the nectar collected from *Robinia* flowers and separated two oligosaccharides, one of which was a maltosyl-sucrose. The same trisaccharide was detected in the digest of sucrose by enzymes from the honeydew of the citrus mealy bug, the soft scale (*Coccus hesperidum* L.) and a purified hog intestinal invertase[141-143].

After an investigation of the formation of honeydew by insects growing on citrus plants, Wolf and Ewart[142] found that the melezitose-containing honeydew of the cottony-cushion scale, *Icerya purchasi Mask.* contains an enzyme capable of forming melezitose from sucrose. Bacon and Dickinson[144] clarified the relationship between the insects and the mother plants and showed that an enzyme preparation from aphids, which feed on the lime tree, produces free fructose and glucose and melezitose when incubated with sucrose. This action involves the transfer of an α-glucosyl group from a sucrose molecule to the third position of the fructose moiety of another sucrose molecule.

Disaccharides resulting from α-glucosyl transfer from sucrose have been identified after the action of enzymes of several common microorganisms. Yasumura[145] found two disaccharides in the partial hydrolyzates of sucrose produced by an enzyme from brewer's yeast. One was identified as turanose [O-α-D-glucopyranosyl-($1 \rightarrow 3$)-D-fructofuranose] and the other as maltulose [O-α-D-glucopyranosyl-($1 \rightarrow 4$)-D-fructose]. Ishizawa[146], using isomaltose as the donor and a maltase from Takadiastase, obtained a new disaccharide which was tentatively identified as O-α-D-glucopyranosyl-($1 \rightarrow 1$)-D-fructose on the basis of its optical rotation.

In the course of studies on the metabolism of sucrose by a bacterium which grows on sugar beets, Weidenhagen et al.[147] isolated a disaccharide in a crystalline form. This product had a high optical rotation, $[\alpha]_D^{20} = +97.2$. Other evidence including osazone formation, the reducing power and periodate oxidation indicated the structure of this sugar to be O-α-D-gluco-pyranosyl-($1 \rightarrow 6$)-D-fructose. It was named palatinose.

$C_1 : \alpha$-Gl-($1\rightarrow1$)-Fr
$C_3 :$ Turanose
$C_4 :$ Maltulose   + Enz.
$C_6 :$ Palatinose

A reducing disaccharide, composed of D-glucose and D-fructose and named leucrose was isolated in 7.9% yield from the reaction mixture produced by the synthesis of dextran from sucrose by an enzyme from *Leuconostoc mesenteroides*[48, 148] NRRLB-512A. Methylation and other evidence showed that this disaccharide is O-α-D-glucopyranosyl-($1 \rightarrow 5$)-fructopyranose.

(c) β-Glucosyl transfer

The occurrences of the transfer of β-glucosyl groups are much less common than of α-glucosyl groups. Peat, Whelan and Hinson[149] showed that five β-linked disaccharides could be obtained by incubating a 60% glucose solution with a high concentration of almond emulsin over a period of five weeks. This action is probably a relatively unspecific reversal of that of almond β-glucosidase. All of the possible isomeric disaccharides have been isolated after this condensation reaction. These are β,β-trehalose($1 \rightarrow 1$), sophorose($1 \to 2$), laminaribiose($1 \to 3$), cellobiose($1 \to 4$) and gentiobiose ($1 \to 6$), the yield of these sugars was in the order 1.6, 1.4, 1.3, 1.2, 1.1, respectively.

Crook and Stone[150] reported the formation of a series of oligosaccharides by β-glucosyl transfer from cellobiose in the presence of enzymes from several sources. Three disaccharides and two trisaccharides were isolated after column chromatography on activated charcoal of the digest of cellobiose by a partially purified enzyme from *A. niger*.

The disaccharides were identified as sophorose, laminaribiose and gentiobiose. The trisaccharides were β-analogs of panose and dextrantriose as shown by the identification of the disaccharides produced from them by partial hydrolysis. Similar results for cellobiose have been described by several investigators, using enzyme preparations from molds, higher plants, seaweeds and the gut of the snail, *Helix pomatia*[151-153]. D-Xylose and D-galactose were shown to be able to act as acceptors for the β-glucosyl group from cellobiose. Buston and Jabbar[154] found that some higher oligosaccharides could be detected when an enzyme from *Chaetomium globosum*, grown on glucose medium, acted on cellobiose. A trisaccharide was obtained in relatively high yield and identified as cellotriose by paper chromatography, paper ionophoresis, infrared spectroscopy and molecular weight determination.

(d) β-Fructofuranosyl transfer

Bacon and Edelman, and Blanchard and Albon reported independently on the complexity of the hydrolysis of sucrose and the intermediate formation of several oligosaccharides by yeast invertase[166,167]. With yeast and mold-invertase preparations at least eight oligosaccharides were obtained, all of which were further acted upon by these enzymes to give ultimately only free fructose and glucose. These oligosaccharides are composed solely of fructosyl and glucosyl residues in different proportions. Of these oligosaccharides, four are disaccharides, three are trisaccharides and one is a tetrasaccharide.

Fructosyl transfer from sucrose to the primary alcohol group of free glucose and the two such groups of free fructose should give three disaccharides. The fructosylglucose which was formed only when the free glucose concentration had become appreciable was identified as O-β-D-fructofuranosyl-($2 \to 6$)-D-glucopyranose by methylation and hydrolysis[168].

Bell and Edelman[168] separated the difructose fraction into two components. One appeared to be O-β-D-fructosyl-($2 \to 1$)-D-fructose (inulobiose), whereas the other was O-β-D-fructosyl-($2 \to 6$)-D-fructose (levanbiose). During studies of the biosynthesis of oligosaccharides of grasses, Schlubach *et al.*[169] demonstrated the involvement of a non-reducing difructose,

O-$β$-D-fructosyl-$(2 \rightarrow 2)$-$β$-D-fructose as acceptor for the enzymatic transfer of the fructosyl residue of sucrose to form non-reducing oligosaccharides.

The trisaccharide fraction was separated into three components by carbon-Celite or cellulose column chromatography. The trisaccharides were called kestose, 1-kestose and neokestose, but other names also have been used[170-176]. Kestose was produced most effectively when yeast invertase was incubated with a 50% solution of sucrose; its structure is $β$-D-glucopyranosyl-6-O-$β$-D-fructofuranosyl-$β$-D-fructofuranoside. 1-Kestose, sometimes called inulobiosyl-D-glucose, is O-$β$-D-fructofuranosyl-$(2 \rightarrow 1)$-$β$-D-fructofuranosyl-$α$-D-glucopyranoside. It has been formed by enzymes from molds, yeast, artichoke and other higher plants[171,172,176,177]. Neokestose has the structure O-$β$-D-fructofuranosyl-$(2 \rightarrow 6)$-$α$-D-glucopyranosyl-$β$-D-fructofuranoside[170,174,176]. These trisaccharides are produced by fructosyl

transfer to the various possible primary alcohol groups of sucrose. Of these trisaccharides, kestose and 1-kestose are widely distributed in plants, especially in the bulbs and tubers of monocotyledons[172].

Pazur[177] reported the formation of some higher oligosaccharides from sucrose by an *A. oryzae* enzyme. The trisaccharide was of the straight chain $β$-$(2 \rightarrow 1)$ type, but the tetra- and pentasaccharide fractions were probably heterogeneous. On the other hand, alcohols such as methyl, ethyl, *n*-butyl and benzyl alcohols and glycerol can act as acceptors, giving the corresponding alkyl $β$-D-fructofuranosides[173,178-182]. Further, Whelan and Jones[183], using methyl $β$-D-fructofuranoside as the donor and glucose as acceptor demonstrated the formation of 6-fructosyl-D-glucose.

Hestrin *et al.*[184,185] reported on the intermediate formation of several oligosaccharides from sucrose with levansucrase from *Aerobacter levanicum*. In addition to the same oligosaccharide series obtained with yeast invertase, two new disaccharides, 2-O-$β$-D-fructosyl-D-glucose and 3-O-$β$-D-fructosyl-D-glucose were isolated. In this case, D-xylose, L-arabinose, D-glucose, melibiose and lactose could also act as acceptors to give the corresponding disaccharides and trisaccharides[186,187]. Similarly, sucrose was formed when this enzyme was allowed to act on raffinose in the presence of D-glucose[187].

(e) Galactosyl transfer

Wallenfels and Bernt, and Aronson[155-158] have demonstrated the formation of several oligosaccharides by β-galactosyl transfer from lactose by the action of extracts of molds, snail (*Helix pomatia*), *Saccharomyces fragilis*, and *E. coli*. Pazur[159] showed that during the action of yeast lactase preparations on lactose, four oligosaccharides were produced. These sugars were isolated by paper chromatographic procedure and identified as *O*-β-D-galacto-pyranosyl-(1 → 6)-D-glucose, *O*-β-D-galactopyranosyl-(1 → 6)-D-galactose, *O*-β-D-galactopyranosyl-(1 → 6)-*O*-β-D-galactopyranosyl-(1 → 4)-D-glucose, and *O*-β-D-galactopyranosyl-(1 → 6)-*O*-β-D-galactopyranosyl-(1 → 6)-D-galactose. The identifications were made by the partial and complete hydrolysis of these products and their aldobionic acids. Wallenfels and Arens[119], using a crystalline β-galactosidase from *E. coli*, confirmed these results. The action of the transgalactosylases is thus quite analogous to that of mold trans-glucosylases in transferring 1,4-linked glycosyl residues to the 6 position of the acceptor sugars.

The synthesis of β-linked disaccharides containing amino sugars has been achieved using β-galactosidase preparations from *L. bifidus* var. Penn., yeasts, *E. coli*, and mammary organs[114,160,161,162]. The transfer products isolated from the reaction of lactose and *N*-acetylglucosamine were identified as the *O*-β-D-galactopyranosyl-(1 → 3), (1 → 4) and (1 → 6)-*N*-acetyl-D-glucosamines. Two nitrogen-containing disaccharides were obtained by incubating melibiose or phenyl α-D-galactoside and *N*-acetylglucosamine or *N*-acetylgalactosamine with an α-galactosidase from *Trichomonas foetus*[163]. The resulting products were *O*-α-D-galactopyranosyl-(1 → 6)-*N*-acetyl-D-glucosamine and *O*-α-D-galactopyranosyl-(1 → 6)-*N*-acetyl-D-galactosamine.

Blanchard and Albon observed some oligosaccharide formation when yeast enzyme was allowed to act on melibiose. Later, a major component was identified as manninotriose by French[164]. Courtois and Petek[165], studying coffee α-galactosidase, found that D-mannose and sucrose were active as acceptors for α-galactosyl residues, resulting in the formation of epimelibiose [*O*-α-D-galactopyranosyl-(1 → 6)-D-mannose] and raffinose.

(f) Transglucosylation from sugar phosphates

Certain species of bacteria, for example, *Pseudomonas saccharophila*, are unable to utilize free glucose or fructose but can utilize sucrose efficiently. They contain an enzyme, sucrose phosphorylase, capable of catalyzing the phosphorolytic cleavage of sucrose with the production of α-D-glucose

$$\text{Sucrose} + \text{inorganic phosphate} \rightleftarrows \alpha\text{-D-glucose 1-phosphate} + \text{D-fructose}$$

1-phosphate and fructose[188,189]. This reaction is reversible, and the equilibrium constant is 0.053 at pH 6.6 and 30°. The reaction, thus, favors predominantly the breakdown of sucrose.

In the reverse reaction, the glycosyl residue of α-D-glucose 1-phosphate is transferred to fructose, resulting in the formation of sucrose. In addition to fructose, other ketoses, such as D-xylulose, L-ribulose, and L-sorbose can act as the acceptor of the glucosyl group[190-192]. L-Arabinose also can be an acceptor[46]. The following analogs of sucrose and also a new disaccharide were enzymatically synthesized: α-D-glucosyl β-D-xyluloside, α-D-glucosyl α-L-ribuloside, α-D-glucosyl α-L-sorboside and 3-O-α-D-glucopyranosyl-L-arabinopyranose[189].

Doudoroff and Fitting[193] found that the bacterium *Neisseria meningitidis* could utilize maltose much more rapidly than D-glucose. It contains an enzyme which catalyzes the reversible reaction:

Maltose + inorganic phosphate $\rightleftharpoons$ β-D-glucose 1-phosphate + D-glucose

This enzyme was named maltose phosphorylase. The sugar phosphate produced by the phosphorolytic fission of maltose was not α-D-glucose 1-phosphate but was the β-form which was identified by comparison with synthetic material. Other sugar esters or glucosyl compounds could not replace β-D-glucose 1-phosphate as the glucosyl donor. The reaction evidently involved a Walden inversion at the linkage cleaved. Besides D-glucose, D-xylose was one of the few sugars which could act as an acceptor in the reverse reaction[194]. The xylose-containing disaccharide was identified as β-D-glucosyl-D-xyloside.

An analogous synthesis of cellobiose from α-D-glucose 1-phosphate and D-glucose by an enzyme obtained from *Clostridium thermocellum* has been reported[195].

(g) Glycosyl transfer from uridylphosphoglycosyl compounds

The metabolism of ^{14}C-labeled compounds by photosynthesizing higher plants and algae suggested hexose phosphates and uridine diphosphate glucose (UDPG) as precursors for sucrose formation. Leloir and Cardini[196] first demonstrated that wheat germ, corn germ and potato sprouts contain an enzyme which catalyzes a glucosyl transfer from UDPG to fructose to give sucrose and uridine diphosphate (UDP):

$$UDPG + \text{D-fructose} \rightleftharpoons UDP + \text{sucrose} \tag{i}$$

Further evidence[197-199] showed that the reaction for enzymes from wheat germ and sugar-beet leaves apparently involves D-fructose 6-phosphate:

$$\text{UDPG} + \text{D-fructose 6-phosphate} \rightleftharpoons \text{UDP} + \text{sucrose phosphate} \qquad (ii)$$

The crude enzyme preparations contained a specific phosphatase for the sucrose phosphate and with these preparations sucrose was formed.

The high energy bond in a substituted glucosyl phosphate might be important for sucrose synthesis. The equilibrium constant for reaction (i) was shown to be 2 to 8 at 37° and pH 7.4, indicating that this reaction favors sucrose formation. As for sucrose phosphorylase, L-sorbose, D-xylulose and D-rhamnulose acted as acceptors to give the corresponding disaccharides[200].

Cabib and Leloir[201] found an enzyme responsible for the synthesis of trehalose in brewer's yeast extracts, and its action was quite similar to the sucrose synthesizing enzyme. The enzyme has been purified 15 to 20 fold from brewer's yeast and catalyzes the reaction:

$$\text{UDPG} + \text{glucose 6-phosphate} \rightarrow \text{UDP} + \text{trehalose phosphate}$$

This reaction is not reversible. The enzyme preparation also contained a specific phosphatase for the hydrolysis of trehalose phosphate to trehalose.

In the synthesis of lactose by extracts of mammary gland tissue, Gander et al.[202] presented evidence of the involvement of galactosyl transfer from UDP galactose to D-glucose:

$$\text{UDP Gal} + \text{glucose 1-phosphate} \rightarrow \text{lactose phosphate} + \text{UDP}$$

The resulting lactose phosphate was also hydrolyzed by a specific phosphatase. This reaction course was confirmed by tracer experiments[203].

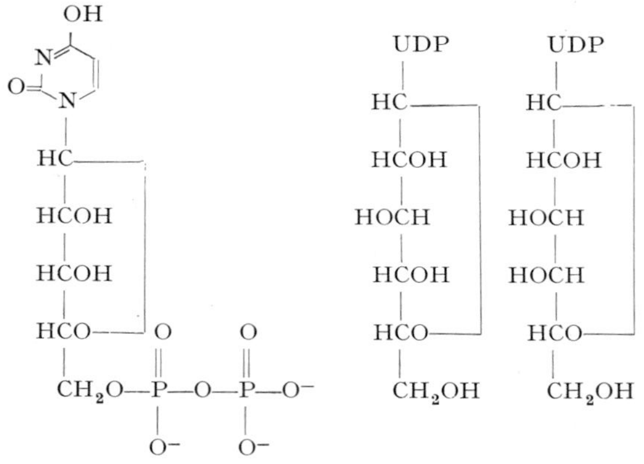

Uridine diphosphate   UDP glucose   UDP galactose

REFERENCES

[1] B. HELFERICH, E. BOHN AND S. WINKLER, *Ber.*, 63 (1930) 989.
[2] W. Z. HASSID AND C. E. BALLOU in W. W. PIGMAN (Ed.), *The Carbohydrate Chemistry, Biochemistry, Physiology*, Academic Press, New York, 1957, p. 478.
[3] F. MICHEEL, *Chemie der Zucker und Polysaccharide*, Geest & Portig, Leipzig, 1956.
[4] A. SATO AND K. ASO, *Nature*, 180 (1957) 984.
[5] S. A. BARKER, E. J. BOURNE AND M. STACEY, *J. Chem. Soc.*, (1953) 3084.
[6] P. BÄCHLI AND E. G. V. PERCIVAL, *J. Chem. Soc.*, (1952) 1243.
[7] J. C. SOWDEN AND A. S. SPRIGGS, *J. Am. Chem. Soc.*, 78 (1956) 2503.
[8] M. L. WOLFROM, L. W. GEORGES AND I. L. MILLER, *J. Am. Chem. Soc.*, 71 (1949) 125.
[9] A. THOMPSON AND M. L. WOLFROM, *J. Am. Chem. Soc.*, 75 (1953) 3605.
[10] A. B. FOSTER, *J. Chem. Soc.*, (1953) 982.
[11] W. W. BINKLEY, *Advances in Carbohydrate Chem.*, 10 (1955) 55.
[12] R. L. WHISTLER AND D. F. DURSO, *J. Am. Chem. Soc.*, 72 (1950) 677.
[13] R. S. ALM, R. J. P. WILLIAMS AND A. TISELIUS, *Acta Chem. Scand.*, 6 (1952) 826.
[14] W. J. WHELAN, J. M. BAILEY AND P. J. P. ROBERTS, *J. Chem. Soc.*, (1953) 1293.
[15] W. H. MCNEELY, W. W. BINKLEY AND M. L. WOLFROM, *J. Am. Chem. Soc.*, 67 (1945) 527.
[16] A. THOMPSON, K. ANNO, M. L. WOLFROM AND M. INATOME, *J. Am. Chem. Soc.*, 76 (1954) 1309.
[17] G. N. KOWKABANY, *Advances in Carbohydrate Chem.*, 9 (1954) 303.
[18] D. FRENCH AND G. M. WILD, *J. Am. Chem. Soc.*, 75 (1953) 2612.
[19] J. R. TURVEY AND W. J. WHELAN, *Biochem. J.*, 67 (1957) 49.
[20] A. JEANS, C. S. WISE AND R. J. DIMLER, *Anal. Chem.*, 23 (1951) 415.
[21] R. J. BAYLY AND E. J. BOURNE, *Nature*, 171 (1953) 385.
[22] A. B. FOSTER, *Advances in Carbohydrate Chem.*, 12 (1957) 81.
[23] S. A. BARKER, E. J. BOURNE, P. M. GRANT AND M. STACEY, *Nature*, 177 (1956) 1125.
[24] A. THOMPSON AND M. L. WOLFROM, *J. Am. Chem. Soc.*, 76 (1954) 5173.
[25] H. BERLIN, *J. Am. Chem. Soc.*, 48 (1926) 1107.
[26] R. L. WHISTLER AND C.-C. TU, *J. Am. Chem. Soc.*, 74 (1952) 3609.
[27] C. S. HUDSON AND S. M. JOHNSON, *J. Am. Chem. Soc.*, 38 (1916) 1566.
[28] W. M. HAWORTH AND W. J. HICKINGBOTTOM, *J. Chem. Soc.*, (1931) 2847.
[29] H. H. SCHLUBACH AND W. SCHETELIG, *Z. physiol. Chem.*, *Hoppe-Seyler's*, 213 (1932) 83.
[30] K. FREUDENBERG, H. KNAUBER AND F. GRAMER, *Chem. Ber.*, 84 (1951) 144.
[31] J. RABATÉ, *Bull. soc. chim.*, 17 (1940) 565.
[32] S. PEAT, J. R. TURVEY AND J. EVANS, *Nature*, 179 (1957) 261.
[33] M. L. WOLFROM AND J. C. DACONS, *J. Am. Chem. Soc.*, 74 (1952) 5331.
[34] M. L. WOLFROM, L. W. GEORGES AND I. L. MILLER, *J. Am. Chem. Soc.*, 71 (1949) 125.
[35] D. FRENCH, *Advances in Carbohydrate Chem.*, 9 (1954) 149.
[36] R. L. WHISTLER, J. BACHRACH AND C.-CTU, *J. Am. Chem. Soc.*, 74 (1952) 3061.
[37] I. LEVI, *Advances in Carbohydrate Chem.*, 4 (1949) 1.
[38] W. N. HAWORTH, J. V. LOACH AND C. W. LONG, *J. Chem. Soc.*, (1927) 3146.
[39] W. N. HAWORTH AND S. PEAT, *J. Chem. Soc.*, (1926) 3094.
[40] F. SMITH AND R. MONTGOMERY, *Chemistry of Plant Gums and Mucilages and some Related Polysaccharides*, Reinhold, New York, 1959, p. 223.
[41] R. KUHN AND H. H. BAER, *Chem. Ber.*, 89 (1956) 504.
[42] P. FLUERY AND J. COURTOIS, *Bull. soc. chim.*, 10 (1943) 245; *Compt. rend.*, 216 (1943) 65.
[43] J. AVERY, W. N. HAWORTH AND E. L. HIRST, *J. Chem. Soc.*, (1927) 2308.
[44] W. N. HAWORTH, E. L. HIRST AND A. LEARNER, *J. Chem. Soc.*, (1927) 2432.
[45] J. COURTOIS AND M. RAMET, *Bull. soc. chem. biol.*, 29 (1947) 240.
[46] W. Z. HASSID, M. DOUDOROFF, A. C. POTTER AND H. A. BARKER, *J. Am. Chem. Soc.*, 70 (1948) 306.
[47] L. HOUGH, D. B. POWELL AND B. M. WOODS, *J. Chem. Soc.*, (1956) 4799.
[48] F. H. STODOLA, E. S. SHARPE AND H. J. KOEPSELL, *J. Am. Chem. Soc.*, 78 (1956) 2514.
[49] A. S. PERLIN, *Anal. Chem.*, 27 (1955) 396.
[50] A. S. PERLIN AND A. R. LANSDOWN, *Can. J. Chem.*, 34 (1956) 451.

[51] D. D. REYNOLDS AND W. L. EVANS, *J. Am. Chem. Soc.*, 60 (1938) 2559.
[52] B. HELFERICH AND W. KLEIN, *Ann.*, 450 (1926) 219.
[53] G. R. WYATT AND G. F. KALF, *J. Gen. Physiol.*, 40 (1957) 833.
[54] H. BLOCK, J. DEFAYE, E. LEDERER AND H. NOLL, *Biochim. Biophys. Acta*, 23 (1957) 312.
[55] T. GENDRE AND E. LEDERER, *Bull. soc. chim.*, (1956) 1478.
[56] E. FISCHER AND K. DELBRÜCK, *Ber.*, 42 (1909) 2776.
[57] M. L. WOLFROM AND A. THOMPSON, *J. Am. Chem. Soc.*, 79 (1957) 4212.
[58] F. SMITH AND R. MONTGOMERY, *Chemistry of Plant Gums and Mucilages and some Related Polysaccharides*, Reinhold, New York, 1959, p. 155; J. K. N. JONES, *J. Chem. Soc.*, (1953) 1672.
[59] A. M. STEPHANE, *J. Chem. Soc.*, (1957) 1919.
[60] F. SMITH, *J. Chem. Soc.*, (1939) 744.
[61] H. C. SRIVASTAVA AND F. SMITH, *J. Am. Chem. Soc.*, 79 (1957) 982.
[62] E. L. HIRST AND A. S. PERLIN, *J. Chem. Soc.*, (1954) 2622.
[63] B. O. LINDGREN, *Acta Chem. Scand.*, 11 (1957) 1365.
[64] A. M. O'NEIL, *J. Am. Chem. Soc.*, 77 (1955) 6324.
[65] R. L. WHISTLER AND D. F. DURSO, *J. Am. Chem. Soc.*, 73 (1951) 4189.
[66] R. MONTGOMERY, F. SMITH AND H. C. SRIVASTAVA, *J. Am. Chem. Soc.*, 79 (1957) 698.
[67] J. K. M. JONES AND M. B. PERRY, *J. Am. Chem. Soc.*, 79 (1957) 2787.
[68] R. KUHN, I. LÖW AND H. TRISCHMANN, *Chem. Ber.*, 90 (1957) 203.
[69] B. LINDBERG, *Acta Chem. Scand.*, 7 (1953) 1119, 1218; B. LINDBERG AND J. PAJU, *Acta Chem. Scand.*, 8 (1954) 817.
[70] F. SMITH AND H. C. SRIVASTAVA, *J. Am. Chem. Soc.*, 78 (1956) 1404.
[71] P. ANDREWS, D. H. BALL AND J. K. N. JONES, *J. Chem. Soc.*, (1953) 4090.
[72] R. L. WHISTLER AND W. M. CORBETT, *J. Am. Chem. Soc.*, 77 (1955) 3822.
[73] R. L. WHISTLER AND W. M. CORBETT, *J. Am. Chem. Soc.*, 77 (1955) 6328.
[74] J. E. COURTOIS, C. ANAGNOSTOPOULOS AND F. PETEK, *Bull. soc. chim. biol.*, 35 (1953) 731.
[75] C. SCHEIBLER AND H. MITTLEMEIER, *Ber.*, 22 (1889) 1680.
[76] C. NEUBERG, *Biochem. Z.*, 3 (1907) 528.
[77] J. E. COURTOIS, *Proc. of the Fourth International Congress of Biochemistry*, Vol. 1, Vienna, Symposium No. 1, Pergamon Press, London, 1958, p. 1.
[78] C. S. HUDSON AND E. P. PACSU, *J. Am. Chem. Soc.*, 52 (1930) 2519.
[79] N. WATTIEZ AND M. HANS, *Bull. acad. roy. méd. Belg.*, 8 (1943) 386.
[80] M. L. WOLFROM, R. C. BURRELL, A. THOMPSON AND S. S. FURST, *J. Am. Chem. Soc.*, 74 (1952) 6299.
[81] S. MURAKAMI, *Acta Phytochim.* (*Japan*), 11 (1940) 213; 13 (1943) 161.
[82] E. E. DICKEY AND M. L. WOLFROM, *J. Am. Chem. Soc.*, 71 (1949) 825.
[83] R. L. WHISTLER AND J. L. HIRKSON, *J. Am. Chem. Soc.*, 76 (1954) 1671.
[84] R. L. WHISTLER AND J. H. DUFFY, *J. Am. Chem. Soc.*, 77 (1955) 1017.
[85] R. L. WHISTLER AND B. F. MOY, *J. Am. Chem. Soc.*, 71 (1949) 5761.
[86] J. M. SUGIHARA AND M. L. WOLFROM, *J. Am. Chem. Soc.*, 71 (1949) 3357.
[87] A. THOMPSON AND M. L. WOLFROM, *J. Am. Chem. Soc.*, 74 (1952) 3612.
[88] R. L. WHISTLER, J. B. BACHRACH AND C. C. TU, *J. Am. Chem. Soc.*, 74 (1952) 3059.
[89] R. L. WHISTLER AND C.-C. TU, *J. Am. Chem. Soc.*, 75 (1953) 645.
[90] R. L. WHISTLER AND C.-C. TU, *J. Am. Chem. Soc.*, 74 (1952) 4334.
[91] R. L. WHISTLER AND C.-C. TU, *J. Am. Chem. Soc.*, 73 (1951) 1389.
[92] R. KUHN, A. GAUHE AND H. H. BAER, *Chem. Ber.*, 86 (1953) 827.
[93] R. KUHN, A. GAUHE AND H. H. BAER, *Chem. Ber.*, 87 (1954) 289.
[94] R. KUHN, H. H. BAER AND A. GAUHE, *Chem. Ber.*, 88 (1955) 1135.
[95] R. KUHN, H. H. BAER AND A. GAUHE, *Chem. Ber.*, 89 (1956) 2514.
[96] P. GYÖRGY, J. R. E. HOOVER, R. KUHN AND C. S. ROSE, *Arch. Biochem. Biophys.*, 48 (1954) 209.
[97] F. H. MALPRESS AND F. E. HYTTEN, *Biochem. J.*, 68 (1958) 708.
[98] R. KUHN, H. H. BAER AND A. GAUHE, *Chem. Ber.*, 91 (1958) 364.
[99] R. KUHN, H. H. BAER AND A. GAUHE, *Chem. Ber.*, 89 (1956) 2513.
[100] R. G. EAGON AND R. DEDONER, *Compt. rend.*, 241 (1955) 579.

101 R. Kuhn and R. Brossmer, *Chem. Ber.*, 89 (1956) 2015.
102 R. Kuhn and R. Brossmer, *Angew. Chem.*, 70 (1958) 25.
103 H. H. Baer, *Fortschr. chem. Forsch.*, 3 (1958) 822.
104 B. Weissmann, M. M. Rapport, A. Linker and K. Meyer, *J. Biol. Chem.*, 205 (1953) 205.
105 B. Weissmann and K. Meyer, *J. Am. Chem. Soc.*, 76 (1954) 1753.
106 H. Masamune, Z. Yosizawa and M. Maki, *Tôhoku J. Exptl. Med.*, 55 (1951) 29.
107 E. A. Davidson and K. Meyer, *J. Am. Chem. Soc.*, 77 (1955) 4796.
108 Z. Yosizawa, *Tôhoku J. Exptl. Med.*, 52 (1950) 145.
109 R. Kuhn and W. Kirschenlohr, *Chem. Ber.*, 87 (1954) 560.
110 R. H. Côté and W. T. J. Morgan, *Nature*, 178 (1956) 1171.
111 R. Kuhn, H. H. Baer and A. Gauhe, *Chem. Ber.*, 87 (1954) 1553.
112 R. Kuhn and W. Kirschenlohr, *Chem. Ber.*, 87 (1954) 1547.
113 R. Kuhn and W. Kirschenlohr, *Ann.*, 600 (1956) 135.
114 F. Zilliken, P. N. Smith, C. S. Rose and P. György, *J. Biol. Chem.*, 208 (1954) 299.
115 E. J. Hehre, *Advances in Enzymol.*, 11 (1951) 297.
116 E. H. Fischer and L. Kothès, *Helv. Chim. Acta*, 34 (1951) 1123.
117 E. H. Fischer, L. Kothès and J. Fellig, *Helv. Chim. Acta*, 34 (1951) 1132.
118 Y. Tsujisaka and F. Fukumoto, *Proc. 10th Symp. Enzy. Chem., Japan*, 1958, p. 84.
119 K. Wallenfels and A. Arens, *Biochem. Z.*, 332 (1960) 247.
120 J. Edelman, *Advances in Enzymol.*, 17 (1956) 189.
121 H. M. Kalcker in W. D. MacElroy and B. Glass (Eds.), *The Mechanism of Enzyme Action*, Johns Hopkins Press, Baltimore, 1954, p. 608.
122 W. W. Pigman, *J. Research Natl. Bur. Standards*, 33 (1944) 105.
123 S. C. Pan, A. A. Anderson and P. Kolachov, *Science*, 112 (1950) 115.
124 S. C. Pan, L. W. Nicholson and P. Kolachov, *J. Am. Chem. Soc.*, 73 (1951) 2547.
125 S. C. Pan, L. W. Nicholson, P. Kolachov, *Arch. Biochem. Biophys.*, 30 (1952) 6.
126 D. French, *Science*, 113 (1951) 352.
127 M. L. Wolfrom, A. Thompson, T. T. Galkowski, *J. Am. Chem. Soc.*, 73 (1951) 4093.
128 K. V. Giri, P. L. Narashimha Rao, K. Saroja and R. Venkataraman, *Naturwissenschaften*, 40 (1953) 484.
129 K. V. Giri, K. Saroja, R. Venkataraman and P. L. Narashimha Rao, *Arch. Biochem. Biophys.*, 51 (1954) 62.
130 K. Saroja, R. Venkataraman and K. V. Giri, *Biochem. J.*, 60 (1955) 399.
131 J. H. Pazur and D. French, *J. Am. Chem. Soc.*, 73 (1951) 3536.
132 J. H. Pazur and D. French, *J. Biol. Chem.*, 196 (1952) 265.
133 K. Aso, K. Shibasaki and F. Yamaguchi, *Hakkô Kôgaku Zasshi*, 30 (1952) 3114.
134 S. A. Barker and T. R. Carlington, *J. Chem. Soc.*, (1953) 3588.
135 S. A. Barker and E. Bourne, *J. Chem. Soc.*, (1952) 209.
136 K. D. Miller, *J. Biol. Chem.*, 231 (1958) 987.
137 K. D. Miller and W. H. Copeland, *J. Biol. Chem.*, 231 (1958) 997.
138 J. W. White Jr. and J. Maher, *J. Am. Chem. Soc.*, 75 (1953) 1259.
139 J. W. White Jr. and J. Maher, *Arch. Biochem. Biophys.*, 42 (1953) 360.
140 M. Zimmermann, *Experientia*, 10 (1954) 145.
141 H. E. Gray and G. Fraenkl, *Science*, 118 (1953) 304.
142 J. P. Wolf and W. H. Ewart, *Science*, 122 (1955) 973.
143 A. Dahlquist and B. Börgstrom, *Acta Chem. Scand.*, 13 (1959) 1659.
144 J. S. D. Bacon and B. Dickinson, *Biochem. J.*, 66 (1957) 289.
145 A. Yasumura, *Seikagaku*, 26 (1954) 200.
146 K. Ishizawa, *Mem. Fac. Agr. Tokyo Univ. Educ.*, 6 (1960) 77.
147 R. Weidenhagen and S. Lorenz, *Z. Zuckerind.*, 11 (1959) 533.
148 F. H. Stodola, H. J. Koepsell and E. S. Sharpe, *J. Am. Chem. Soc.*, 74 (1952) 3202.
149 S. Peat, W. J. Whelan and K. A. Hinson, *Nature*, 170 (1952) 1056.
150 E. M. Crook and B. A. Stone, *Biochem. J.*, 55 (1953) xxv; 65 (1957) 1.
151 W. A. M. Duncan, D. J. Manners and J. L. Thompson, *Biochem. J.*, 73 (1959) 295.
152 K. Giri, V. N. Kigam and K. S. Srinivasan, *Nature*, 173 (1953) 953.
153 P. Kooiman, P. A. Roelofsen and S. Sweeris, *Enzymologia*, 16 (1954) 237.
154 H. W. Buston and A. Jabbar, *Biochim. Biophys. Acta*, 51 (1954) 543.

155 K. WALLENFELS, *Naturwissenschaften*, 38 (1951) 306.
156 K. WALLENFELS AND E. BERNT, *Angew. Chem.*, 64 (1952) 28.
157 K. WALLENFELS, *Angew. Chem.*, 65 (1953) 137.
158 M. ARONSON, *Arch. Biochem. Biophys.*, 39 (1953) 370.
159 J. H. PAZUR, *J. Biol. Chem.*, 208 (1954) 439.
160 A. ALLESSANDRINI, E. SCHMIDT, F. ZILLIKEN AND P. GYÖRGY, *J. Biol. Chem.*, 220 (1956) 71.
161 P. GYÖRGY in G. E. W. WOHLSTENHOLME AND M.O'CONNOR (Eds.), *Ciba Foundation Symposium on Chemistry and Biology of Mucopolysaccharides*, Little, Brown and Co., Boston, 1958, p. 140.
162 F. ZILLIKEN, P. N. SMITH, C. S. ROSE AND P. GYÖRGY, *J. Biol. Chem.*, 217 (1955) 79.
163 W. M. WATKINS, *Nature*, 181 (1958) 117.
164 D. FRENCH, *Advances in Carbohydrate Chem.*, 9 (1954) 157.
165 J. E. COURTOIS AND F. PETEK, *Bull. soc. chim. biol.*, 39 (1957) 715.
166 J. S. D. BACON AND J. EDELMAN, *Arch. Biochem.*, 28 (1950) 467.
167 P. H. BLANCHARD AND N. ALBON, *Arch. Biochem.*, 29 (1950) 220.
168 D. J. BELL AND J. EDELMAN, *J. Chem. Soc.*, (1954) 4652.
169 H. H. SCHLUBACH, *Fortschr. org. chem. Naturst.*, 15 (1958) 1.
170 N. ALBON, D. J. BELL, P. H. BLANCHARD, D. GROSS AND J. T. RUNDELL, *J. Chem. Soc.*, (1953) 24.
171 J. S. D. BACON, *Biochem. J.*, 57 (1954) 320.
172 J. S. D. BACON, *Biochem. J.*, 73 (1959) 507.
173 F. J. BEALING AND J. S. D. BACON, *Biochem. J.*, 49 (1951) I XXV; 53 (1953) 277.
174 D. GROSS, P. H. BLANCHARD AND D. J. BELL, *J. Chem. Soc.*, (1954) 1727.
175 H. C. S. DE WALLEY AND D. GROSS in D. GLICK (Ed.), *Methods of Biochem. Analysis*, Vol. 1, Interscience, New York, 1954, p. 307.
176 J. S. D. BACON AND J. EDELMAN, *Biochem. J.*, 48 (1951) 114.
177 J. H. PAZUR, *J. Biol. Chem.*, 199 (1952) 217.
178 J. S. D. BACON, *Biochem. J.*, 50 (1952) 18.
179 J. S. D. BACON AND D. J. BELL, *J. Chem. Soc.* (1957) 3581.
180 F. J. BEALING, *Biochem. J.*, 55 (1953) 93.
181 K. ISHIZAWA, Y. IRIKI AND T. MIWA, *Sci. Repts. Tokyo Kyôiku Daigaku*, 8 (1957) 102.
182 F. KURASAWA, S. SAITO, N. HOMMA AND Y. YAMAMOTO, *J. Agr. Chem. Soc. Japan*, 29 (1955) pp. 211, 332, 336.
183 W. J. WHELAN AND D. M. JONES, *Biochem. J.*, 54 (1953) 34.
184 S. HESTRIN, D. S. FEINGOLD AND G. AVIGAD, *Biochem. J.*, 64 (1956) 340.
185 D. S. FEINGOLD, G. AVIGAD AND S. HESTRIN, *Biochem. J.*, 64 (1956) 351.
186 G. AVIGAD, *J. Biol. Chem.*, 229 (1957) 121.
187 S. HESTRIN, D. S. FEINGOLD AND G. AVIGAD, *J. Am. Chem. Soc.*, 77 (1955) 6710.
188 M. DOUDOROFF, H. A. BARKER AND W. Z. HASSID, *J. Biol. Chem.*, 168 (1947) 725.
189 W. Z. HASSID AND M. DOUDOROFF, *Advances in Enzymol.*, 10 (1950) 123.
190 W. Z. HASSID, M. DOUDOROFF, H. A. BARKER AND W. H. DORE, *J. Am. Chem. Soc.*, 68 (1946) 1465.
191 M. DOUDOROFF, W. Z. HASSID AND H. A. BARKER, *J. Biol. Chem.*, 168 (1947) 733.
192 W. Z. HASSID, M. DOUDOROFF, H. A. BARKER AND W. H. DORE, *J. Am. Chem. Soc.*, 67 (1945) 1394.
193 C. FITTING AND M. DOUDOROFF, *J. Biol. Chem.*, 199 (1952) 153.
194 E. W. PUTMAN, C. FITTING AND W. Z. HASSID, *J. Am. Chem. Soc.*, 77 (1955) 4351.
195 C. J. SIH AND R. H. MACBEE, *Proc. Montana Acad' Sci.*, 15 (1955) 21.
196 L. F. LELOIR AND C. E. CARDINI, *J. Biol. Chem.*, 214 (1955) 157.
197 C. E. CARDINI, L. F. LELOIR AND J. CHIRIBAGO, *J. Biol. Chem.*, 214 (1955) 149.
198 J. E. TURNER, *Biochem. J.*, 67 (1958) 450.
199 D. F. BURMA AND D. C. MORTIMER, *Arch. Biochem. Biophys.*, 62 (1956) 16.
200 R. C. BEAN AND W. Z. HASSID, *J. Am. Chem. Soc.*, 77 (1955) 5737.
201 E. CABIB AND L. F. LELOIR, *J. Biol. Chem.*, 231 (1958) 259.
202 J. E. GANDER, W. E. PETERSEN AND P. D. BOYER, *Arch. Biochem. Biophys.*, 69 (1957) 85.
203 E. DIAMONT, V. R. SMITH AND H. A. LARDY, *J. Biol. Chem.*, 201 (1953) 85.

Chapter VII

Polysaccharides

Section a

General

D. HORTON AND M. L. WOLFROM

Department of Chemistry, The Ohio State University, Columbus, Ohio (U.S.A.)

1. Introduction

The carbohydrate content of living tissue is found principally in the form of polysaccharides, which are high-molecular weight polymers of the simple sugars. They function most commonly as skeletal constituents conferring rigidity on aggregates of soft living tissue, or as reserve food sources, readily convertible to metabolizable sugars when required. The bulk of the dry weight of the higher land plants and of the seaweeds is composed of polysaccharides, while lesser, though highly significant amounts are found in the tissues of the animal species and of the lower plants.

Polysaccharides may be regarded as polycondensation products of the monosaccharides glycosidically linked with the elimination of water to form linear or branched chains, the glycoside function being a mixed acetal from the organic chemical standpoint. The molecular weight of a polysaccharide is relatively high and has to be estimated by physicochemical methods. An oligosaccharide is a substance composed of monosaccharides whose number is definitely ascertainable by classical chemical methods.

The glycose residues in a polysaccharide are generally linked according to a regular repeating plan and the chain lengths of individual molecules vary. A chemically homogeneous polysaccharide is generally a mixture of similarly constituted macromolecules of varying molecular size forming a polymer-homologous series.

A wide variety of polysaccharide types has been found in nature, even though very many of these contain but one monosaccharide species as the structural unit. Even the most complex seldom contain more than three or four such units. Many more polysaccharides undoubtedly still await discovery and identification in the tissues of rarer biological species. The structural units of the polysaccharides are not limited solely to the simple aldose or ketose sugars, but may include uronic acids and amino sugars; all types may occur alone, or severally in combination. Amino sugar-containing polysaccharides, though seldom found in the higher plants, occur widely in the animal kingdom and in those plants (saprophytes) which live on organic matter. It is perhaps significant that those forms of life which have an abundance of combined nitrogen in their food intake utilize nitrogenous sugars extensively in their metabolic processes, while the higher plants,

TABLE I

POLYSACCHARIDES CLASSIFIED ACCORDING TO SOURCE AND FUNCTION

Source	Function		
	Skeletal	Food reserve	Other function
Plant Kingdom			
Embryophyta	cellulose	amylose	gums
Bryophyta (mosses)	pentoglycans	amylopectin	mucilages
Tracheophyta (vascular plants)	pectic substances	fructans	
Thallophyta	galactans	laminaran	
Phaeophyta (brown algae)	agar	floridean starch	
Rhodophyta (red algae) and other algae	carrageenan	mannan	
	alginic acid		
	fucan		
	cellulose		
	pectic substances		
Schizomycophyta	chitin	starches	extracellular
Myxomycophyta	cellulose	levans	polysaccharides
Eumycophyta (bacteria, molds, and fungi)	mannans	glycogen	
Animal Kingdom			
Vertebrata	chondroitin sulfuric acids	glycogen	heparin hyaluronic acid blood group substances galactan
Invertebrata	chitin cellulose	glycogen galactan	

TABLE II

CLASSIFICATION OF POLYSACCHARIDES ACCORDING TO
CHEMICAL STRUCTURE

Type		Examples
Homoglycans, linear	Glucans	cellulose, amylose, chitin, laminaran, lichenan, crown gall polysaccharide, pustulan
	Galactans	agar, carrageenan, pectic galactan
	Mannans	ivory nut mannan, salep mannan
	Xylans	esparto xylan
	Fructans	inulin
Homoglycans, branched	Glucans	glycogen, amylopectin, floridean starch, bacterial dextrans, pyrodextrins
	Galactans	*Helix* galactan
	Mannans	yeast mannan, *Porphyra umbilicalis* mannan
	Arabinans	peanut arabinan
	Fructans	asparagosan, irisan, sinistran, bacterial levans
Heteroglycans	Glucomanno-glycans	konjakmannan, softwood hemicellulose glucomannoglycans
	Galactomanno-glycans	guaran, carob gum
	Arabinogalacto-glycans	softwood hemicellulose arabinogalacto-glycans
	Arabinoxyloglycans	cereal hemicellulose arabinoxyloglycans
	Others	some plant gums and mucilages (see Table III, p. 227)
Heteroglycans (containing neutral sugars and uronic acids)	Glucuronoxylo-glycans	hardwood hemicellulose B
	Others	many plant gums and mucilages (see Table IV, p. 229)
Glycuronans (containing only uronic acis)	Galacturonans	pectic substances
	Guluronomann-uronoglycans	alginic acid
Mucopolysaccharides (containing amino sugars and uronic acids)		heparin, hyaluronic acid, chondroitin sulfuric acids, blood group substances

which rely on an often scarce supply of combined nitrogen for the synthesis of vital proteins, utilize nitrogen-free sugars almost exclusively.

It is convenient to discuss the polysaccharides under several broad headings from the standpoint of their biological function. The amino sugar-containing polysaccharides of the animal kingdom (excluding the skeletal polysaccharide *chitin*) form a special class, the *mucopolysaccharides*, and form the subject of Section e (p. 262) of this Chapter on Polysaccharides. Section b (p. 189) of the present Chapter deals with polysaccharides in general, but excludes from consideration those polysaccharides built up exclusively from uronic acid residues, the *glycuronans* (*polyuronides*); these are discussed in Section c (p. 233). Section d (p. 246) is devoted to those polysaccharides which are produced by bacteria and other microorganisms.

2. Classification

Polysaccharides may be classified according to source and function into broad divisions which conveniently divide the wide field into several smaller groups. Such a division in terms of biological origin and purpose is outlined in Table I. As a means of classification, however, it suffers from several limitations. In particular, it presupposes knowledge of the function of the polysaccharide, and this information is frequently lacking. A second disadvantage arises from the fact that the same polysaccharide may fall into several groups. Furthermore, such a classification would not include artificially modified or degraded polysaccharides.

Some improvement may be made by classifying the polysaccharides from the standpoint of their chemical structure. Those containing only one glycose species are termed *homoglycans*, and may be subdivided into linear and branched-chain types. Polysaccharides containing two or more types of monosaccharide unit are termed *heteroglycans*. Heteroglycans which also contain uronic acid residues form a third group, while homoglycans containing only uronic acid residues fall into a fourth group, the *glycuronans* (polyuronides). Heteroglycans containing uronic acid and amino sugar residues are termed the *mucopolysaccharides* (Section e).

Such a chemical classification is necessarily incomplete, since details of structure are not available for all known polysaccharides. Table II, however, lists the more important polysaccharides classified according to this scheme

Chapter VII

Section b

Polysaccharides

(Excluding Glycuronans,
Bacterial Polysaccharides and Mucopolysaccharides)

D. HORTON and M. L. WOLFROM

Department of Chemistry, The Ohio State University, Columbus, Ohio (U.S.A.)

1. Nomenclature

Polysaccharides are named systematically by substituting "an" for the "ose" suffix of the glycose or monosaccharide unit. "Glycose" denotes any sugar, hence "glycan" is synonymous with "polysaccharide". "Mannan" is thus the systematic name for a homoglycan built from D- or L-mannose units. A glycan containing two or more species of glycose units (a heteroglycan) is named from the stem names of the constituent glycoses, taken alphabetically, with the suffix "glycan". The composition, if known, is inserted parenthetically after the name. Thus the polysaccharide *guaran*, which contains D-galactose and D-mannose units in the molar ratio 1:2 is systematically named D-galacto-D-mannoglycan (1:2). The trivial names for the more recently discovered polysaccharides are assigned by adding the standard suffix "an" to the stem name, which is generally derived from the source from which the polysaccharide was first isolated, for example, *asparagan*, *laminaran*, and *lichenan*. Non-systematic names established by long usage include *amylopectin, amylose, cellulose, chitin, glycogen, inulin, pectin,* and *starch*.

2. Examination of polysaccharides by physical methods

Polysaccharides are carbohydrate high polymers, macromolecules whose molecular weights may range from a few thousand to several millions. Some are essentially linear chains of monosaccharide units, while others are highly branched. The physical characteristics of such structures, while resembling in many ways those of high polymers in general, are, however, influenced by the presence of a large number of hydroxyl groups along the polymer chain. These groups confer on the polysaccharides those individual features which distinguish them from other polymers not so constituted. The units in the chain are generally linked in a regular repeating sequence and represent polymer molecules with a high degree of order. Elaborate procedures are often needed to isolate polysaccharides from natural products in a pure undegraded state suitable for physicochemical study (see p. 197).

The two principal biological groups of polysaccharides, the skeletal and the reserve food polysaccharides, exhibit notable differences in their general physical properties. The former, strongly hydrogen bonded intermolecularly, are in most cases quite insoluble in water, and swell little on immersion in water. They are relatively unreactive with reagents which cannot readily penetrate the molecular aggregates. Polysaccharides of the second group, in contrast, can usually imbibe water readily and may swell greatly. Many of them finally lose their rigidity to form a viscous colloidal solution. Chemical attack generally proceeds readily on such solutions. The lyophilic nature of these polysaccharides results from the lack of intermolecular hydrogen bonding, which thus allows the hydroxyl groups of the molecule to engage in hydrogen bonding with water molecules, and permits ready dispersion of the macromolecules in an aqueous medium. Aqueous solutions of salts which can break down hydrogen bonding, lithium thiocyanate for example, can be used to bring many otherwise insoluble polysaccharides into solution. Under certain conditions, some food reserve polysaccharides, amylose, for example, will spontaneously associate by inter- and intra-molecular hydrogen bonding to give an insoluble form which precipitates from solution (retrogradation). Some lyophilic polysaccharides form rigid gels in water and play an important part in the structural support of living tissue, especially in the seaweeds.

Polysaccharides whose molecules are essentially linear in structure can be distinguished from highly branched molecules by studying the film-forming ability of the material. A solution of the polysaccharide in water or other solvent is spread on a glass plate and allowed to dry. Insoluble poly-saccharides may be acetylated; the acetates are soluble in chloroform. A linear polymer of at least fifty monosaccharide units [degree of polymeri-zation, $(DP) > 50$], will give a tough pliable film which may readily be removed from the plate. It will have good tensile strength. Under these conditions a branched-chain polysaccharide yields a film which is difficult to remove from the plate, breaks easily on distortion, and has little tensile strength. An increasingly stronger and more pliable film is obtained with a linear polymer as the DP increases. The X-ray diffraction pattern of such a film under conditions of mechanical strain can be used to give information about the orientation of the macromolecules within the film, and also the nature and dimensions of the crystal lattice which may form. Plastic flow takes place under mechanical strain and tends to orient the linear molecules along the line of strain, making the film anisotropic to polarized light. A similar molecular alignment, causing anisotropy, occurs when such anisodimensional molecules exist in a solution which is subjected to shear, and experimental methods are available for using this phenomenon of *streaming birefringence* for the determination of the shape and flexibility of polysaccharide molecules. It has also been used as a method for molecular weight determination.

(a) Molecular weight of polysaccharides

Most of the methods generally used on high polymers for molecular weight and $\overline{DP}$ determinations may be used with polysaccharides. A polysaccharide is never composed solely of molecules with the same $\overline{DP}$ but exists as a mixture of polymer-homologous molecules with the same empirical formula whose $\overline{DP}$'s cover a range of values, giving a molecular weight "spectrum" or distribution about a mean value. It is necessary to calculate an *average* molecular weight value for the polymer. If this average is made on the basis of the relative *numbers* of molecules of a given size present in the mixture, the result is called the *number average molecular weight* M_n. If the calculation is based instead on the relative *weights* of molecules of a given size present, a *weight average molecular weight* $\overline{M}_w$ will result. Each molecular species will contribute equally to the number average, whereas the species that have the greater molecular weight will contribute more to the weight average. Therefore M_w will always be greater than M_n, and a wide molecular weight distribution curve will produce a larger difference between $\overline{M}_w$ and M_n, and in a narrow distribution curve the averages will approach each other.

The averages may be expressed in the form:

$$\text{Number average } \overline{M}_n = \frac{\sum_i M_i N_i}{\sum_i N_i}$$

$$\text{Weight average } \overline{M}_w = \frac{\sum_i M_i^2 N_i}{\sum_i M_i N_i}$$

where M_i is the molecular weight of particles of chain length i, and N_i is the number of particles of chain length i.

Bibliography p. 231

A perfectly homogeneous polymer containing molecules all of equal size would give the same value in each case, but the polymolecular[*] polymers encountered in practice give a lower value for $\overline{M}_n$ than for $\overline{M}_w$. The ratio of the molecular weight averages $\overline{M}_n/\overline{M}_w$ is less than unity, and is a measure of the molecular weight inhomogeneity of the polymer.

Methods for molecular weight determination which depend on colligative properties of the polymer in solution, that is, on the number of particles present, give a number average molecular weight; osmotic pressure measurements are an example. Methods involving measurements which depend on the physical size, and hence the weight, of the molecule (as the light-scattering methods) give the weight average. In general, molecular weight determination procedures involving an equilibrium state are amenable to fundamental thermodynamic consideration for calculation of absolute values, and are not influenced by the shape of the molecule. However, kinetic methods, though often founded on semi-empirical relationships which require calibration with polymers of known molecular weight distribution, are often of great value in furnishing information on the shape and flexibility of the molecule.

In the polysaccharide field, the most useful procedures for measuring weight average molecular weights are the light-scattering and the sedimentation methods. Viscosity methods are also used. Number average molecular weights may be measured by osmometry, or by chemical determination of reducing end-groups in the polysaccharide. *Isothermal distillation* is a useful method for determining number average molecular weights below $2 \cdot 10^4$, a region difficult to measure by other methods.

(i) *Osmotic pressure methods*

The number average molecular weight of a polysaccharide may be calculated from its osmotic pressure in solution, according to the Van 't Hoff formula, but any association of the molecules in solution will give spurious high values. This may be overcome by using a limiting value of osmotic pressure/concentration extrapolated to zero concentration. Alternatively, a modified Van 't Hoff expression:

$$\frac{\pi}{C} = \frac{RT}{\overline{M}_n} + BC^n$$

(π = osmotic pressure, C = concentration, R = gas constant, T = absolute temperature, B and n are empirical constants) which introduces a concentration-dependent correction term employing two empirical constants,

---

[*] A *polymolecular* system contains a mixture of homologs of one polymer species.

may be used. The method is very useful with polysaccharides whose molecular weights range from about 10^4 to $5 \cdot 10^5$. Below this limit, diffusion of the solute through the membrane is of serious consequence; above the limit the observed osmotic pressure is too small to be measured with any degree of accuracy. Polyvinyl alcohol membranes, claimed to be semipermeable down to $\overline{M}_n \approx 2 \cdot 10^3$, should be valuable in the osmometric study of low molecular weight polysaccharides.

(ii) End-group determination

Most, but not all polysaccharides have a terminal reducing saccharide unit. Each macromolecule has only one such group, which can be quantitatively determined by its copper reducing value, or by hypoiodite oxidation. The $\overline{DP}$ and $\overline{M}_n$ of the polysaccharide can then readily be calculated. A linear polysaccharide has, in addition to the reducing end-group, a non-reducing end-group which differs from the sugar residues along the chain. It is possible to determine this group quantitatively by methylation procedures (see p. 200) or, in certain cases, by periodate oxidation (see p. 202); such procedures serve to confirm the values obtained by reducing end-group determination. A branched-chain polysaccharide has more than one non-reducing end-group per molecule, and comparison of the number of such groups with the number of reducing groups gives a measure of the degree of branching in the molecule.

(iii) Viscosity methods

The weight average molecular weight of linear polymers in solution may be calculated from viscosity measurements using the Staudinger equation:

$$\lim_{C \to 0} \left[\frac{\eta_{sp}}{C} \right] = K_m \overline{M}_w$$

where $\eta_{sp} = \eta_{rel} - 1$, $\left(\eta_{rel} = \dfrac{\text{viscosity of solution}}{\text{viscosity of solvent}} \right)$, C = concentration, and K_m is an empirical constant evaluated by using a polymer of known molecular weight. The term on the left-hand side of the Staudinger equation is the *intrinsic viscosity* of the polymer. The method gives good results for polysaccharides with molecular weights below 10^4. Above this limit the shape of the polymer chain becomes of increasing significance, and better results are obtained if the right-hand term in the Staudinger equation is modified to $K_m \overline{M}_v^a$ where a is a constant which depends on the shape of the molecules; for a randomly coiled, solvated chain it has a value close to 0.80,

Bibliography p. 231

but for a matted coil it has a value of only 0.5, while for an extended rod-like molecule it may be as high as 2.0. The term $\overline{M}_v$ is a more complex average than the weight average, termed the *viscosity average molecular weight*. It involves the exponent a and is expressed as:

$$\text{Viscosity average } \overline{M}_v = \left[\frac{\sum\limits_i M_i^{a+1}\, N_i}{\sum\limits_i M_i N_i} \right]^{1/a}$$

It can be seen to reduce to M_w when a is unity. For accurate results with molecular weights greater than 10^5 the Staudinger equation must be further modified.

(iv) Sedimentation rate

Polysaccharide molecules in solution are prevented from settling under normal gravitational forces by the kinetic motion of the solvent molecules, which diffuse and maintain a solution of uniform concentration. When, however, the gravitational force is greatly increased, as in the ultracentrifuge, the heavier molecules tend to fall through the solution at a rate which depends on their molecular weight and shape. The sedimentation of a polysaccharide in a centrifuge cell may be followed by measurements of light absorption or refractive index at different levels in the cell. A polysaccharide with a narrow molecular weight range will give a sharp sedimentation boundary, while a mixture of different polysaccharides which differ appreciably in molecular weight will give a boundary for each component. A polysaccharide with a wide molecular weight range will give a diffuse boundary. The weight average molecular weight can be calculated if the *sedimentation constant* (defined as the value of sedimentation velocity/centrifugal acceleration extrapolated to zero concentration) and the *diffusion constant* of the polysaccharide (a measure of its tendency to re-disperse itself in the medium) are evaluated from the experimental data. The method is based on a kinetic system and can yield information concerning the shape of the molecular kinetic unit as well as its molecular weight. The molecular weight obtained is, however, completely independent of any assumptions as to the shape of the macromolecule.

(v) Sedimentation equilibrium

A solution of a polysaccharide in the ultracentrifuge will, in time, reach a steady state when the sedimentation effect and the diffusion resulting from thermal agitation are in equilibrium. The molecules undergo no net movement up or down the cell, but occupy a position dependent on their molecular weight, with the heaviest molecules nearest the bottom of the cell. The shape of the molecules is of no consequence. If the concentration gradient down the cell is determined by light absorption methods, the weight average molecular weight, which varies along the cell, is given by the equation:

$$\overline{M}_{wx} = \frac{RT}{(1 - V\rho)\omega^2 x} \cdot \frac{d \ln C}{dx}$$

where x = distance from the axis of rotation, R is the gas constant, T is the absolute temperature, V is the partial specific volume of the dissolved polymer, ρ is the density of the solvent, ω is the angular velocity of the rotor and C is the concentration of the solution. Alternatively, the change in refractive index along the cell may be used as a measure of concentration. In this case the result is a fourth type of molecular weight average, the *Z average molecular weight*, expressed as:

$$\overline{M}_z = \frac{\sum_i M_i^3 N_i}{\sum_i M_i^2 N_i}$$

(vi) Light scattering

Essentially the method gives a weight average molecular weight by measuring the turbidity of the solution, which causes light from a narrow parallel beam to be scattered in all directions on passing through the solution. For low molecular weight polymers this scattering is symmetrical, but when the size of the molecules exceeds about a twentieth of the wavelength of the light used, the scattering becomes dissymmetrical. Molecular weights are calculated from a relationship the constants in which can be derived from first principles. This method is extremely sensitive to large molecules and is well adapted to ranges of low concentration where associative effects do not affect the accuracy of the result.

(vii) Other methods for molecular weight determination

Cryoscopic methods, which are very useful in other fields, are of little value in the study of polysaccharides, since the relative freezing point depressions observed are very small and very sensitive to small quantities of low molecular weight impurities, especially inorganic salts. *Isopiestic* (isothermal distillation) methods have been used to some extent with polysaccharides (see p. 192). The application of *streaming birefringence* in molecular weight determination has already been mentioned (p. 191). Some determinations have made use of *ultrafiltration* techniques and of *diffusion*

Bibliography p. 231

constant measurements. *Electrophoretic* methods, which involve migration of charged particles in a solution to which a potential difference is applied, have also been used.

(b) Other structural information by physical methods

Most polysaccharides are macroscopically amorphous, but molecules of the linear polysaccharides of natural and artificial fibers, and stretched films are generally oriented parallel to one another, and appear partially or almost completely crystalline on X-ray crystallographic examination. Some unstretched linear molecules, amylose (in its complexes) for example, also exhibit partial crystallinity. In a number of cases the size of the unit cell of the crystal lattice has been evaluated. Comparison of the crystallographic data with scale models of short lengths of the polysaccharide chain has been used to reveal the manner in which inter- or intra-molecular hydrogen bonding hold the chains in the rigid framework of a crystal lattice.

Study of the *specific optical rotation* of polysaccharides, either at a fixed wavelength (usually the sodium D line, $\lambda = 5893$ Å) or at a series of wavelengths in the visible and near ultraviolet (optical rotatory dispersion) can yield useful information, particularly about the configuration of the glycosidic linkages. Polyhydroxy compounds form complexes with certain ions, cuprammonium ions, and borate ions for instance, and such complexing will sometimes bring an otherwise insoluble polysaccharide into aqueous solution. Cellulose, for example, dissolves in aqueous cuprammonium hydroxide. These complexes tend to lock the previously flexible six-membered rings in the polysaccharide chain into fixed conformations; such structures exhibit exalted optical rotations and electrical conductivity changes which can give structural information on the position of the linkages in the polysaccharide.

The *infrared* spectral analysis of polysaccharides is becoming increasingly important as more infrared absorption peaks are related to characteristic molecular groupings. The presence of such substituents as acetamido groups, carboxyl groups, or sulfate ester groups can be recognized, and the configuration of the interglycosidic link may in many cases be determined. The disappearance of the characteristic hydroxyl absorption peak on methylation or acylation of a polysaccharide is a useful rapid test for completion of a reaction.

3. Examination of polysaccharides by chemical methods

Only a few of the many isomeric monosaccharide sugars are found as structural units of the polysaccharides. The *hexoses* D-glucose, D-galactose, D-mannose and D-fructose are common; L-galactose is occasionally encountered. The *pentoses* D-xylose and L-arabinose are commonly found, while D-arabinose occurs less frequently. The *amino sugars* 2-amino-2-deoxy-D-glucose and 2-amino-2-deoxy-D-galactose are widespread in the polysaccharides from animal tissues, others are relatively rare. Four *uronic acids* are generally encountered: D-glucuronic, D-galacturonic, D-mannuronic and L-guluronic acids. The two 6-deoxy sugars L-fucose (6-deoxy-L-galactose) and L-rhamnose (6-deoxy-L-mannose) complete the list. Other sugars are found in certain polysaccharides, but are rare. The amino group in the amino sugar-containing polysaccharides is generally acetylated. The hydroxyl groups on certain polysaccharides may be partially esterified or etherified.

(a) Isolation of pure polysaccharides

It is imperative that a polysaccharide isolated for structural study be rigorously purified to ensure homogeneity. It is regrettable that much careful structural work done in the past has afforded misleading results since it has been shown by more recent techniques that the polysaccharide preparations used in many instances contained more than one component. Methods used for the isolation of individual polysaccharides vary widely and it is not possible to describe any standard procedure. In favorable cases, however, a water-soluble polysaccharide may, for example, be isolated from a tissue homogenate by filtration to remove insoluble matter, deproteinization (as by the Sevag procedure) and precipitation of the polysaccharide with an organic solvent, generally ethanol. It is important to ensure that enzymes which may be liberated when the tissue is homogenized be rapidly inactivated, otherwise extensive modification of the polysaccharide may take place. A water-insoluble polysaccharide may be separated in a fairly pure state by extraction of contaminating material with a suitable solvent. Wood cellulose is freed from xylans in this way by extraction with hot alkali. When such vigorous conditions are employed it is often difficult to avoid some degradation of the polysaccharide.

Closer examination of purified polysaccharide preparations, as by sedimentation studies, will frequently reveal that more than one polysaccharide is still present. Fractional precipitation with organic solvents has been widely used for the purification of such mixtures of water-soluble polysaccharides. In most cases, however, this procedure merely subdivides the polymolecular system into fractions on a molecular weight basis. Each individual fraction represents a narrow molecular weight range, but still remains a mixture of polysaccharide types. In this case the more recently developed separation techniques are of great value. Numerous methods are available and involve selective precipitation with detergents or metal ions, chromatographic techniques, ultrafiltration, sedimentation, solvent distribu-

Bibliography p. 231

tion, electrodialysis, electrophoresis, and other procedures. Sedimentation and electrophoretic methods are particularly valuable for rapid small-scale analytical tests of homogeneity. The electrophoretic mobility of a polysaccharide molecule, that is, its tendency to migrate along an applied potential gradient, is chiefly dependent on the net charge on the molecule. Even molecules with no readily ionizable groups, such as carboxyl groups, are generally slightly charged, and in alkaline solution slight ionization of the hydroxyl groups increases this charge and confers considerable electrophoretic mobility on many polysaccharides. Complex formation with certain charged ions, as borate ions, will increase the charge and modify the electrophoretic behavior of the polysaccharide. Many polysaccharides which were believed to be homogeneous until quite recently, for instance many glycogens, amylopectins, and plant gums, have been resolved into more than one component by electrophoresis.

The absolute purity of a polysaccharide preparation is always open to some doubt, but it is generally considered to be pure when it exhibits the same physical characteristics after isolation by different methods. Considerable experimental skill is required in the isolation of a pure undegraded polysaccharide.

Analysis of the polysaccharide

The elementary analysis of a polysaccharide, in agreement with its molecular formula, is a valuable but by no means the only criterion of purity. The sulfur and nitrogen values obtained for polysaccharides containing sulfate or amino sugar residues give a measure of these constituents. Amino sugars may also conveniently be determined by the Elson–Morgan colorimetric method on the hydrolyzed polysaccharide. Acidic groups, as carboxyl groups of uronic acids, may be determined by direct titration, or by decarboxylation or colorimetric methods.

(b) Identification of the monosaccharides

Total acidic hydrolysis of the polysaccharide yields a mixture of the component monosaccharides, which are readily separated and identified chromatographically. Paper chromatography is useful as a rapid analytical tool to preface the isolation of larger quantities of the sugars which can then be unequivocally identified as crystalline derivatives.

(c) Fragmentation analysis

Once the component monosaccharides have been identified, an extension of the hydrolytic degradation procedure, fragmentation analysis, can be used to gain insight into the position and nature of the interglycosidic linkages. Acidic hydrolysis is not taken to completion, and, in addition to the monosaccharides, a range of oligosaccharides is formed. The lower oligosaccharides are conveniently separated by adsorption of the neutralized hydrolyzate on a carbon column, where they will remain during elution of the monosaccharides with water. The low-molecular weight oligosaccharides may then be removed from the column by elution with aqueous ethanol, and isolated individually by further chromatography, either as the free sugars or as the acetylated derivatives. Silicate extrusion chromatography is a valuable technique for separating the acetates, and the pure oligosaccharide acetates show much better crystallizing properties than the free sugars. These oligosaccharides represent portions of the original polymer chain, and preserve the linkages found therein, and knowledge of their structure can thus help to elucidate the structure of the polysaccharide. Since many disaccharides and trisaccharides are known, it is often possible to identify the di- and tri-saccharide components of the fragmented polysaccharide by direct comparison. The structure of unknown oligosaccharides may be elucidated by established methods, and in certain cases they may be synthesized for direct comparison. A valuable procedure for identifying the reducing monosaccharide unit of an oligosaccharide is to "mark" this residue, either by oxidation to the glyconic acid, or (better) by reduction to the glycitol. The monosaccharide aldonic acid or alditol may then be isolated and characterized from the hydrolyzed oligosaccharide derivative to identify the terminal reducing sugar residue. The position of linkage of the penultimate group in the reducing unit may be established by methylation analysis of the oxidized or reduced oligosaccharide.

Acetolysis provides a useful variation on the hydrolysis procedure; it involves the fragmentation of the polysaccharide in mixed acetic and sulfuric acids at low temperatures, to produce oligosaccharide acetates directly.

Mercaptolysis, that is, treatment of a polysaccharide with an alkanethiol and concentrated hydrochloric acid, causes fragmentation of the macromolecule with the formation of dialkyl dithioacetals at the reducing end of each fragment. Reaction may be partial or complete; the oligosaccharide and monosaccharide dialkyl dithioacetals generally crystallize well and are often suitable characterization derivatives for the structural components of the polysaccharide.

The *rate of acidic hydrolysis* of a polysaccharide can give useful information. Furanoside units are very rapidly hydrolyzed under mild conditions. Pentopyranosides hydrolyze somewhat faster than hexopyranosides. Uronic acids linked to neutral sugars yield glycuronic acid → glycose "disaccharides" (aldobiouronic acids) which are resistant to hydrolysis.

A reliable proof that a given polysaccharide is a heteroglycan and not a mixture of homoglycans is afforded by the isolation, by fragmentation analysis, of a disaccharide containing two different monosaccharide units. Precautions to avoid reversion (see below) must be observed; this difficulty is readily circumvented by the use of dilute solutions of the carbohydrate.

(d) Enzymic hydrolysis

Pure enzymes are highly specific and only hydrolyze one type of interglycosidic linkage. This affords a valuable method for the identification of a particular type of linkage, and is useful in studies of branched-chain polysaccharides, since the hydrolysis halts at the branch point. Care must, however, be exercised in the interpretation of results of studies made with crude enzyme preparations, since contaminating enzymes may permit a wide range of other reactions to yield untrustworthy results and vitiate the specificity of the pure enzyme.

It is wise to avoid the use of a high concentration of polysaccharide in hydrolytic or enzymic degradation studies owing to the possibility of *acid reversion* or enzymic *transglycosylation* taking place. Reversion involves the interaction of mono- or oligo-saccharides with the elimination of water to produce oligosaccharides with structures different from those of the genuine fragmentation products. Similarly, transglycosylation is the process whereby the enzyme, whose action is reversible in the presence of high concentrations of reaction products, transfers glycosyl units to other fragments present in the mixture, giving rise to new oligosaccharides.

(e) Acylation and alkylation reactions

Acetylation of a polysaccharide, followed by acetyl group determination, is a convenient method for determining the total hydroxyl group content of the polysaccharide. Primary and secondary hydroxyl groups may be quantitatively distinguished by reaction with triphenylmethyl (trityl) chloride or with p-toluenesulfonyl chloride. Both reagents react selectively with primary hydroxyl groups. Primary p-tolylsulfonyloxy groups react quantitatively with sodium iodide to form sodium p-toluenesulfonate and a deoxy-iodo derivative of the sugar; the reaction serves to distinguish these groups from the more difficultly formed secondary p-tolylsulfonyloxy groups.

(f) Methylation

Total methylation of all available hydroxyl groups in a polysaccharide generally requires initial methylation by the Haworth method (dimethyl sulfate and aqueous sodium hydroxide) to introduce sufficient lipophilic methoxyl groups to confer solubility in organic solvents, followed by several successive methylations by the Purdie method (methyl iodide and silver oxide), until the methoxyl content of the product approaches a limiting value. This *exhaustive methylation* procedure can be tedious, and improved methods have recently been developed to achieve total methylation in as few stages as possible. One such procedure involves the alternate addition of sodium metal and methyl iodide to a suspension of the polysaccharide in liquid ammonia. Methylation of the polysaccharide with the Purdie reagents, but in excess *N,N*-dimethylformamide solution, also gives good results. The silver oxide used in all of these methylations tends to oxidize and degrade the polysaccharides somewhat, and the use of *N,N*-dimethylformamide, methyl iodide and barium oxide for methylation has been advocated to overcome this drawback; a trace of barium hydroxide promotes the reaction. A relatively undegraded methylated polysaccharide may be obtained if low molecular weight fragmentation products are removed by *dialysis* after each methylation.

Other methylation procedures of value in the polysaccharide field have been advocated. Methylation of a solution of the polysaccharide in tetrahydrofuran with solid sodium hydroxide and dimethyl sulfate can be used to totally methylate an already partially methylated polysaccharide. Etherification takes place readily; the solvent appears to stabilize the alkoxide intermediate in the reaction long enough to facilitate ether formation at the expense of competing side reactions. Another useful methylation procedure involves treatment of the polysaccharide with methyl iodide and thallous hydroxide.

Uronic acid-containing polysaccharides are particularly difficult to methylate completely. Total methylation can be achieved if the carboxyl groups are esterified and then reduced (potassium borohydride or diborane) to primary alcohol groups.

Total acidic hydrolysis of a *fully methylated polysaccharide* is one of the most useful tools for structure determination available to the carbohydrate chemist. The hydrolysis is generally initiated in methanolic hydrogen chloride or formic acid (which will dissolve the methylated polysaccharide) and completed with dilute mineral acid. The resultant partially methylated monosaccharides bear hydroxyl groups at the points of linkage in the original polysaccharide, and monosaccharides from branch points will have three such hydroxyl groups. The separation and identification of the partially methylated sugars, once a difficult problem when fractional high-vacuum distillation was the only method available, is now accomplished more simply by chromatography. Exploratory work can be carried out by paper chromatography, and the pure methyl ethers are isolable by column techniques. Many partially methylated monosaccharide derivatives have been synthesized as reference compounds. The technique of *gas–liquid partition chromatography* has recently been applied to the separation of mixtures of methylated monosaccharides (as their methyl glycosides) with highly successful results. It offers a powerful new tool which will undoubtedly find extensive use in future investigations on polysaccharide structure.

(g) *Oxidation of polysaccharides*

vic-Diol groupings interact with the glycol-cleaving reagents, sodium metaperiodate and lead tetraacetate, scission of the carbon–carbon bond takes place and a dialdehyde is formed. Since the monosaccharide units of a polysaccharide are linked in the cyclic hemiacetal form, the backbone of the molecule is left intact after oxidation, and each glycol-containing saccharide unit will remain in place in the chain as a dialdehyde. The dialdehyde itself probably cyclizes by hydration and hemiacetal formation. The molar uptake of oxidant per anhydrosaccharide unit provides evidence for the location of hydroxyl groups in the repeating unit. Lead tetraacetate oxidation sharply differentiates *cis*-1,2-diols from *trans*-1,2-diols; the former react far more rapidly than the latter. The end-groups of a linear polysaccharide contain one more hydroxyl group than the repeating unit, and thus give a different oxidation pattern. The reducing end-group can yield definite quantities of formaldehyde and formic acid, the non-reducing end-group will yield formic acid only. Direct titration of formic acid produced, and determination of formaldehyde by precipitation as the dimedone derivative or (better) colorimetrically with chromotropic acid, give values from which the $\overline{DP}$ of the polysaccharide may be calculated. Polysaccharides formed from units which contain three contiguous hydroxyl groups, as $(1 \rightarrow 6)$-linked hexoglycans, yield one mole of formic acid per anhydrosaccharide unit; in these cases no reliable estimate of the small yield of formic acid produced by end-group oxidation can be made. The behavior of branched-chain polysaccharides on glycol cleavage is more complex since the units at the branch points have one fewer hydroxyl group than the repeating unit. In many cases the branch-point monosaccharide has no *vic*-diol group, and remains as the only intact monosaccharide after hydrolysis of the oxidized polysaccharide. The degree of branching may often be calculated from the formic acid produced by end-group oxidation. The reaction conditions for glycol-cleavage oxidation must be carefully controlled to minimize non-stoichiometric "over-oxidation".

A valuable adjunct to the periodate oxidation technique is the *Barry degradation*, which can give information on the sequence of units in a polysaccharide. It is particularly useful in assigning a single structure to a polysaccharide from several possible structures which may be proposed from the results of methylation studies. The periodate-oxidized polysaccharide is initially treated with phenylhydrazine to convert the aldehyde groups into their phenylhydrazones, and it is then subjected to excess phenylhydrazine in aqueous ethanol, whereupon the fragments of those monosaccharides which were oxidized by periodate are split off as phenylosazones. Saccharide residues in the polysaccharide which are not subject to periodate oxidation are unaffected by this treatment. The phenylosazone fragments split off during the degradation may be identified and related to the structure of the original polysaccharide. Fragments frequently encountered include triose phenylosazone, D-*glycero*-tetrose phenylosazone, glyoxal bis(phenylhydrazone), and the osazones of oligosaccharides. If the polysaccharide backbone is resistant to periodate oxidation [as in a $(1 \rightarrow 3)$-linked hexoglycan], the Barry degradation will only remove the end-groups; other linear polysaccharides generally undergo complete degradation. It is frequently advantageous to perform the degradation several times on the same material to obtain structural information on a branched-chain polysaccharide.

A related type of degradation (Smith degradation) involves borohydride reduction of the periodate-oxidized polysaccharide, followed by acid hydrolysis. Fragments of the oxidized units in the polysaccharide appear as alcohols in the hydrolysis products. These can be identified and related to the structure of the original polysaccharide, affording similar structural evidence to the Barry degradation.

Polysaccharides containing free primary alcohol groups can be oxidized to the corresponding carboxylic acids with nitrogen dioxide, or oxygen and a platinum catalyst; hexose units are thus converted into hexuronic acids.

Elementary oxygen slowly oxidizes many polysaccharides, particularly under alkaline conditions; the main reaction appears to be fragmentation of the molecules into shorter chains. This is of consequence in the weakening of fabrics composed of polysaccharide fibers (cotton, rayon) during atmospheric weathering, and on laundering.

(h) *Alkaline degradation of polysaccharides*

Polysaccharides do not at once undergo the radical changes that take place with the monosaccharides when treated with alkali. Glycosidic linkages are ordinarily stable to alkali, hence there is no random fragmentation of a polysaccharide chain such as takes place during acidic hydrolysis. A stepwise degradation takes place, however, from the reducing end of the molecule at a rate which is influenced by the position at which the penultimate sugar residue is attached. If this linkage is $(1 \rightarrow 3)$, the terminal residue is rapidly detached, but $(1 \rightarrow 4)$ and $(1 \rightarrow 6)$ links are much more stable, while $(1 \rightarrow 2)$ links are resistant to the action of alkali. Molecular rearrangements take place in the terminal residue prior to its elimination as an acidic derivative. These rearrangements are facilitated by a 3-O-substituent, but are inhibited by a substituent at position 2. The acidic derivative formed, a saccharinic acid, can often be identified and related to the particular linkage involved.

4. Homopolysaccharides

Within this section, only those polysaccharides which contain at least 95% of a single structural monosaccharide will be considered. As techniques for the separation of polysaccharides are improved it is probable that some polysaccharides at present classified as heteropolysaccharides will be resolved into homopolysaccharide components.

The common glucans, cellulose, starch, and glycogen are unlikely to contain even small quantities of sugars other than D-glucose. In other cases, as in the xylans from wood, the distinction between homo- and hetero-polysaccharides is not so clear and some reclassification will undoubtedly take place when more investigations are made.

(a) Cellulose

Cellulose is not only the most widespread polysaccharide, it is indeed the most abundant organic compound found in nature, and it is put to a multitude of different uses by man. It is hardly surprising that the cellulose macromolecule has been the subject of more study than any other high polymer. While its principal occurrence is in the higher plants, it is also produced by many lower plants, by bacteria, and by a few of the lower animals. It is a linear glucan with β-D-($1 \rightarrow 4$) linkages and has a measured $\overline{DP}$ of at least 3000. The $\overline{DP}$ prior to isolation may be much larger than this.

The purest form of cellulose found naturally is in the seed hair of the cotton plant, which is 98% cellulose, but many other plant sources are rich in the polysaccharide. Commercially, wood is the most important source of cellulose. Wood chips are extracted with hot alkali in the "pulping" process to remove most of the lignin*, hemicellulose**, gums, and other components

---

* *Lignin* is a non-carbohydrate component of wood, and is removed during "pulping". *Holocellulose* is wood from which lignin has been extracted, generally by treatment with sodium chlorite. It contains most of the original wood polysaccharides, in a relatively undegraded state.

** The term *hemicellulose*, applied to the non-cellulosic cell-wall polysaccharides which can be extracted from wood and other plant material with alkali, is of little precise structural significance. Xylans form the principal component, but mannans, glucomannoglycans, galactans, arabinogalactoglycans, arabinoxyloglycans and uronic acid-containing xylans (acidic hemicelluloses, hemicellulose B) and pectic substances may also be present. These polysaccharides are discussed individually elsewhere in this chapter. It is not yet firmly established whether hemicellulose materials are covalently linked to cellulose and lignin, or whether they are held by secondary forces, or merely entrained mechanically.

which accompany cellulose in native wood (see Fig. 1), to leave only the insoluble cellulose. Most of this commercial cellulose is used for paper manufacture, smaller quantities are used for the production of rayon. "Pulping" with alkaline sodium sulfide at 160–175° (kraft process) gives a pulp which produces a strong brown paper. Other processes involve treatment with sodium hydroxide (soda process) or with calcium bisulfite (sulfite process). Some depolymerization takes place during the alkaline treatment when cellulose is extracted from plant materials.

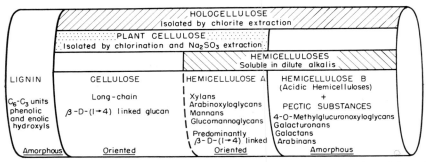

Fig. 1. Schematic representation of the major constituents of wood cellulose. Adapted from A. G. Norman, Ref. 30, p. 464. Reproduced by permission of the publishers, Interscience, New York, 1954.

The bast fibers of many plants are rich in cellulose, and a number of them, as flax (*Linum usitatissimum*), jute (*Corchorus capsularis*), hemp (*Cannabis sativa*), and ramie (*Boehmeria nivea*) are important in the manufacture of textiles and rope. Some leaf fibers, those from sisal (*Agave sisalana*), and Manila hemp (*Musa textilis*), for example, are also rich in cellulose, and are used similarly.

Cellulose is extremely insoluble in most solvents, except strong mineral acids, which rapidly depolymerize it. It will, however, dissolve in solutions of cuprammonium hydroxide or cupriethylenediamine. When care is taken to exclude oxygen, which rapidly degrades the dissolved polysaccharide, the cuprammonium solution may be used for viscometric measurements of molecular weight. Insoluble cellulose is regenerated from cuprammonium solution on acidification; *cuprammonium rayon* is made in this way. Alkaline sodium ferric tartrate solutions dissolve cellulose. The solutions are stable to atmospheric oxygen, and are to be preferred for viscosity measurements.

Fibrous cellulose, as isolated from natural sources, is shown by X-ray diffraction diagrams to be partially crystalline. The animal cellulose tunicin, isolated from the outer mantles of certain marine organisms of the subphylum *Tunicata*, shows the highest crystallinity of those studied. Ramie fiber cellulose also shows above average crystallinity but all natural cellulose samples studied give the same X-ray pattern. It is probable that the linear molecules are associated for parts of their length in an ordered, parallel arrangement, usually along the fiber axis, to form crystalline micelles approximately 50 Å in diameter and 600 Å or more long. Interspersed between the micellar regions are believed to be amorphous regions where the chains are less highly oriented.

Crystallographic analysis of the micellar regions reveals a monoclinic unit cell with the dimensions $a = 8.2$ Å, $b = 10.3$ Å, $c = 7.9$ Å, and $\beta = 83°$ The spatial arrangement of the molecules within the cell is shown in Fig. 2

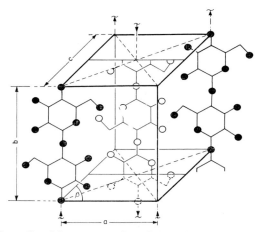

Fig. 2. Spatial representation of the unit cell of cellulose[*].

Two extended cellulose chains pass, probably in opposite directions, through the cell, along the longest (b) axis, and the cell itself contains one cellobiose unit (length 10.3 Å) from each chain. The units along the b axis (which is also the fiber axis) are thus firmly linked by covalent bonds (bond energy *ca.* 50 kcal per mole). The cellobiose units are linked along the a axis by hydrogen bonding (energy about 15 kcal per mole), and along the c axis by the much weaker Van der Waals forces. Natural fibers vary in the ratio of crystalline to amorphous cellulose. The tensile strength of the fiber increases with increasing crystallinity, but at the same time the elasticity decreases. Highly crystalline fibers are brittle. The crystal structure of regenerated cellulose (cellulose II) is slightly different from that of natural cellulose (cellulose I).

Cellulose will imbibe water and swell to a certain extent, but will not

[*] After K. H. MEYER AND L. MISCH, *Helv. Chim. Acta*, 20 (1937) 237.

dissolve. Aqueous solutions of salts which will break down hydrogen bonding will cause extensive swelling and may result in complete dispersion of the polysaccharide.

The swelling of cellulose in water and hydroxylic solvents takes place initially by sorption into the amorphous regions, and no change in the X-ray pattern is observed at this stage. Some swelling agents may then enter the miceliar regions and modify the crystal structure (swollen cellulose, cellulose II). A few solvents can break down the crystallites altogether. Sodium hydroxide solution causes swelling of natural cellulose by penetration of the amorphous regions and conversion of the crystallites to the cellulose II structure. This is the basis of the mercerization process; cotton is treated under tension with sodium hydroxide solution, and the resulting *mercerized cotton* is of improved appearance, and accepts dyes readily.

The chemical structure of cellulose is well established. Total hydrolysis yields D-glucose as the sole product, and hydrolysis of the permethylated polysaccharide gives high yields of 2,3,6-tri-O-methyl-D-glucose, which would be expected from a $(1 \rightarrow 4)$-linked glucan. The alternative $(1 \rightarrow 5)$-linked structure is ruled out since the polysaccharide does not show the acid lability characteristic of furanosides, nor have any $(1 \rightarrow 5)$-linked oligosaccharides been isolated on partial hydrolysis. Optical rotation studies indicate that the glycosidic linkages have the β-D configuration and the infrared absorption spectrum confirms this. From this evidence cellulose can be assigned the structure:

Cellulose

Much supplementary evidence has accrued to support this structure. Acetolysis, or partial hydrolysis with subsequent acetylation, yields the octaacetate of the disaccharide cellobiose, a diglucosaccharide known to be β-D-$(1 \rightarrow 4)$-linked, and an homologous series of higher saccharides, all β-D-$(1 \rightarrow 4)$-linked. No evidence of chain branching is found. Cellulose reacts with one mole of periodate per component D-glucose unit, with scission of the C-2 to C-3 bond. No periodate-resistant residues are found, which is indicative of the absence of branching.

Estimates of the $\overline{DP}$ of cellulose by chemical methods give low values

Bibliography p. 231

probably because of degradation. Physical methods are hampered by the difficulty of obtaining undegraded cellulose in solution, but recent estimates by most of the commonly used physical methods indicate a linear molecule with a $\overline{DP}$ of at least 3,000.

(i) Modifications of cellulose

Cellulose can be considered as a polyhydric alcohol with one primary and two secondary hydroxyl groups per D-glucose residue available for substitution. A number of cellulose derivatives are highly important commercially. Substitution of the hydroxyl groups with lipophilic residues renders the polysaccharide soluble in organic solvents. Substitution reactions initially take place heterogeneously in the amorphous regions of the cellulose fiber, and subsequently dissolution of the solubilized partially substituted molecule allows reaction to go to completion in a homogeneous solution.

Viscose rayon is produced by extruding a solution of cellulose xanthate, produced from "soda cellulose" and carbon disulfide, into dilute acid, which breaks down the cellulose xanthate and reprecipitates the cellulose in a form suitable for spinning. *Acetate rayon* is produced by extruding a solution of cellulose acetate; the organic solvent is allowed to evaporate to leave a fiber of cellulose acetate. Cellulose acetate is also used in plastics and paints manufacture. *Cellulose nitrate* (nitrocellulose, guncotton) is used as a propellant. *Ethers* of cellulose are used as protective colloids (see p. 221) and as detergents.

(ii) Biological degradation of cellulose

Many bacteria, fungi, and *Actinomyces* produce cellulolytic enzymes. Most higher animals cannot metabolize cellulose, but *herbivorous vertebrates*, whose intestinal flora contain cellulose-splitting anaerobic bacteria make use of cellulose indirectly in this manner. *Actinomyces* species are mainly responsible for the aerobic breakdown of cellulose in the soil, while many fungi will attack wood and utilize its cellulose metabolically.

(b) Chitin

The cuticle or exoskeleton of the *Arthropoda* and other invertebrate phyla is formed from a framework of the nitrogen-containing polysaccharide chitin, together with proteins, inorganic salts, lipids, pigments, and the like, to confer added rigidity. Other tissues of these lower animals may also be rich in chitin. Saprophytic plants, such as fungi (*Eumycophyta*) generally utilize chitin in partial or total replacement of cellulose as a cell-wall structural material.

Chitin is generally prepared by extraction with acid and alkali successively to remove salts and proteins. It dissolves only in concentrated acids, which degrade it, and in aqueous solutions of salts, lithium thiocyanate for example, which by virtue of their high hydrating ability can break down hydrogen bonding. In chemical structure chitin resembles cellulose closely, with the exception that the hydroxyl group at position 2 on the D-glucose residues in cellulose is replaced in chitin by the acetamido ($-NHCOCH_3$) group. The physical properties of chitin closely resemble those of cellulose, but it is still more insoluble and unreactive. The structure of the crystalline regions in both polysaccharides is probably closely similar. Total acidic hydrolysis of chitin yields the monosaccharide unit, 2-amino-2-deoxy-D-glucose as the amine salt, together with one equivalent of acetic acid. Fragmentation analysis of de-*N*-acetylated chitin (chitosan) has been used to isolate a homologous series of chitosaccharides, isolated as their *N*-acetyl derivatives. These are β-D-(1 → 4)-linked 2-acetamido-2-deoxy-D-glucose residues and represent fragments of the chitin molecule. (See also Chapter VII, Section e, p. 226.)

Chitin

(c) Starch

Starches are plant reserve food polysaccharides, glucans linked predominantly α-D-(1 → 4). Starches with linear molecules are termed *amyloses*, while highly branched starch molecules, with α-D-(1 → 6)-linked branch points are termed *amylopectins*. Small differences exist between individual samples of each constituent from different plant species. Plants store starch in *starch granules*. These vary in size from 3 to 100 μ in diameter, and contain both amylose and amylopectin. Starch has a negligible osmotic pressure, and the plant is thus able to store large reserves of D-glucose in a readily accessible form without disturbing the water balance of the tissues. Most plant cells contain a few starch granules, but many plants have accumulations of large parenchymatous cells whose principal function is the storage of starch. Such reserves may be found in root tissue (root vegetables, tubers), stems (corms, for example), or leaves (bulbs). In each case the original tissue is greatly enlarged to accommodate the reserve starch. The highest concentrations of starch are found in seeds, cereal grains in particular; those of corn (maize) contain 80% starch.

Bibliography p. 231

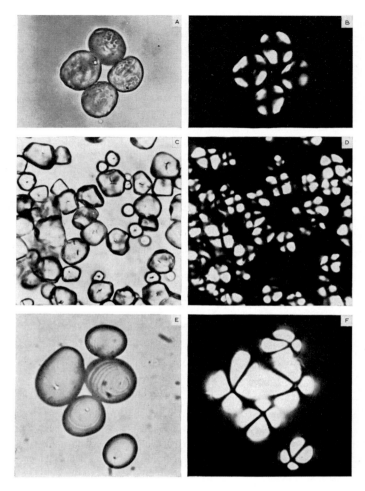

Fig. 3. (A) Wheat starch. (B) Wheat starch under polarized light. (C) Corn starch. (D) Corn starch under polarized light. (E) Potato starch. (F) Potato starch under polarized light. (G) Regal lily starch. (H) Navy bean starch. (I) Rice starch. (J) Wrinkled pea starch. (K) Cassava starch. (L) Oat starch, showing a large compound granule. Magnification × 235. All photographs kindly provided by Professor R. M. Sandstedt of the University of Nebraska.

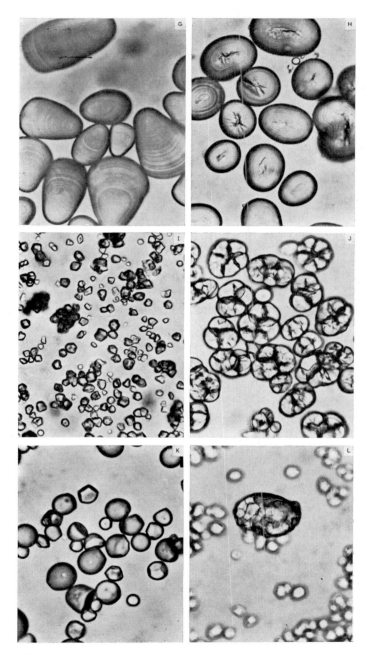

Starch is separated on a large scale from plant materials by milling the plant tissue in water suspension to release the granules, which are then separated from accompanying protein by "tabling" or by continuous centrifugation techniques. The size and shape of starch granules are characteristic of their source (Fig. 3). When placed in cold water, the granules swell to a limited extent. On heating the suspension, a temperature is reached when rapid swelling of the granules takes place and the suspension becomes gelatinous. This "pasting" temperature is characteristic of the starch type. At this stage a small amount of material diffuses out of the swollen granules. At a higher temperature the granule "sacs" break down and all of the contents are liberated.

A starch typically contains 25% amylose and 75% amylopectin, although the so-called waxy, or glutinous starches contain very little amylose. By selective breeding, varieties of corn producing starch of up to 70% amylose content have been developed. The components may be separated by the selective precipitation of amylose from the mixture by polar organic molecules. 1-Butanol, for example, may be added to a hot starch solution, whereupon an amylose–butanol complex separates out as a solid on cooling. The complex is readily broken down to give pure amylose. Amylopectin may be recovered from the remaining solution. An industrial process utilizes a selective precipitation of amylose by inorganic salts.

Molecular weight determinations made on whole starches are of little value owing to the heterogeneity of the material, but reported values indicate that in contrast to cellulose, starches occur with a very broad spectrum of molecular weights.

Treatment of whole starch with hot alkali causes degradation of the amylose fraction starting at the reducing end, and converts it into D-glucoisosaccharinic acid [3-deoxy-2-C-(hydroxymethyl)-D-*erythro*- or -D-*threo*-pentonic acid]. The short reducing chain of amylopectin is similarly degraded, but the degradation does not continue along the side chains, and there is thus little overall degradation of this fraction.

(i) Amylose

Total acidic hydrolysis of amylose yields D-glucose as the sole product, and the permethylated polysaccharide can be hydrolyzed to give 2,3,6-tri-O-methyl-D-glucose in high yield, together with a very small quantity of 2,3,4,6-tetra-O-methyl-D-glucose. The α-D configuration can be assigned to the glycosidic linkages from the optical rotation and infrared spectrum of the polysaccharide. These results indicate a linear α-D-$(1 \rightarrow 4)$-linked glucan structure for amylose.

The small quantity of tetramethyl ether arises from the non-reducing end-group. The alternative $(1 \rightarrow 5)$-linked furanoside structure is ruled out by fragmentation analysis, which yields a homologous series of α-D-($1 \to 4$)-linked glucosaccharides of which the first is maltose (4-O-α-D-glucopyranosyl-D-glucose).

Amylose

The acetate of amylose may be cast into strong pliable films, which on stretching give fiber-type X-ray patterns; this confirms the linear structure of the amylose molecule. Early estimates of the $\overline{DP}$ of amylose, calculated from the methylation results, gave low values (about 350); some degradation undoubtedly occurred during the methylation procedure. Estimates based on the release of formic acid from the non-reducing end-group on oxidation with periodate give values close to 1000, and the results obtained by osmometry are in good agreement with this value. Physical methods which give weight average values indicate that the $\overline{DP}$ may be as high as 4000.

In aqueous solution, amylose has a strong tendency to form molecular associations which cause the polysaccharide to precipitate spontaneously. This *retrogradation*, as it is termed, is troublesome when making physical measurements on amylose solutions.

Some workers believe that very occasional linkages other than α-D-($1 \to 4$) occur in the amylose molecule, but no definitive evidence for this has yet been adduced.

The two principal amylolytic enzymes, *β-amylase* and *α-amylase* are so named because the former causes optical rotational changes in a positive direction and the latter causes a fall in the specific rotation, when allowed to act on a solution of amylose. The amylases often occur together in plants, and they may be separated and isolated in pure crystalline form. In animal tissues, only α-amylase is found, occurring in saliva and pancreatic juice as a digestive enzyme. β-Amylase hydrolyzes amylose to maltose by detaching the disaccharide fragments stepwise from the non-reducing end of the amylose molecule, and the viscosity of the solution falls slowly. The purest β-amylase preparations appear to not completely degrade amylose, and it is possible that the reaction stops at some "anomalous linkages" resistant to the enzyme.

The liquefying, or α-amylases appear to attack the molecule in a different manner. Fragmentation into short chains takes place and the amylose

Bibliography p. 231

solution very rapidly loses viscosity as a result. The products are termed *dextrins*.

The *phosphorylases* can completely convert amylose into α-D-gluco-pyranose 1-phosphate when inorganic phosphate is present. The reaction is reversible, provided a fragment of an amylose chain containing three or more D-glucose residues is present to act as an initiator. Amylose may be converted into amylopectin by the branching enzyme (Q enzyme) which is present in many crude phosphorylase preparations. This branching enzyme causes transglycosylation by simultaneous scission of (1 → 4) links and synthesis of (1 → 6) links.

The *amylose complexes*, which readily form on addition of certain alcohols to amylose solutions, are highly crystalline and their X-ray diagrams have been interpreted to indicate that the amylose molecule has a helical structure enclosing the complexed molecule.

Iodine reacts with amylose to give a characteristic deep blue-colored complex containing one iodine molecule for each seven or eight D-glucose residues. At least 30–35 D-glucose units are required for full development of the blue color, and degraded amylose molecules with shorter chains give a red color. If fewer than six units are present, no color is formed. A potentiometric titration based on the formation of the amylose-iodine complex is a good method for the quantitative determination of amylose in a mixture. The amylose-iodine complex is believed to be a helically-coiled amylose molecule with a period of six D-glucose units, with iodine atoms situated in the core of the helix.

(ii) Schardinger dextrins

Enzymes from *Aerobacillus macerans* can convert amylose into crystalline α-D-(1 → 4)-linked dextrins containing six, seven, or eight D-glucose residues (α-, β- and γ-dextrins), with the reducing end of the oligosaccharide linked glycosidically α-D-(1 → 4) to its own non-reducing end to form a macrocyclic structure. These cycloamyloses form characteristic crystalline complexes with iodine. It is conceivable that they may be formed from a helical amylose molecule by enzymic transglycosylation between adjacent turns of the helices.

(iii) Amylopectin

Total hydrolysis of amylopectin gives D-glucose as the only sugar constituent. Hydrolysis of the fully methylated polysaccharide yields, in addition to 2,3,6-tri-O-methyl-D-glucose, a greater quantity of 2,3,4,6-tetra-O-methyl-D-glucose than is produced by amylose under these conditions, together with an equimolar amount of 2,3-di-O-methyl-D-glucose. These results are in agreement with the assignment of a (1 → 4)-linked glucan structure with branch points ($I \to 6$)-linked. The tetramethyl ether residues would arise from the non-reducing ends, and the dimethyl ether residues would come from the branch points. Independent confirmation of the existence of branch points is desirable since small quantities of 2,3-di-*O*-methyl-D-glucose could conceivably arise from an incompletely methylated polysaccharide, or by demethylation. Fragmentation analysis affords direct evidence on this point by the isolation of the disaccharide isomaltose (6-*O*-α-D-glucopyranosyl-D-glucose) and the trisaccharide panose (*O*-α-D-glucopyranosyl-($I \to 6$)-*O*-α-D-glucopyranosyl-($I \to 4$)-D-glucose), which clearly arise from α-D-($I \to 6$)-linked branch points.

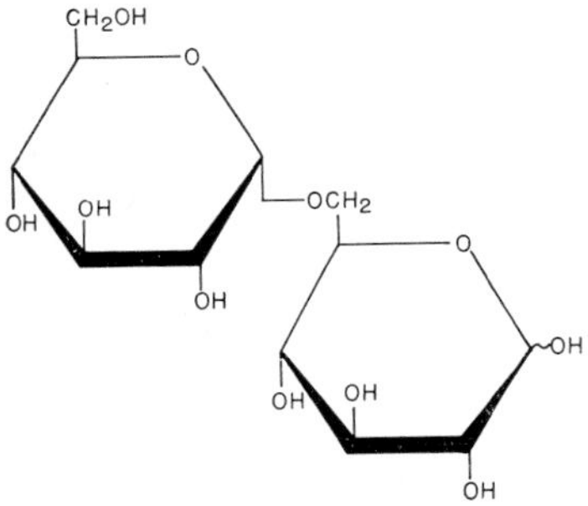

Isomaltose 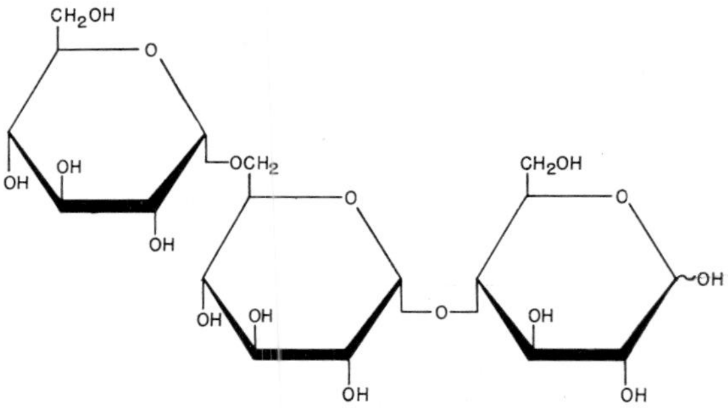   Panose

The proportion of the products found on methylation linkage-analysis indicates that in contrast to amylose, amylopectin has only short α-D-($I \to 4$)-linked chains. Periodate oxidation studies confirm this result, and from the formic acid produced by oxidation of the non-reducing end-groups, it can be shown that a non-reducing end-group occurs once in every 20–25 D-glucose units. The reducing power of amylopectin is very small indeed, and the very high ratio of non-reducing to reducing end-groups indicates that amylopectin is a very large highly branched molecule built up from many short amylose-like chains joined by α-D-($I \to 6$) links to form a ramified structure.

Streaming birefringence measurements indicate that the amylopectin molecule is approximately spherical in shape, and weight average molecular weight measurements (light scattering) indicate a very high molecular weight ranging up to 10^8. Number average values by osmometry range from 10^6 to 10^7.

X-ray crystallographic examination of amylopectin reveals it to be amorphous. The molecule is believed to be a multiply branched bush-like structure with no definite principal chain.

The enzyme β-amylase, which operates exclusively from the non-reducing end of the α-D-(1 → 4)-linked D-glucan chain, degrades the pendant α-D-(1 → 4)-linked chains of amylopectin, until a branch point is reached, when the reaction can go no further. The product is termed a limit dextrin (β-amylase limit dextrin), and is envisaged as a pruned amylopectin molecule.

The limit dextrin contains one end-group for every 10–12 D-glucose residues. A similar limit dextrin is formed when phosphorylase acts on amylopectin in the presence of inorganic phosphate.

A "debranching" enzyme has been isolated [R enzyme (from higher plants), or amylo-(1 → 6)-glucosidase (from rabbit muscle)], which will remove the (1 → 6)-linked "stubs" from the outside of the β-amylolysis limit dextrin molecule. The product is then once more susceptible to β-amylolysis and will give rise to a new limit dextrin with a smaller molecule. The process may be repeated a number of times and may be visualized as the stripping of successive layers from the surface of the three-dimensional amylopectin molecule.

Scission of the amylopectin molecule on both sides of the branch-point can occur with α-amylase, and a mixture of α- and β-amylases degrades amylopectin principally to maltose. The trisaccharide maltotriose [O-α-D-glucopyranosyl-(1 → 4)-O-α-D-glucopyranosyl-(1 → 4)-D-glucose] is also present in the reaction products; the enzymes are apparently unable to split this trisaccharide.

Amylopectin differs from amylose in that its retrogradation from solution is slow. The setting of starch gels (cornstarch puddings) and the staling of bread are, however, due to amylopectin separation. With iodine amylopectin gives a purple to red color, and it may be distinguished from amylose in a potentiometric titration with iodine, since it does not form a complex.

Amylopectin contains a small quantity of covalently linked phosphate as a 6-ester, which cannot be removed without extensive degradation of the polysaccharide. β-Amylolysis does not remove this phosphate, which remains in the limit dextrin. It has been shown that although α-D-(1 → 4) and α-D-(1 → 6) linkages predominate in amylopectin, a very small number of α-D-(1 → 3) links also occur.

(iv) Modified starches (dextrins)

Degradation and modification of starches by the action of heat, acid, enzymes, or oxidizing agents, alone or in combination, produces substances of wide commercial interest as adhesives and as sizing materials.

Heat treatment of starch containing a trace of acid produces *pyrodextrins*, used principally as adhesives. The related British gums are produced at a higher temperature in the absence of acid. These products are manufactured on an empirical basis and vary widely in viscosity, solubility and adhesive power according to small variations in the preparative procedure. During the dextrination process the α-D-$(1 \rightarrow 4)$ links of the linear part of the molecules are broken down and linkages are re-formed in different positions to give a highly branched molecule containing significant amounts of β-D-$(1 \rightarrow 6)$, β-D-$(1 \rightarrow 4)$, and β-D-$(1 \rightarrow 2)$ links in addition to those originally present. Other linkages, and β-D-1,6-anhydro end-groups, may also be present. The resultant dextrins do not form complexes with iodine, and give less maltose than does starch on β-amylase hydrolysis. These observations reflect the increased branching of the molecule.

Oxidative modification of starches with hypochlorite or peroxide yields dextrin-like substances which are used as adhesives. The reaction is complex, some depolymerization takes place, and carboxyl groups are formed.

Degradation of starches with malt diastatic enzymes (which contain α- and β-amylase) depolymerize starch to give "soluble starch". "Thin-boiling starches" are produced by mild acid hydrolysis of starch. D-Glucose is produced commercially by the total acidic hydrolysis of starch.

Derivatives of starch. The esters and ethers of starch do not find the wide field of uses of their cellulose counterparts. Starch nitrate is used as a high explosive. Slight derivatization of starch yields a number of commercially useful products.

(d) Glycogen

The glycogens are food reserve polysaccharides found throughout the animal kingdom, in vertebrates, invertebrates, and also in some bacteria and yeasts. All animal cells appear to contain some glycogen, but the polysaccharide is particularly concentrated in liver tissue. Muscle tissue is also rich in glycogen. Glycogen closely resembles amylopectin in chemical structure; it is a multiply branched α-D-$(1 \rightarrow 4)$-linked glucan with α-D-$(1 \rightarrow 6)$ links at the branch points. It can be extracted from glycogen-rich tissue, for example liver, by dissolution of the tissue in hot 30% potassium hydroxide and precipitation of the glycogen by the addition of ethanol. This frequently used procedure, however, undoubtedly causes degradation of the short reducing chain. Extraction of the tissue with hot water, dilute trichloroacetic acid, chloral hydrate, or dimethyl sulfoxide are more satisfactory procedures, and cause little degradation of the polysaccharide. Purified glycogen resembles amylopectin; it is amorphous, strongly dextrorotatory and it forms an opalescent, negligibly reducing solution in water. It can be quantitatively hydrolyzed to D-glucose. Small differences are observed between glycogens from different biological sources, and it has been reported that many glycogen samples are polydisperse and can be resolved by electrophoresis.

Glycogen differs only slightly from amylopectin, and studies such as methylation, hydrolysis, and periodate oxidation yield closely similar results for the two polysaccharides. These do establish, however, that there are fewer D-glucose residues per non-reducing end-group (12–18 according to the source) than in amylopectin, which indicates that glycogen is more highly branched than amylopectin. The behavior of glycogen with β-amylase lends support to the view that the α-D-(1 → 4)-linked chains on the outside of the molecule are shorter than those in amylopectin, since the enzyme degrades glycogen to maltose in 45% yield (β-amylolysis limit of 45%) whereas the β-amylolysis limit for amylopectin is about 55%. The resulting limit dextrin has only 5.5 D-glucose residues for each non-reducing end-group, and the adjacent branch points in the interior of the molecule are only separated by 3–4 D-glucose residues. The exterior chains in the original glycogen molecule are generally about twice this length.

Glycogen resembles amylopectin in giving a limit dextrin (φ-dextrin) when treated with pure phosphorylase and inorganic phosphate. If "de-branching" enzymes are present, complete degradation to α-D-glucopyranose 1-phosphate takes place. The "debranching" enzymes have no effect on the intact glycogen molecule, and act only when the exterior chains have been shortened to one or two units in length.

Molecular weight measurements on glycogens are complicated by the fact that samples often contain components which are readily water-soluble, together with fractions which are almost insoluble in water. These may be separated by sedimentation or electrophoretic methods. Weight average values for the soluble fractions are of the order of $5 \cdot 10^6$, while water-insoluble glycogens have molecular weights up to $15 \cdot 10^6$. The molecules do not have the kinetic behavior expected from spherical particles, and are believed to be flat ellipsoids in shape.

With iodine, glycogen stains a red-brown color; the exterior chains of the molecule are too short to form a stable complex.

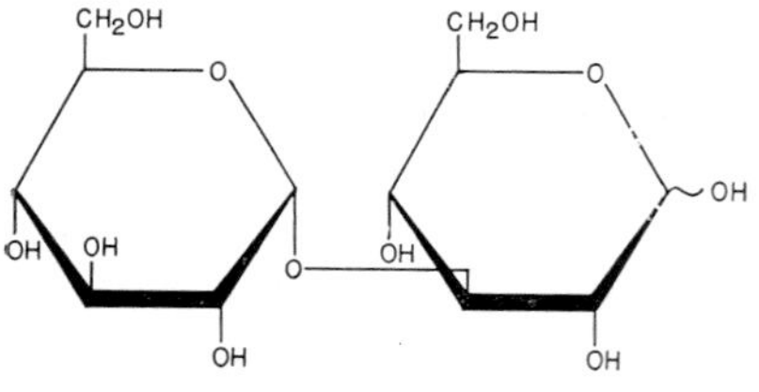

Nigerose 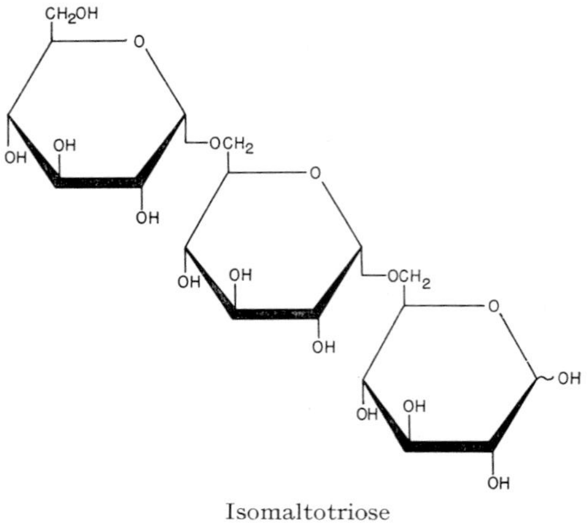   Isomaltotriose

There is evidence that some "anomalous" linkages are present in glycogen, since on fragmentation analysis the polysaccharide yields, in addition to the oligosaccharides maltose, isomaltose, maltotriose, and panose which would be expected on the basis of the accepted structure, small quantities of *nigerose* and *isomaltotriose*. The presence of nigerose (3-*O*-α-D-glucopyranosyl-D-glucose) is indicative of some α-D-(1 → 3) links, while the isolation of iso-maltotriose [*O*-α-D-glucopyranosyl-(1 → 6)-*O*-α-D-glucopyranosyl-(1 → 6)-D-glucose] shows that some cumulative α-D-(1 → 6) links are present.

(e) Other glucans

(i) Laminaran

The reserve polysaccharide of the *Laminaria* genus of brown seaweeds, laminaran, yields 2,4,6-tri-*O*-methyl-D-glucose on methylation and hydrolysis. Graded hydrolysis yields the β-D-(1 → 3)-linked glucose disaccharide *laminaribiose*. From these results and the study of other fragmentation

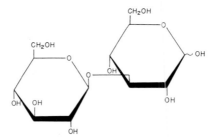

Laminaribiose

products it is believed that laminaran contains linear β-D-(1 → 3)-linked chains of D-glucose units with occasional β-D-(1 → 6) links, possibly forming branch points. Some, if not all chains are terminated by D-mannitol residues.

(ii) Lichenan and isolichenan

The lichen *Cetraria islandica* (Iceland moss) contains the structural polysaccharide lichenan, which is insoluble in cold water, and the related water-soluble polysaccharide isolichenan. Periodate oxidation and methylation studies indicate that lichenan is a linear glucan containing both β-D-(1 → 3) and β-D-(1 → 4) linkages in a ratio approximately 2:5, while isolichenan is similarly constituted but with the linkages in the ratio 3:2. Isolichenan has a $\overline{DP}$ of 42–44.

(iii) Floridean starch

Floridean starch occurs in many red algae (*Rhodophyta*), *Dilsea edulis* for

Bibliography p. 231

example. It contains α-D-$(1 \rightarrow 4)$ and α-D-$(1 \rightarrow 6)$ links together with a significant amount of the α-D-$(1 \rightarrow 3)$ variety. It gives a brown or violet color with iodine, but differs markedly from amylopectin and glycogen in its physical properties and in certain biological tests.

Other glucans have been described. The *crown gall polysaccharide*, produced by the organism *Phytomonas tumefaciens* is believed to be a $(1 \rightarrow 2)$-linked glucan. *Barley glucan* is a linear glucan with equal numbers of β-D-$(1 \rightarrow 4)$ and β-D-$(1 \rightarrow 3)$ links; it resembles the plant gums in properties. *Baker's yeast* glucan contains β-D-$(1 \rightarrow 3)$- and β-D-$(1 \rightarrow 6)$-linked units in a linear polymer. *Pachyman* from the tree root fungus *Poria cocos* Wolf, is a β-D-$(1 \rightarrow 3)$-linked glucan. The lichen *Umbilicaria pustulata* produces the β-D-$(1 \rightarrow 6)$-linked glucan *pustulan*. Many bacteria produce glucans (see Section d, p. 246).

Glucans have been produced synthetically by "reversion" techniques. The hydrogen-ion catalyzed polymerization of D-glucose yields highly branched glucans containing $(1 \rightarrow 6)$ and some $(1 \rightarrow 4)$ links, with the α-D configuration predominating when the reaction takes place at low temperatures.

(f) Mannans

The presence of mannans in the crude cellulose of softwoods has frequently been reported but it is probable that in most of these instances the polysaccharide involved is a glucomannoglycan (see p. 225). A true mannan (ivory nut mannan) forms about 60% of the endosperm of the seed of the tagua palm (*Phytelephas macrocarpa*) and its X-ray diffraction pattern resembles that of cellulose. The D-mannose units are mainly β-D-$(1 \rightarrow 4)$-linked in a linear molecule. Similar mannans are found in the tubers of some *Orchidaceae* species (salep mannan) and in the green coffee bean.

The red seaweed *Porphyra umbilicalis*, which is widely used as a food, contains a predominantly β-D-$(1 \rightarrow 4)$-linked mannan along with other polysaccharides (sulfated galactans). The mannan appears to have a branched chain structure with one branch point for every 12 D-mannose residues.

Yeast cells contain, in addition to glucans, a highly branched mannan (yeast gum) which contains $(1 \rightarrow 2)$, $(1 \rightarrow 3)$, and $(1 \rightarrow 6)$ linkages, predominantly of the α-D-configuration.

(g) Galactans

Galactans are found in association with galacturonans and arabinans in the pectic substances, which occur without exception in all the higher plants. These gelling factors occur in the cell walls, in the cell itself, and in the intercellular layers where they appear to promote cell adhesion. Citrus fruit rind is a particularly rich source of pectic substances, and they are extracted commercially from this source for use in the gelation of fruit juices for jellies, jams, and the like. Separation of the galactan from the two accompanying polysaccharides is difficult, but the seeds of *Lupinus albus* offer a rich source of galactan, since the pectin present has an unusually high galactan content. Structural studies indicate that the galactan has a linear β-D-$(1 \to 4)$-linked molecule with a $\overline{DP}$ of about 120. A similar galactan has been isolated from the seeds of *Strychnos nux-vomica*.

The gel-forming cell wall polysaccharide *agar* from the seaweed *Gelidium amansii* and other red algae (phylum *Rhodophyta*) is likewise a galactan, in this case containing sulfate half-ester groups. Agar is used as a food ingredient in the Orient, and elsewhere it is extensively used as a laboratory culture medium for microorganisms. It is used in the bakery and confectionery industry as a gelling agent for icing and candies, and in dental work for impression molds. Agar contains residues of both D- and L-galactose, the latter as the 3,6-anhydro derivative. Acetylated agar can be resolved into two fractions. One (agarose) has been shown by methylation, mercaptolysis, and fragmentation studies to have a linear structure with the two components alternating along the chain. The D-galactopyranose residues are β-D-$(1 \to 4)$-linked to the 3,6-anhydro-L-galactopyranose residues, which are in turn α-L-$(1 \to 3)$-linked to the D-galactopyranose residues. Some of the D-galactose units may be sulfated at C-6. The second fraction of agar (agaropectin) contains most of the sulfate residues of the original polysaccharide. It contains O-β-D-galactopyranosyl-$(1 \to 4)$-3,6-anhydro-L-galactose units, but its full structure is not yet known. The occurrence of both D- and L-galactose in the same molecule is noteworthy and it is of interest that end-group interchange in the galactose unit will result in enantiomorphism.

Another sulfated galactan, *carrageenan*, can be extracted with hot water from the red seaweed, Irish moss (*Chondrus crispus* and *Gigartina stellata*). By virtue of its ability to form a reversible gel with water, carrageenan finds many similar uses to agar, and is extracted commercially for use as a stabilizer and homogenizer (protective colloid) in chocolate milk, ice cream, other foodstuffs, toothpaste, and pharmaceutical products. The commercially extracted polysaccharide contains several components, the two main ones being termed $\varkappa$-carrageenan and λ-carrageenan. $\varkappa$-Carrageenan contains D-galactopyranose 4-sulfate and 3,6-anhydro-D-galactopyranose residues, believed to be linked in a linear chain with alternating α-D-$(1 \to 3)$ and β-D-$(1 \to 4)$ linkages similar to those found in agarose. Some of the D-galactose 4-sulfate residues are probably substituted at C-6 with D-galactose 3,4-disulfate residues. Some workers consider that $\varkappa$-carrageenan contains two α-D-$(1 \to 3)$-linked D-galactopyranose 4-sulfate units alternating with single 3,6-anhydro-D-galactopyranose units.

Bibliography p. 231

λ-Carrageenan is a linear galactan containing only D-galactopyranose 4-sulfate residues, and is predominantly α-D-(1 → 3)-linked.

Carrageenans have been shown by sedimentation, osmotic pressure, viscosity, and light-scattering methods to have molecular weights in the range $1.2 \cdot 10^5$ to $1.7 \cdot 10^6$. Many other red algae, for instance *Furcellaria fastigata, Hypnea musciformis*, and *Iridaea* species produce galactans which resemble *Chondrus* carrageenan and are utilized commercially. The galactan from *F. fastigata* is known as Danish agar or furcellaran.

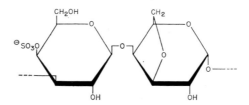

Repeating unit of ϰ-carrageenan molecule

Galactans of animal origin are rare. The snail *Helix pomatia* and a few other cold-blooded animals produce a highly branched levorotatory galactan containing D-galactose and a lesser amount of L-galactose. Methylation studies indicate that (1 → 3) and (1 → 6) links are present, probably as a dichotomously branched structure. A water-soluble dextrorotatory galactan has been extracted from beef lung. It likewise contains (1 → 3) and (1 → 6) links but contains no L-galactose.

Fucan. Several of the brown seaweeds *Phaeophyta* contain the highly sulfated polysaccharide fucan (fucoidin), which is built up of L-fucose (6-deoxy-L-galactose) residues with sulfate half-ester groups (calcium salt). The polysaccharide contains predominantly α-L-(1 → 2) linkages, together with some α-L-(1 → 3) and α-L-(1 → 4) linkages.

The 2-*O*-methyl ether of L-fucose is a structural unit in plum leaf polysaccharides.

(h) Fructans

Polysaccharides containing D-fructose as the structural unit occur as reserve carbohydrates in the higher plants, particularly in the *Compositae* and *Graminae* families, and are termed *fructans*. Fructose polysaccharides elaborated by microorganisms are termed *levans* and are discussed in section d of this chapter (p. 246). Two main types of fructans are distinguishable, the *inulin* group, which are (2 → 1) glycosidically linked, and the *phlean* group, which have (2 → 6) links. D-Fructose is in the furanose form in both groups.

Inulin, the best known fructan, forms the major reserve polysaccharide in tubers of many *Compositae*, for example dahlia (*Dahlia rosea*), dandelion (*Taraxacum officinale*), Jerusalem artichoke (*Helianthus tuberosus*), and chicory (*Chicorium intybus*), from which sources it may be obtained by hot water extraction and crystallization. In common with all furanosides, inulin undergoes rapid hydrolysis with dilute acid. Methylation and periodic acid oxidation studies indicate that the molecule is a chain of β-D-$(2 \rightarrow 1)$-linked fructofuranose residues.

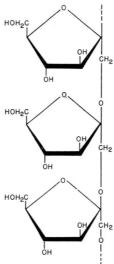

Section of inulin molecule

The presence of a small amount of D-glucose in inulin hydrolyzates suggests that the complete molecule is a chain of about 35 D-fructofuranose residues terminated at the reducing end by a D-glucose unit in a sucrose-type linkage.

Other fructans in the inulin group include *asparagosan, asphodelan, graminan, irisan, sinistran, tritican,* and *kritesan*. These fructans are in most cases very difficult to purify, but appear to resemble inulin in structure.

The $(2 \rightarrow 6)$-linked fructans of the phlean group, found in the *Gramineae*, include *phlean, poan, secalan,* and *pyrosan*. These are likewise difficult to purify, and their detailed structures are not yet known.

(k) Pentoglycans

(i) *Xylan*

Polysaccharides containing D-xylose residues are present in the cell walls of practically all land plants, and are particularly abundant in plant tissues which have undergone secondary thickening (Fig. 1, p. 205). Crude hemi-

Bibliography p. 231

cellulose extracts may be treated with lime water to precipitate pectic substances, and acidification (acetic acid) of the remaining solution causes precipitation of neutral D-xylose-containing polysaccharides (hemicellulose A); the filtrate then contains acidic D-xylose-containing polysaccharides (acidic hemicelluloses, hemicellulose B). Hardwoods are particularly rich in the hemicellulose B fraction, while cereal residues (husks, stalks, cobs, and the like) contain hemicellulose A as the main component of the hemicellulose extract. Both hemicellulose A and hemicellulose B have been shown to have a linear β-D-(1 → 4)-linked xylan as the basic structure, but the chain may be more or less extensively substituted with L-arabinofuranose or 4-O-methyl-D-glucuronic acid residues; the acidic hemicelluloses are rich in the latter component. The two hemicellulose fractions are thus strictly termed hetero-glycans, and are discussed further under the headings Arabinoxyloglycans (p. 226) and Acidic Hemicelluloses (p. 230).

True xylans are relatively rare. The xylan from esparto grass gives only D-xylose on hydrolysis, and it has been shown to be a chain of β-D-(1 → 4)-linked D-xylopyranose units. It has a $\overline{DP}$ of about 75 and has a single (1 → 3)-linked branch point. The xylan backbone resembles cellulose in structure. Chemically combined D-glucuronic acid is the biochemical precursor of the D-xylose units forming the xylan.

True xylans have been found in algae. The xylan from the red seaweed *Rhodymenia palmata* contains 80% of β-D-(1 → 4) links and 20% of β-D-(1 → 3) links, while the green seaweed *Caulerpa filiformis* contains a xylan with only β-D-(1 → 3) links.

Xylans hydrolyze readily, and xylan-containing residues are treated with hot hydrochloric acid on an industrial scale to produce 2-furfuraldehyde in high yield.

(ii) Arabinan

D-Arabinan is the only pentoglycan other than D-xylan found in nature, and it is widely distributed as one of the three components of the pectic substances. Separation of arabinan from accompanying galactan is difficult. The pectin from peanuts (*Arachis hypogea*) is low in galactan and is a con-venient source of pure arabinan. On hydrolysis it yields L-arabinose as the sole product. Structural studies indicate that the backbone of the molecule is a chain of α-L-(1 → 5)-linked L-arabinofuranose residues, with single L-arabinofu-ranose residues α-L-(1 → 3)-linked to every second unit on the main chain.

5. Heteropolysaccharides

A great diversity of polysaccharides which contain more than one mono-saccharide type in their molecule are known. In this section, consideration will be limited to polysaccharides containing neutral sugars, and to polysaccharides containing neutral sugars and uronic acids. Such polysaccharides appear to be found exclusively in the plant kingdom.

(a) Heteropolysaccharides containing neutral sugars only

Relatively few polysaccharides of this type have been described until recently, but the last few years have seen the isolation of an increasing number of such substances, particularly from woods, grasses, and cereals. Many "xylans" are correctly termed arabinoxyloglycans and are discussed below. It is probable that some polysaccharides at present believed to be heteropolysaccharides, may be resolvable into homopolysaccharide components. The isolation by fragmentation analysis of an oligosaccharide containing more than one monosaccharide species is considered diagnostic of a true heteropolysaccharide, provided the conditions of isolation preclude reversion.

(i) Glucomannoglycans

A number of polysaccharides which yield D-glucose and D-mannose on hydrolysis have been described. The flour extracted from the corms of *Amorphophallus konjak*, which is used as a food in the Far East, contains a glucomannoglycan(2:3), *konjakmannan*. The molecule has a $(1 \rightarrow 4)$-linked main chain, with branches linked $(1 \rightarrow 3)$, and has 10–11 residues per terminal unit. Glucomannoglycans have been found in other *Amorphophallus* species, and in the seeds of some *Iris* species.

Hemicelluloses from many woods, particularly conifers (softwoods) contain glucomannoglycans which may be isolated by fractionation procedures. The glucomannoglycan from western red cedar (*Thuja plicata* Donn) is a typical example. It contains D-glucose and D-mannose only, in the ratio 2:5, and is a short-chain, essentially linear, β-D-$(1 \rightarrow 4)$-linked polymer. Similar glucomannoglycans have been isolated from western hemlock (*Tsuga heterophylla*), sitka spruce (*Picea sitchensis*) and other softwoods. Glucomannoglycans from Norwegian spruce (*Picea abies*) are α-D-$(1 \rightarrow 4)$-linked.

(ii) Galactomannoglycans

The endosperms of the seeds of *Leguminosae* species are frequently rich in galactomannoglycans, mucilaginous branched-chain polysaccharides which function as food reserves. The galactomannoglycans of guar (*Cyamopsis tetragonolobus*) seeds and carob tree (*Ceratonia siliqua*) seeds are extracted commercially for use as textile sizes, in paper manufacture, and as food thickeners.

Guaran, the galactomannoglycan(1:2) from guar seeds is believed to be a linear β-D-$(1 \rightarrow 4)$-linked mannan with single D-galactopyranose units

Bibliography p. 231

α-D-($1 \to 6$)-linked to every other D-mannose residue. It has a molecular weight (by osmotic pressure) of about $2.2 \cdot 10^5$, and it forms strong films which appear partially crystalline when stretched, which emphasizes the fact that the short-unit side chains in the molecule do not destroy the linear physical characteristics of the backbone.

The galactomannoglycan from carob (locust) beans resembles guaran in structure, but has fewer D-galactose unit side chains. A similar polysaccharide can be extracted from the endosperm of tara (*Caesalpina spinosa*) seed. Galactomannoglycans have been extracted from alfalfa (lucerne, *Medicago sativa*), clover (*Trifolium pratense*), and from fenugreek (*Trigonella foenum-graecum*) seeds.

(iii) Arabinogalactoglycans

In addition to polysaccharides based on a mannan chain (glucomanno-glycans), the hemicellulose fraction of softwoods (*Coniferales*) is rich in D-galactans which have L-arabinose substituent units. Several such arabino-galactoglycans extracted from *Coniferales* hemicelluloses have been studied and have been shown to contain D-galactose and L-arabinose residues in the approximate ratio 6:1. Those from European larch (*Larix decidua*) and white spruce [*Picea glauca* (Moench) Voss] are highly branched, with β-D-($1 \to 3$)-linked D-galactopyranose chains carrying side chains of two β-D-($1 \to 6$)-linked D-galactopyranose residues. Most of the L-arabinose occurs as 3-O-β-L-arabinopyranosyl-L-arabinofuranosyl side chains. Other arabino-galactoglycans from Jack pine (*Pinus banksiana* Lamb), Western larch (*Larix occidentalis*) and Eastern larch (*Larix laricina*) have been described. Arabinogalactoglycans from Douglas fir (*Pseudotsuga taxiflora*) and black spruce (*Picea mariana*) have a $\overline{DP}$ (from osmotic pressure measurements) of about 330.

(iv) Arabinoxyloglycans

The xylan fraction of hemicellulose extracts generally contains some covalently bound L-arabinose. Certain *Gramineae* (cereal) hemicelluloses contain larger quantities of L-arabinose in the xylan fraction. These cereal arabinoxyloglycans all have the same basic structure, a linear β-D-($1 \to 4$)-linked xylan with short or unit L-arabinofuranose side-chains linked through position 2 (sometimes position 3) of the D-xylose residue. The arabinoxylo-glycans from wheat, rye, and barley flours are typical examples. They differ mainly in the degree and mode of substitution of the L-arabinofuranose residues on the xylan chain. Wheat straw, barley husk, and corn (maize) cob arabinoxyloglycans have similar structures. Small amounts of D-glucuronic acid and D-galactose residues are sometimes present in the cereal fiber arabinoxyloglycans.

(v) *Others*

Some heteropolysaccharides, not containing uronic acid residues, but containing three or more monosaccharide components, have been described, and their compositions are summarized in Table III. Most form aqueous solutions of a gummy or mucilaginous nature, and some are used commercially as hydrocolloids.

TABLE III

COMPOSITION OF POLYSACCHARIDES CONTAINING THREE
OR MORE NEUTRAL SUGARS

Name	Source	Composition, %				
		D-Glucose	D-Galactose	D-Mannose	L-Arabinose	D-Xylose
Iris polysaccharide	*Iris sibirica*	48	3	48		
Rye flour arabinoxylo-glycan	*Secale cereale*	5			29	60
Salai tree poly-saccharide	*Boswellia serrata*		+		+	+
Tamarind seed poly-saccharide	*Tamarindus indica* L.	53	17		30	

(b) *Heteropolysaccharides containing uronic acids*

The polysaccharides which contain both neutral sugars and uronic acids present to the investigator one of the most complex fields in carbohydrate chemistry. The countless permutations of principal chains, side chains, linkages, and structural units reach their greatest diversity in this field, and available knowledge of the whole subject is necessarily very incomplete. Most of the polysaccharides in this section are found as principal constituents in the plant gums, and the most thorough investigations have naturally been made on those materials which are of commercial importance. The uronic acid-containing fractions from hemicellulose are in many cases true heteropolysaccharides, and are also discussed in this section.

Many plant species produce water-soluble gums (hydrocolloids) which contain polysaccharides of highly individual structure, and generalizations concerning their constitution cannot easily be made. A few plant gums do not contain uronic acids, and have been listed in Table III. The uronic acid-containing gums most commonly contain D-glucuronic acid; a lesser number have been found to contain D-galacturonic acid as the acidic component.

Plant gums are solid exudates produced by some trees, notably of the family *Leguminosae* in response to some physical injury to the bark of the tree. *Gum arabic*, produced by *Acacia senegal*, and *gum tragacanth*, from *Astragalus* species, are important commercially, as adhesives, and for other

Bibliography p. 231

purposes. The resinous plant exudates which dissolve in organic solvents do not contain polysaccharides and will not be considered here.

(i) Gum arabic

Gum arabic of commerce comes mainly from North Africa (Sudan and Senegal), and is partially soluble in cold water to form a viscous, adhesive solution. In addition to its use as an adhesive it is used as a protective colloid and thickening agent in foodstuffs, medicines, inks, and water colors. The natural gum is almost neutral and is the salt of the acidic polysaccharide *arabic acid* with calcium, magnesium, and potassium ions. The molecular weight of sodium arabate as determined by osmotic pressure, ultracentrifugation, or diffusion methods, is about $2.5 \cdot 10^5$. Light-scattering and viscosity methods give higher values (about 10^6). Total hydrolysis of arabic acid yields L-arabinose, L-rhamnose, D-galactose, and D-glucuronic acid in the approximate proportions $3:1:3:1$. The probable structure for the repeating unit of arabic acid was deduced as a result of much detailed experimental work involving selective hydrolysis of furanoside residues, isolation and identification of aldobiouronic acids, methylation, and other methods. The proposed structure for the repeating unit is given in Fig. 4.

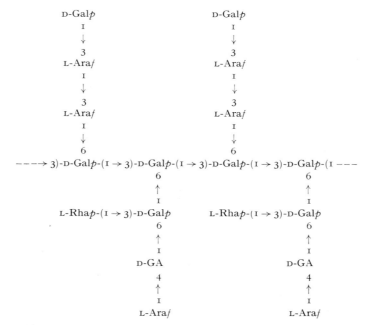

Fig. 4. Proposed structure for the repeating unit of gum arabic.

TABLE IV

COMPOSITION OF GUMS AND MUCILAGES CONTAINING URONIC ACIDS

Gum	Source	D-Glucuronic acid	D-Galacturonic acid	D-Galactose	D-Mannose	L-Arabinose	D-Xylose	L-Rhamnose	Others (%)
					Composition, %				
Arabic	Acacia senegal	16		52		19		12	D-Glucose, (40) D-fructose (10)
Asparagus	Asparagus filicinus	5			45				
Black wattle	Acacia mollissima Willd	9		42		42		7	
Cherry	Prunus virginiana L.	9		26	13	29		23	
Cholla	Opuntia fulgida		8	25		50	16	trace	
Corn hull	Zea mays	7–12		7		35	48		
Damson	Prunus insitia	16		30	15	38	trace		
Egg plum	Prunus domestica	15		40		34	11		
Flax seed	Linum usitatissimum		+						L-Galactose (8)
Ghatti	Anogeissus latifolia Wall	12		27	8	9	25	13	3-O-Methylpentose (trace)
Grapefruit	Citrus maxima	31		53		41			
Iles mannan	Amorphophallus oncophyllus	4		41		16			D-Glucose (49), pentoses (2)
Karaya	Sterculia urens		36	33				32	
Karroo	Acacia karroo Hayne	12		50		36		2	
Lemon	Citrus limonia	22		55		22			4-O-Methyl-D-glucuronic acid, 6-deoxyhexose (traces)
Mesquite	Prosopis juliflora D.C.	18[a]		31		51			
Myrrh	Commiphora myrrha	38[a]		50		12			
Okra	Bamia fellahi		6	80		3		10	
Peach	Prunus persica	7		36		43	14	trace	
Plantago seed	Plantago ovata Forsk		+	+		+	+	+	
Sapote	Sapota achras	16							
Slippery elm	Ulmus fulva		33	+		30	54	33	3-O-Methyl-D-galactose, D-glucose, L-fucose (traces)
Tororo-aoi	Abelmoschus manihot		++	+		++	++	+	
Tragacanth	Astragalus species		++	+		++	++	+	L-Fucose

[a] 4-O-Methyl ether.

Another *Acacia* gum, *black wattle gum*, has been shown to contain the same four components as gum arabic, in the proportions 6:1:5:1.

(*ii*) *Gum tragacanth*

Tragacanth is collected in a similar manner to gum arabic from trees of the genus *Astragalus*, principally in the Near Eastern countries. It resembles gum arabic in its physical properties and finds similar uses. The gum is heterogeneous, containing a water-soluble fraction (tragacanthin) and a water-insoluble fraction (bassorin). The crude gum contains L-arabinose, D-xylose, L-fucose, D-galactose, and D-galacturonic acid but its detailed structure is not known.

(*iii*) *Mesquite gum*

Mesquite gum, the exudate of *Prosopis piliflora* D.C. is of little commercial importance, but structural studies have been made which suggest that it has a (1 → 3)-linked main chain of D-galactopyranose residues, with 6-linked side chains. These may be short (1 → 3)-linked chains of L-arabinofuranose residues, or similar chains attached through D-galactose or 4-O-methyl-D-glucuronic acid residues.

(*iv*) *Other plant gums and mucilages*

Some of the major results of studies made on other plant gums and mucilages are summarized in Table IV.

(*v*) *Acidic hemicelluloses*

Uronic acid-containing xylans (hemicellulose B, glucuronoxyloglycans) may be isolated from hemicellulose extracts after removal of the neutral polysaccharides (hemicellulose A, see p. 224), by the addition of alcohol to the acidified solution. Xylans containing the highest proportion of uronic acid are found in wood hemicelluloses, particularly hardwoods; hemicelluloses from cereal sources yield predominantly arabinoxyloglycans. Glucuronoxyloglycans from beech, oak, elm, maple, pine, larch, spruce, hemlock, birch, and aspen have all been shown to have the same general structure, a β-D-(1 → 4)-linked D-xylopyranose backbone with 4-O-methyl-D-glucuronic acid units linked α-D-(1 → 2) to the D-xylose residues as side chains. Small numbers of (1 → 3)-linked L-arabinofuranose side chains may also be present. In most cases the xylan backbone has been shown to be linear, with a $\overline{DP}$ of about 100. The vigorous conditions used in the isolation of most of these polysaccharides may, however, cause some degradation.

BIBLIOGRAPHY

[1] G. O. ASPINAL, Structural Chemistry of the Hemicelluloses, *Advances in Carbohydrate Chem.*, 14 (1959) 429.

[2] D. J. BELL, *Introduction to Carbohydrate Biochemistry*, 3rd ed., University Tutorial Press, London, 1952.

[3] J. M. BOBBITT, Periodate Oxidation of Carbohydrates, *Advances in Carbohydrate Chem.*, 11 (1956) 1.

[4] J. BONNER, *Plant Biochemistry*, Academic Press, New York, 1950.

[5] H. O. BOUVENG AND B. LINDBERG, Structural Polysaccharide Chemistry, *Advances in Carbohydrate Chem.*, 15 (1960) 53.

[6] W. BROCK NEELY, Infrared Spectra of Carbohydrates, *Advances in Carbohydrate Chem.*, 12 (1957) 13.

[7] G. V. CAESAR, Starch Nitrate, *Advances in Carbohydrate Chem.*, 13 (1958) 331.

[8] M. L. CALDWELL AND M. ADAMS, Action of Certain Alpha Amylases, *Advances in Carbohydrate Chem.*, 5 (1950) 229.

[9] J. COMPTON, The Molecular Constitution of Cellulose, *Advances in Carbohydrate Chem.*, 3 (1948) 185.

[10] G. F. D'ALELIO, *Fundamental Principles of Polymerization*, John Wiley & Sons, New York, 1952.

[11] P. J. FLORY, *Principles of Polymer Chemistry*, Cornell University Press, Ithaca, N.Y., 1953.

[12] A. B. FOSTER, Zone Electrophoresis of Carbohydrates, *Advances in Carbohydrate Chem.*, 12 (1957) 81.

[13] A. B. FOSTER AND J. M. WEBBER, Chitin, *Advances in Carbohydrate Chem.*, 15 (1960) 371.

[14] D. FRENCH, The Schardinger Dextrins, *Advances in Carbohydrate Chem.*, 12 (1957) 189.

[15] C. T. GREENWOOD, Aspects of the Physical Chemistry of Starch, *Advances in Carbohydrate Chem.*, 11 (1956) 335.

[16] P. H. HERMANS, *Physics and Chemistry of Cellulose Fibres*, Elsevier, Amsterdam, 1949.

[17] E. HEUSER, *The Chemistry of Cellulose*, John Wiley & Sons, New York, 1944.

[18] O. HOFFMANN–OSTENHOF, *Enzymologie*, Springer, Vienna, 1954.

[19] J. HONEYMAN (Ed.), *Recent Advances in the Chemistry of Cellulose and Starch*, Interscience, New York, 1959.

[19a] J. HONEYMAN, *Ann. Rep. Chem. Soc. (London)*, 57 (1960) 328.

[20] M. L. HUGGINS, *Physical Chemistry of High Polymers*, John Wiley & Sons New York, 1958.

[21] R. W. KERR (Ed.), *Chemistry and Industry of Starch*, Academic Press, New York, 1950.

[22] TH. LIESER, *Kurzes Lehrbuch der Cellulosechemie*, Bornträger, Berlin-Nikolasee, 1953.

[23] D. J. MANNERS, The Molecular Structure of Glycogens, *Advances in Carbohydrate Chem.*, 12 (1957) 261.

[24] R. J. McILROY, *The Chemistry of Polysaccharides*, Longmans, Green & Co., New York, 1948.

[25] K. H. MEYER, *Natural and Synthetic High Polymers*, 2nd ed., Interscience, New York, 1950.

[26] F. MICHEEL, *Chemie der Zucker und Polysaccharide*, parts III, VI and VII, Geist & Portig, Leipzig, 1956.

[27] T. MORI, Seaweed Polysaccharides, *Advances in Carbohydrate Chem.*, 8 (1953) 315.

[28] K. MYRBÄCK, Products of the Enzymic Degradation of Starch and Glycogen, *Advances in Carbohydrate Chem.*, 3 (1948) 251.

[29] R. F. NICKERSON, The Relative Crystallinity of Celluloses, *Advances in Carbohydrate Chem.*, 5 (1950) 103.

[30] E. OTT, H. M. SPURLIN AND M. W. GRAFFLIN (Eds.), *Cellulose and Cellulose Derivatives*, 2nd ed., Interscience, New York, 1954.

[31] W. G. OVEREND, Carbohydrates, *Ann. Rep. Chem. Soc. (London)*, 55 (1958) 315.

[32] W. W. PIGMAN (Ed.), *The Carbohydrates*, Academic Press, New York, 1957.

[33] W. J. POLGLASE, Polysaccharides Associated with Wood Cellulose, *Advances in Carbohydrate Chem.*, 10 (1955) 283.

[34] R. E. REEVES, Cuprammonium Glycoside Complexes, *Advances in Carbohydrate Chem.*, 6 (1951) 107.

[35] J. A. RADLEY, *Starch and Its Derivatives*, 3rd ed., John Wiley & Sons, New York, 1954.

[36] W. RUHLAND, *Encyclopedia of Plant Physiology*, Vol. VI, Springer, Berlin, 1958.

[37] F. SMITH AND R. MONTGOMERY, *The Chemistry of Plant Gums and Mucilages*, Reinhold, New York, 1959.

[38] L. STOLOFF, Polysaccharide Hydrocolloids of Commerce, *Advances in Carbohydrate Chem.*, 13 (1958) 265.

[39] L. STOLOFF, in G. F. SPRINGER (Ed.), *Polysaccharides in Biology*, 4th conf., Josiah Macy Jr. Foundation, 1959; p. 283.

[40] R. L. WHISTLER, Xylan, *Advances in Carbohydrate Chem.*, 5 (1950) 269.

[41] R. L. WHISTLER AND J. N. BeMILLER, Alkaline Degradation of Polysaccharides, *Advances in Carbohydrate Chem.*, 13 (1958) 289.

[42] R. L. WHISTLER AND J. N. BeMILLER (Eds.), *Industrial Gums, Polysaccharides and their Derivatives*, Academic Press, New York, 1959.

[43] R. L. WHISTLER AND C. L. SMART, *Polysaccharide Chemistry*, Academic Press, New York, 1953.

[44] L. E. WISE (Ed.), *Wood Chemistry*, Reinhold, New York, 1944.

[45] M. L. WOLFROM (Ed.), *Carbohydrate Chemistry of Substances of Biological Interest*, IVth International Congress of Biochemistry, Vienna, 1958.

[46] M. L. WOLFROM, in D. E. H. FREAR (Ed.), *Agricultural Chemistry*, Vol. 1, Van Nostrand, New York, 1950.

Chapter VII

Section c

Polyuronides

Z. I. KERTESZ

New York State Agricultural Experiment Station,
Cornell University, Geneva, N.Y. (U.S.A.)

1. Introduction

The uronic acids are aldehydecarbonic acid derivatives of the hexose sugars. When written in the open-chain formula, these hexuronic acids are characterized by the presence of an aldehyde group at C-1 and a carboxyl group at C-6, thus they are both aldehydes and acids. The polyuronides are the corresponding polysaccharides (or polysaccharide derivatives) in which n hexuronic acids are combined according to the principles of glycoside formation with the exclusion of $(n - 1)$ molecules of water to form macromolecules containing many hexuronic acid residues.

Almost half of the known polysaccharides, now numbering nearly 200, contain some uronic acid units[1]. The proportion of these units in the polysaccharide may be small as in the case of some gums and exudates of plants and in various polysaccharides produced by microorganisms. Uronic acid units may account for about one-half of the building units of the polymer as in hyaluronic acid which is composed of equal parts of D-glucuronic acid and N-acetyl-D-glucosamine. Or the uronic acid may be the predominant monomer in the polysaccharide as is D-galacturonic acid in the pectins occurring in plant tissue and D-mannuronic acid in alginic acid isolated from seaweeds. In addition to D-glucuronic acid, D-galacturonic acid, and D-mannuronic acid, some other uronic acids have been found to occur in polysaccharides: the L-iduronic acid in chondroitin sulfate B may be noted as such an example[2].

The term polyuronide implies a macromolecular structure predominantly composed of anhydrouronic acid units. Today, only two groups of compounds fitting this definition are known to exist. Accordingly, the present discussion deals with the polygalacturonide pectins and the polymannuronide alginic acids which are entirely or almost entirely built of anhydrouronic acid residues. Hyaluronic acid and some other polysaccharides containing lower proportions of uronic acid units are discussed elsewhere (see p. 270).

2. The pectic polyuronides (pectins)

(a) Occurrence

The pectic polyuronides occur in all plant tissues[3,4,5]. In some instances they make up as much as one-third of the dry matter in the tissue as in the albedo of citrus fruit, or they may be present in only trace quantities as in woody tissues. Succulent, rapidly growing plant tissues usually contain a higher proportion of pectin than stems and woody tissues. The pectins are universally present in cell walls of higher plants but occur also in the intercellular cementing material (middle lamellae) and in the cell sap. Pectic substances have been also detected in the cell walls of algae[6]. The synthesis of pectic polyuronides in plants appears to occur when the cell nuclei are beginning to divide. The location of pectins in the plant indicates that they are predominantly structural constituents, lending succulent plant tissues heir typical firmness. In more mature tissues this function is taken over

TABLE I

PROPORTION OF PECTIC SUBSTANCES IN SOME PLANTS[*]

Tissue	Total % pectic substances
Apples (flesh)	0.5–1.0
Apple pomace (wet)	1.5–2.5
Lemon peel	2.5–4.0
Orange peel	3.5–5.5
Sugar beet (root) pulp	1.0
Carrot (root)	1.0–3.0
Grapes (fruit)	0.5–1.0
Strawberries (fruit)	0.3–0.6
Tomatoes (fruit)	0.1–0.3
Maple wood[**]	4.4
White pine sapwood[**]	0.3
Lettuce (leaves)	0.4
Water melon (flesh)	0.02

[*] Data from various sources, see ref.[3]. Expressed as % calcium pectate on fresh weight basis. The pectin content of the same plant will vary widely under different conditions, in various phases of growth, maturity, etc.
[**] On dry matter basis.

by cellulose and lignin. It is also assumed that, due to the highly hydro-
philic character of various pectic substances, they might play a role in
the water household of the plant[3].

(b) Definition and nomenclature

Pectin was discovered by Braconnot[7] in 1825, but not until 1917 was the
major building unit of all pectins, D-galacturonic acid, discovered by
Ehrlich[8] and Suarez[9]. The presence of methyl ester groups in pectins was
discovered by Von Fellenberg[10] in 1913. Yet it was only in the early 1930's
that any degree of unanimity could be attained in the classification and
nomenclature of pectic substances. A major factor in this development was
the then increasing and now general acceptance of the macromolecular
concept for pectins[11, 12, 13], a subject discussed below.

Today the terms *pectic substances* or *pectic materials*[14] are used as group
designations for complex colloidal macromolecular polygalacturonic acids
which contain a large proportion of anhydrogalacturonic acid residues
existing in linear chain-like combination. "Pectins" is also used as a broad
generic term for these compounds. The carboxyl groups of the polygalacturonic acids may be esterified to varying degrees by methyl groups and
partly or completely neutralized by one or more bases. Acetyl groups are
present in some pectins, the pectin isolated from sugar-beet residue being
a classical example. Some galactose and arabinose units occur almost invariably in pectin preparations. Certain investigators maintain that this
indicates their occurrence in the linear polyuronide structure typical of
pectins while others believe that they are "ballast materials" from admixed
co-occurring polyoses (galactans and arabans) of sufficiently similar properties to make complete separation difficult. Galactose and arabinose can be
completely removed from pectin preparations only by drastic methods
causing partial degradation of the macromolecule and thus this dilemma is
not resolved in a satisfactory manner. Some additional carbohydrates like
sorbose, rhamnose, and xylose have also been reported to occur at times in
pectins in trace quantities[3].

Protopectin is the water-insoluble "parent" polyuronide of plants from
which all the other pectic materials are assumed to derive. The structure of
protopectin is still uncertain[15]. Its typical insolubility in water has been
ascribed to the association of the polygalacturonic acid units with cellulose,
crosslinking with polyvalent ions, and its being constituted of very large polyuronide molecules. The pectinic acids, which include the commercial pectins,
are water-soluble polygalacturonides usually possessing over 50% of the
carboxyl groups in the form of methyl ester. The typical pectins are capable
of forming gels (jellies) in the presence of over 50% sugar. Low-ester or

TABLE II

RANGES OF COMPOSITION OF (DRY) PURIFIED ISOLATED PECTINS AND
OF "PURE" PECTIC AND PECTINIC ACIDS

Source	% Polyuronide content	% Methoxyl content	% Acetyl content
Hypothetical pure polygalacturonic acid (pectic acid)	100	0	0
Hypothetical pure polygalacturonic acid methyl ester (pectinic acid)	84	16	0
Apple pectins	70–80	6–9	0*
Citrus pectins	75–85	7–10	0*
Beet pectin	60–65	5–7	5–10

* Small proportions of acetyl groups (0.1–1.0%) are often found in the digests of purified apple and citrus pectins. The rest of the preparation in the case of most pectins is made up by 2–8% arabinose, 0.1–6.0 galactose, and a variety of other minor constituents.

low-methoxyl pectins[16] are pectinic acids in which the proportion of ester groups has been intentionally reduced by acid, alkali, or enzyme treatment to below 50%. The low-ester pectins are capable of forming firm gels with traces of polyvalent ions (usually calcium) even in the absence of sugar. The theoretically maximum proportion of methyl ester in a pure polygalacturonic acid is 16.35% (expressed as CH_3O). Allowing for the presence of impurities (or non-uronide constituents), the 50% ester content dividing line is usually taken to be around 7% ester (as CH_3O) in the preparation. The pectic acids are polygalacturonic acids essentially free of methyl ester groups and of sufficiently high (average) molecular weights to be classified as "colloids". The salts of pectic acids are the acid and neutral pectates. Pectic acid and some pectates, as acid calcium pectate, for instance, are almost entirely insoluble even in boiling water.

(c) Structure

The uronic acid units occurring in pectic polyuronides possess a cyclic semi-acetal or oxide "pyranoside" structure in which an oxygen bridge exists between C-1 and C-5. Thus the basic building unit of the pectic substances is α-D-galactopyranosyluronic acid[17, 18]. In the linear skeleton of all pectic substances these units are connected through α-(1 → 4)-glycosidic bonds. Since the aldehyde groups of all but the anhydrogalacturonic acid unit in the end position are engaged in the (1 → 4) intermolecular linkages, the polygalacturonic acids possess only one free aldehyde group, the so-called "reducing end group"[3, 19].

(d) Macromolecular concepts and heterogeneity

For a century the development of pectin chemistry was severely handicapped by the aim of investigators to identify its structure in terms of a constant, relatively small molecular size[20]. It is clear today that any sample of a pectic substance is in reality a mixture of polygalacturonic acids of various

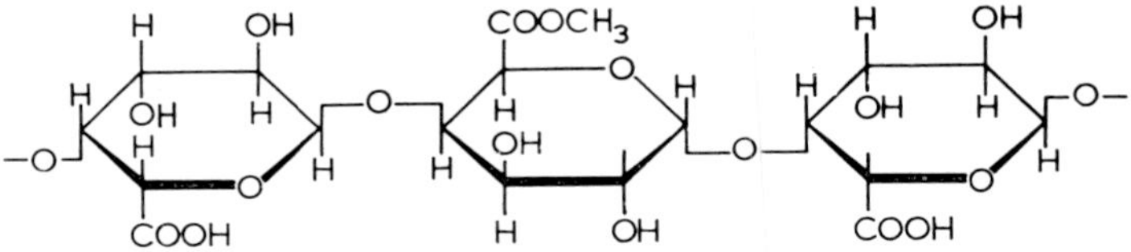

Fig. 1. Part of a pectinic acid macromolecule.

large sizes[11]. The size distribution pattern will depend mostly on the origin of the pectin and the method of preparation. In addition to the occurrence in any sample of polygalacturonic acids of various molecular sizes (of different degrees of polymerization) and the proportionate distribution of these fractions, the individual polygalacturonic acid molecules will also differ in the proportion and distribution of the methyl ester groups. Although this matter is not yet clearly understood, the possibility exists that other factors related to the structure and shape of the molecules further add to the heterogeneity of polygalacturonic acid molecules[3]. On account of these variations it is today practically impossible to obtain two pectin preparations which are identical in all respects and thus will show completely identical properties. The reported (average) molecular weight values for pectinic and pectic acids run from about 10,000 to several hundred thousands but the values obtained for both the weight and number-average molecular weights will depend somewhat on the methods of measurement.

(e) Biogenesis and fate of pectic substances in plant tissues

It has been assumed for some time that the polygalacturonide pectins in plants are derived from the oxidation of polygalactans[21]. Further, it was assumed that the pectic polygalacturonides are eventually decarboxylated to give rise to the polypentosan arabans. This hypothesis received a serious setback when upon critical examination such a transformation became unlikely since galactans appear to possess β-D-galactopyranoside structures whereas pectins contain the alpha form[22]. Further, arabans contain branched α-D-arabofuranoside residues. Thus the transformation would have to proceed through complete hydrolysis and resynthesis. Recently Leloir[23] presented a scheme indicating the possible interconversion of several uridine diphosphate (UDP) sugar compounds, including UDP-L-arabinose, UDP-galacturonic acid, and UDP-galactose. Whether this mechanism will explain the interrelation of arabinose, galactose, and galacturonic acid occurring in pectic substances is not clear today. However, UDP-galacturonic acid has been isolated from *Pneumococcus*[24] and an enzyme occurring in Mung beans (*Phaseolus aureus*) has been shown to be capable of converting UDP-glucuronic acid to UDP-galacturonic acid and UDP pentose[25].

Radioactive carbon supplied in the form of $^{14}CO_2$ is quickly incorporated into the pectins of plants and fruit[26] and [1-^{14}C]glucose and [1-^{14}C]galactose, supplied to boysenberries and strawberries, seem to be equally suitable for incorporation into the pectins[27]. In most instances some randomization of the ^{14}C occurs but the intact hexose carbon skeleton was predominantly preserved. Of course, these tests do not necessarily indicate the actual pathways through which the normal synthesis of pectin occurs in plants. As a matter of fact, we do not know the pathways of pectin formation in plants and today even a method of synthesis of the polymer by a template mechanism cannot be excluded.

We also lack any knowledge of the ultimate fate of pectic substances and galacturonic acid in plant tissues. Little proof exists whether pectic substances may or may not serve as reserve carbohydrates that can be metabolized by the cell. From the fragmentary information on hand, it is not even certain that these polyuronides, once formed, actually disappear from the tissue. The decreasing proportion of pectin in a tissue can be often explained by "dilution" with newly formed constituents and higher proportion of water[3]. Such retention of the pectic polyuronides by the tissue would be in harmony with their known structural function.

(f) Properties and application

Pectins can be isolated from all plant tissues but for commercial purposes apple pomace and citrus peel serve mostly as raw materials[3]. The extraction with hot acid is followed by precipitation of the pectins with ethanol or other means, separation, drying, purification, and standardization. Due to the easy destruction of the useful properties by mishandling during manufacture, the procedure is a difficult one and demands exact scientific control.

Pectinic acids form viscous solutions and show the typical properties of macromolecular polysaccharides. Pectinic acids are susceptible to thermal and oxidative degradation and to the effect of alkali. The latter saponify the methyl ester groups and also affect the polygalacturonic acid structure in some not clearly understood manner.

The pectin of commerce is an off-white colored powder which is soluble in hot water to the extent of 2–3%. Some pectin is also sold in the form of concentrates ("liquid pectin"). The major use for manufactured pectins is in the production of fruit preserves, marmalades, jams, jellies, etc. while smaller quantities are being used by the pharmaceutical trade and for a variety of other purposes. The pectin sold to food manufacturers is standardized with added glucose for its "jelly grade". This value expresses the proportion of sugar which one part of (dry) pectin can turn into a satisfactory jelly under carefully standardized conditions[3].

(g) Methods of analysis[3, 28]

The various groups of pectic substances are usually characterized by their solubility behavior. Polygalacturonides, like other polyuronides, can be quantitatively estimated by the amount of carbon dioxide formed upon heating with hot acid[29]. Pectic substances of all sorts have been commonly determined by the formation and weighing of water-insoluble pectic acid[30] or calcium pectate[31] but unfortunately it is difficult to get these precipitates free from impurities (particularly other polysaccharides) present in the material analyzed. Today, the most common method of estimation is the spectrophotometric measurement of the colored complex formed upon the addition of alcoholic carbazole[32] to the material to be analyzed after alkali treatment and heating with concentrated sulfuric acid[28].

The methyl ester groups in pectinic acids can be estimated by measurement of the amount of alkali required for their saponification[10] or by other classical methods of organic chemistry.

In addition to determining the presence of polyuronide pectins in a sample of unknown composition, usually some information must be obtained on the macromolecular characteristics of the pectin[3]. This is most commonly done by the determination of the intrinsic viscosity values of pectin solutions, measured in the presence of agents depressing charge effects (0.2% sodium chloride) and counteracting the effect on the viscosity of even trace quantities of polyvalent ions present. The latter is usually accomplished by determining the viscosity in solutions containing, in addition to the sodium chloride, a sequesterer like 0.8% polyphosphate (Calgon) or Versene. The isolation, determination, and characterization of pectins is a time-consuming and fairly complicated operation.

(h) Enzymes acting upon pectic substances[33, 34]

Pectins represent complex molecules providing many opportunities for different types of enzyme action. Our understanding of the enzymic hydrolysis of protopectin is so unsatisfactory that a discussion of protopectinase seems unwarranted. The polyuronic skeleton of pectinic acids and pectic acids can be degraded through glycosidic hydrolysis by the various polygalacturonases (formerly designated as pectinases) with the formation of smaller polygalacturonic acid molecules, then oligogalacturonides, and finally D-galacturonic acid. Polygalacturonases occur commonly in nature and practically all classes of microorganisms seem to be able to attack and digest pectins[3]. However, there is some doubt about the occurrence of polygalacturonases in higher plants. Depending on the source of the enzyme preparation, polygalacturonases usually show considerable substrate specificity in attacking pectinic acids or pectic acids, and whether the polygalacturonic acid skeleton is attacked in the random manner or preferentially at the end groups. There are pronounced differences in the size-specificities of polygalacturonases obtained from various sources and additional differences are exhibited with respect to pH optima and other experimental conditions. Thus far no entirely satisfactory system of classification of polygalacturonidases has been presented. Increase in reducing power (free aldehyde groups) and changes in viscosity have been extensively used in studies of polygalacturonases. However, the use of paper chromatography has been the key to the characterization of different polygalacturonases, their preferred substrates, and reaction products[35].

The action of pectinesterase (the pectase of the older literature) results in the liberation of methanol from the ester groups in pectinic acids leading eventually to the formation of ester-free pectic acid (polygalacturonic acid)[10]. Again, the pectinesterases of various origins possess different properties and it is interesting to note that they hydrolyze the ester groups of large pectinic acid molecules with much more facility than D-galacturonic acid methyl ester[36]. Pectinesterase action can be followed by estimation of the amount of methanol formed[37], or by following the changes in ester groups by saponification with alkali[38]. Pectinesterases occur commonly in higher plants as well as in microorganisms.

Pectic enzymes (usually representing a mixture of various enzymes) are manufactured and used on a large scale[3, 33], the major applications being in fruit juice clarification, as an aid in wine manufacture, and in other instances where a partial or complete destruction of the naturally occurring pectic substances is desirable.

3. Alginic acids and alginates (algin)

(a) Occurrence and terminology

The polymannuronide alginates (algin) occur in brown algae, especially in members of the kelp order (*Laminariales*). Algin was discovered in 1883 by Stanford in the viscous fluid contained in the "blisters" of kelp[39]. The original term "algin" was proposed to designate the substance *in situ* in the plant, but it is now loosely applied in a generic manner to designate alginic acid, sodium alginate, soluble alginates, and alginic compounds in general. Since sodium alginate is the most common alginate, the term has been also used interchangeably with sodium alginate[40].

Apparently the alginates have in brown algae a structural function similar to that of the pectins in the higher plants. On the Pacific Coast of North America, the giant kelp *Macrocystis pyrifera* is the sole source of algin manufacture, while on both sides of the Atlantic Ocean *Laminaria digitata*, the horsetail kelp and *L. saccharina*, the broadleaf kelp, are used. Additional varieties serve as starting material in algin manufacture in Great Britain and other countries.

(b) Manufacture and properties

The available seaweed resources have been estimated to run annually into millions of tons[1]. The dry matter in kelp may contain up to 40% alginic acid. The commercial manufacture of algin is based on the principle that the natural algin of kelp, presumably a combination of alginic acid and calcium alginate, can be converted by sodium carbonate solution into the soluble sodium salt. From the extract the alginic acid is precipitated by strong mineral acid, purified and bleached, and usually converted into the sodium salt since this is more stable than alginic acid. In contrast to pectins which are quite resistant to acids, alginates are rapidly decomposed at pH values below 4.

Alginic acid is a white or somewhat off-white powder only slightly soluble in boiling water. The alkali metal salts of alginic acid are water-soluble and form at low concentrations highly viscous solutions. When dried, alginic acid solutions become hard, horny, and resistant to solvents. Alginic acid is a weak acid, and forms many derivatives of unusual and useful properties[40].

Algin and alginic acid are manufactured in many countries and are extensively used in food products. Algin is the most important stabilizer of ice cream in both the United States and in Great Britain and algin and its various derivatives are extensively used in pharmaceutical and cosmetic products, in the paper and textile industries, and for many other purposes.

(c) Structure

Nelson and Cretcher[41] in 1929 showed that D-mannuronic acid is a constituent of alginic acid. It is now generally accepted that alginic acid is a linear polymer of anhydro-β-D-mannuronic acid. The anhydromannuronic acid units most likely possess a pyranose ring structure and the neighboring units are connected through $(1 \to 4)$-glycosidic linkages[42].

References p. 244

Some investigators claim that alginic acid is unique in that D-mannuronic acid units seem to make up its entire structure[1] whereas others believe that the less than theoretical yields of carbon dioxide obtained by the hot acid decarboxylation of alginic acid indicates the presence of a small proportion

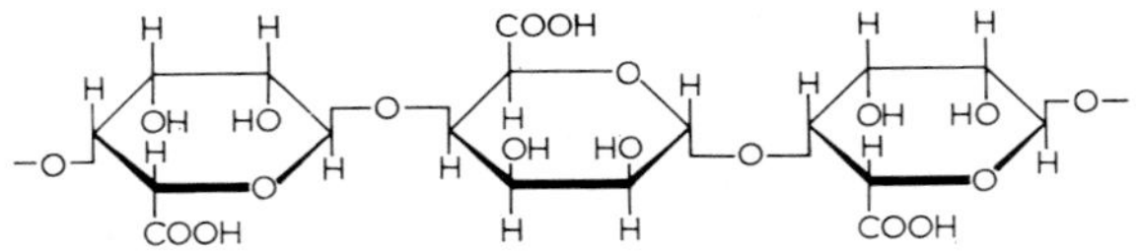

Fig. 2. Part of an alginic acid macromolecule.

(5–8%) of other molecules in the polymer chain[40]. Chandra, Hirst, Percival, and Ross[43] found 6% of a glucose derivative in fully methylated and then hydrolyzed alginic acid. The significance of the presence of the non-uronide carbohydrates is just as unsettled as is the meaning of the presence of non-galacturonide carbohydrates in pectin digests. Molecular weight determinations by various methods indicate that sodium alginate has average molecular weights ranging from 38,000 to 200,000, corresponding to degrees of polymerization in the range of 180 to 930 anhydromannuronic acid units.

It is not known why seaweeds possess polymannuronide alginates in contrast to the polygalacturonide pectins common in all higher plants. The biogenesis of alginic acid is also unknown, and we lack any substantial hypothesis concerning their derivation.

(d) Methods of analysis

Decarboxylation with hot acid and determination of the carbon dioxide formed is one of the important methods used in the determination of polymannuronic acids[29]. Percival and Ross[44] described improvements in the application of the carbazole method to algin. Recently proposed analytical methods include oxidation with cerium sulfate[45], and quantitative thermal decomposition[46] at 255°.

(e) Enzymes acting upon alginates

Much less is known about the enzymes acting upon alginic acid and alginates than about enzymes acting on pectic substances. Waksman and Allen[47] found that many molds that are able to digest pectins will not attack algin. However, it is clear that algin-splitting bacteria occur in sea water and in planktons[48]. Norman and Bartholomew[49] note that pure algin is attacked by many soil organisms and later investigations[50] showed that algin-digesting organisms were more common in soils than in sea water. It is difficult to say today whether this observation reflects the true situation or it is only the consequence of the technique of investigation used. Certainly, just as pectin-digesting microorganisms must be common since we are not overwhelmed by the accumulated residues of plant growth, algin-digesting organisms must occur commonly in the seas since the millions of tons of seaweed produced annually seem to disappear. The fact remains that little is known about the enzymes acting on alginic acid and alginates and such enzymes have not been applied for the elucidation of the structure of these polyuronides as it has been so successfully done with many other polysaccharides.

REFERENCES

[1] R. L. WHISTLER AND CHARLES L. SMART, *Polysaccharide Chemistry*, Academic Press, New York, 1953.

[2] P. HOFFMAN, A. LINKER AND K. MEYER, *Science*, 124 (1956) 1252.

[3] Z. I. KERTESZ, *The Pectic Substances*, Interscience, New York, 1951.

[4] H. DEUEL, J. SOLMS AND H. ALTERMATT, *Vierteljahresschr. naturforsch. Ges. Zürich Beih.*, 98 (1953) 49.

[5] H. J. PHAFF AND M. A. JOSLYN, *Wallerstein Lab. Commun.*, 10 (1947) 133.

[6] H. KYLIN, *Kgl. Fysiograf. Sällskap. i Lund. Förh.*, 16 (1946) 102.

[7] H. BRACONNOT, *Ann. chim. phys., Ser. 2*, 28 (1825) 173.

[8] F. EHRLICH, *Chem. Ztg.*, 41 (1917) 196.

[9] M. L. SUAREZ, *Chem. Ztg.*, 41 (1917) 87.

[10] T. VON FELLENBERG, *Mitt. Lebensm. u. Hyg.*, 4 (1913) 122, 273.

[11] H. MEYER AND H. MARK, *Der Aufbau der hochmolekularen Naturstoffe*, Akad. Verlagsgesellschaft, Leipzig, 1930.

[12] S. MORRELL, L. BAUR AND K. P. LINK, *J. Biol. Chem.*, 105 (1934) 1.

[13] F. A. HENGLEIN in W. RUHLAND (Ed.), *Handbuch der Pflanzenphysiologie*, Vol. 6, Springer, Berlin, 1958, p. 406.

[14] Z. I. KERTESZ, G. L. BAKER, G. H. JOSEPH, H. H. MOTTERN AND A. G. OLSEN, *Chem. Eng. News*, 22 (1944) 105.

[15] F. A. HENGLEIN, *Makromol. Chem.*, 1 (1943) 121.

[16] G. L. BAKER in E. M. MRAK AND G. F. STEWART (Eds.), *Advances in Food Research*, Vol. 1, Academic Press, New York, 1948, p. 395.

[17] P. A. LEVENE AND L. C. KREIDER, *J. Biol. Chem.*, 120 (1937) 591.

[18] G. H. BEAVAN AND J. K. N. JONES, *J. Chem. Soc.*, (1947) 1218.

[19] C. L. HINTON, *Fruit Pectins, Their Chemical Behaviour and Jellying Properties*, Chem. Publishing Co., New York, 1940.

[20] F. EHRLICH AND F. SCHUBERT, *Ber.*, 62 (1929) 1974.

[21] F. EHRLICH, *Cellulosechemie*, 11 (1930) 161.

[22] E. L. HIRST AND J. K. N. JONES in W. W. PIGMAN AND M. L. WOLFROM (Eds.), *Advances in Carbohydrate Chemistry*, Vol. 2, Academic Press, New York, 1946, p. 235.

[23] L. F. LELOIR in G. F. SPRINGER (Ed.), *Polysaccharides in Biology*, Transactions of the third Conference, Josiah Macy Jr. Foundation, New York, 1958.

[24] E. E. B. SMITH, G. T. MILLS AND E. M. HARPER, *Biochim. et Biophys. Acta*, 23 (1957) 662.

[25] D. S. FEINGOLD, E. F. NEUFELD AND W. Z. HASSID, *Science*, 128 (1959) 1144.

[26] L. HOUGH AND J. B. PRIDHAM, *Nature*, 177 (1956) 1039.

[27] C. G. SEEGMILLER, R. JANG AND W. J. MANN, *Arch. Biochem. Biophys.*, 61 (1956) 422.

[28] H. S. OWENS, R. M. MCCREADY, A. D. SHEPHERD, T. H. SCHULTZ, E. L. PIPPEN, H. A. SWENSON, J. C. MIERS, R. F. ERLANDSEN AND W. D. MACLAY, *Methods used at Western Regional Research Laboratory for Extraction and Analysis of Pectic Materials*, AIC-340, U.S. Dept. Agr., 1952.

[29] R. M. MCCREADY, H. A. SWENSON AND W. D. MACLAY, *Ind. Eng. Chem., Anal. Ed.*, 18 (1946) 290.

[30] H. J. WICKMANN, *J. Assoc. Offic. Agr. Chemists*, 7 (1923) 107.

[31] M. H. CARRÉ AND D. HAYNES, *Biochem. J.*, 16 (1922) 60.

[32] Z. DISCHE, *J. Biol. Chem.*, 167 (1947) 189.

[33] A. L. DEMAIN AND H. J. PHAFF, *Wallerstein Lab. Commun.*, 20 (1957) 119.

[34] Z. I. KERTESZ in S. P. COLOWICK AND N. O. KAPLAN (Eds.), *Methods of Enzymology*, Vol. 1, Academic Press, New York, 1955, p. 627.

[35] D. S. PATEL AND H. J. PHAFF, *Food Research*, 25 (1960) 47.

[36] Z. I. KERTESZ, *J. Biol. Chem.*, 121 (1937) 589.

[37] M. HOLDEN, *Biochem. J.*, 40 (1946) 103.

[38] R. J. MCCOLLOCH AND Z. I. KERTESZ, *Arch. Biochem.*, 13 (1947) 217.

[39] E. C. C. STANFORD, *Chem. News*, 47 (1883) 257.

40 C. K. TSENG in R. E. KIRK AND D. F. OTHMER (Eds.), *Encyclopedia of Chemical Technology*, Vol. 1, Interscience, New York, 1947, p. 343; A. B. STEINER AND W. H. McNEELY in *Natural Plant Hydrocolloids (A symposium)*, Am. Chem. Soc., Washington, 1954.

41 W. L. NELSON AND L. H. CRETCHER, *J. Am. Chem. Soc.*, 51 (1929) 1914.

42 E. L. HIRST, J. K. N. JONES AND W. O. JONES, *J. Chem. Soc.*, (1939) 1880.

43 S. K. CHANDRA, E. L. HIRST, E. G. V. PERCIVAL AND A. G. ROSS, *J. Chem. Soc.*, (1952) 1833.

44 E. G. V. PERCIVAL AND A. G. ROSS, *J. Soc. Chem. Ind. (London)*, 67 (1948) 420.

45 A. GADEKE, *Z. anal. Chem.*, 131 (1950) 428.

46 A. S. PERLIN, *Can. J. Chem.*, 30 (1952) 278.

47 S. A. WAKSMAN AND M. C. ALLEN, *J. Am. Chem. Soc.*, 56 (1934) 2701.

48 S. A. WAKSMAN AND L. CAREY, *J. Bacteriol.*, 28 (1934) 213.

49 A. G. NORMAN AND W. V. BARTHOLOMEW, *Soil Sci.*, 56 (1943) 143.

50 J. E. HANSEN AND E. KASS, *Acta Pathol. Microbiol. Scand.*, 23 (1946) 140.

Polysaccharides of Bacteria, Moulds, Yeasts and Protozoa

S. A. BARKER

Chemistry Department, The University, Edgbaston, Birmingham
(Great Britain)

1. Introduction

Polysaccharides produced by micro-organisms range from the most simple homopolysaccharides such as cellulose, starch and dextran which contain only a single monosaccharide repeating unit to the most complex or hetero-polysaccharides which can contain as many as five different monosaccharides. In addition, these polysaccharides can occur as lipopolysaccharide complexes or have attached to them amino acids in peptide linkage. Yet another type is exemplified by luteic acid which is a malonyl ester of a polyglucosan. Since the chemistry of some of the simple polysaccharides is dealt with elsewhere (see Chapter VII b, p. 189) no further mention will be made here other than in Table I, where lists of organisms known to elaborate them have been tabulated together with adequate references. However, some of the homopolysaccharides that are more peculiarly microbial in origin are discussed below. Of the more complex polysaccharides, only hyaluronic acid, which is an important constituent of human and animal tissues, is found outside the world of micro-organisms.

2. Polyglucosans

(a) Crown gall polysaccharide

Crown gall disease, the formation of tumours or galls in plants or trees, is caused by *Agrobacterium tumefaciens*, which is a gram-negative pathogen. When cultured in a sucrose-containing medium it elaborated a polyglucosan[1] which was isolated from the concentrated centrifuged medium by alcohol

TABLE I

OCCURRENCE OF HOMOPOLYSACCHARIDES

Polyglucosans

Cellulose [β-(1 → 4)-polyglucosan]
  Acetobacter xylinum[6], *Acet. pasteurianum*[7], *Acet. rancens*[7], *Acet. kützengianum* (N.C.T.C. 3924)[8], *Acet. acetigenum*[9].
Crown gall polysaccharide [β-(1 → 2)-polyglucosan]
  Agrobacterium tumefaciens[1, 2, 3].
Luteose [β-(1 → 6)-polyglucosan] as its malonyl ester
  Penicillium luteum Zukal[10, 11], *Penicillium islandicum*[12].
Yeast glucan [main polymeric linkage β-(1 → 3)]
  Saccharomyces cerevisiae[13].
Amylose [main polymeric linkage α-(1 → 4)]
  Acetobacter pasteurianum[14], *Acet. mucosum*[15], *T. neoformans*[16].
Starch [main polymeric linkage α-(1 → 4)]
  E. coli[17], *Corynebacterium diphtheriae*[18], *Clostridium butyricum*[19], *Aspergillus niger*[20], *Torulopsis innocua*[21], *T. mucorugosa*[21], *T. liquefaciens*[21], *Polytomella coeca*[22].
Glycogen-amylopectin [main polymeric linkage α-(1 → 4)]
  Neisseria perflava[23], *Pneumococcus*[24] Types I, II and III, *Bacillus megatherium*[25], *Mycobacterium tuberculosis*[26], *Saccharomyces cerevisiae*[27], *Cycloposthium*[28], *Tetrahymena pyriformis*[29].
Dextran [main polymeric linkage α-(1 → 6)]
  Acetobacter capsulatum[30], *Streptococcus bovis*[31], *Strep. viridans*[32], *Strep. viscosum*[32], *Leuconostoc mesenteroides*[33], *Leuconostoc dextranicum*[34], *Betabacterium vermiforme*[35], *Betacoccus arabinosaceous*[36], *Streptobacterium dextranicum*[32].
Nigeran [alternate α-(1 → 3) and α-(1 → 4) linkages]
  Aspergillus niger[37] "152".

Polyfructosans

Levan [main polymeric linkage β-(2 → 6)]
  Pseudomonas fluorescens[38], *Ps. chlororaphis*[38], *Ps. aureofaciens*[38], *Alcaligenes viscosus*[39], *Aerobacter levanicum*[40], *Strep. salivarius*[41], *Bacillus subtilis*[42], *B. mesentericus*[42], *B. megatherium*[43], *B. polymyxa*[44], *B. cereus*[45], *B. pumilus*[45].

Polymannans

Mannan
  Desulfovibrio desulphuricans[46], *Bacillus polymyxa*[47] C3, *Penicillium charlesii* Smith[48], *Saccharomyces cerevisiae*[49], *Saccharomyces rouxii*[50].

Polygalactans

Galactan
  Penicillium charlesii Smith[51], *Aspergillus niger*[52], *Mycoplasma mycoides*[53].

Poly-2-N-acetamido-2-deoxy-glucosan

Chitin
  Aspergillus niger[54], *Neurospora crassa*[55], *Saccharomyces cerevisiae*[56], *Nadsonia fulvescens*[57], *Rhodotorula glutinis*[57], *Sporobolomyces roseus*[57], *Endomycopsis capsularis*[57], *Endomyces decipiens*[57], *Eremascus fertilis*[57], *Coccidioides immitis*[58].

precipitation in yields as high as 3 g/l culture. The polysaccharide $[\alpha]_D^{25}$ —10° (in water) was completely hydrolysed by N HCl at 98° for 1.5 h to yield 93–95% reducing sugar characterised as D-glucose by optical rotation and isolation as D-glucobenzimidazole. Since the rotation increased to +52° during hydrolysis of the polyglucosan, a predominance of β-glucosidic linkages was indicated. The molecular weight (3600 ± 200) of the polysaccharide was relatively low. Acetylation of the polysaccharide gave a triacetate $[\alpha]_D^{25}$ +57.5° (in chloroform).

From a study of the optical activity of the 2-, 3-, 4- and 6-monomethyl derivatives of methyl β-glucopyranoside in water and cuprammonium hydroxide it was concluded[2] that since the behaviour of methyl-2-O-methyl-β-D-glucopyranoside closely resembled that of the crown gall polyglucosan, the latter was presumably composed of glucopyranose units linked chiefly through the 2 position. This was confirmed[3] by methylation of the polysaccharide and isolation of 3,4,6-tri-O-methyl D-glucopyranose from the hydrolysate of the polysaccharide ether. The tri-O-methyl sugar was characterised by oxidation to 3,4,6-tri-O-methyl δ-gluconolactone which, on treatment with phenylhydrazine, gave the phenylhydrazide of 3,4,6-tri-O-methyl-D-gluconic acid. The same tri-O-methyl sugar on direct treatment with phenylhydrazine gave 3,4,6-tri-O-methyl-D-glucosazone identical with that obtained from 3,4,6-tri-O-methyl-D-fructose.

(b) Polysaccharide II

The culture filtrates of human and bovine strains of *Mycobacterium tuberculosis* contain a polysaccharide which has been obtained electrophoretically homogeneous[4]. Although not strictly a homopolysaccharide its relation to the crown gall polyglucosan makes it suitable for inclusion here. This polysaccharide was designated polysaccharide II to distinguish it from another in the medium containing mannose, galactose and arabinose units. Polysaccharide II did not give a red-brown colour with iodine and was therefore not the glycogen detected by previous workers. Moreover, it had high biological specificity and some antigenicity. The polysaccharide showed $[\alpha]_D^{24}$ +165° (water) which on acid hydrolysis fell to +58°. Although the major component of the hydrolysate was glucose (isolated as its diethyl mercaptal pentacetate and anilide) a second unidentified sugar was detected. Polysaccharide II was completely resistant to β-amylase.

More detailed studies[5] showed that the polysaccharide existed as a lipid complex and that after defatting it had $[\alpha]_D$ +183.5° (water) and gave 94.1% reducing sugar after acid hydrolysis. The unidentified sugar was recognised as D-glucosamine by the formation of its N-(2,4-dinitrophenyl) derivative. Methylation of the polysaccharide and subsequent hydrolysis gave one principal component corresponding to 3,4,6-tri-*O*-methyl-D-glucose identified by conversion to its osazone and to 3,4,6-trimethyl-D-gluconophenylhydrazide. The major portion of the polysaccharide II structure therefore consists of D-glucopyranose units linked α-(1 → 2) and arranged in long linear chains having a molecular weight of the order of $4.9 \cdot 10^5$.

(c) Yeast glucan

The cell wall polysaccharide of baker's yeast has long been recognised as glucan — a polyglucosan. Both Zechmeister and Toth[59], and Hassid, Joslyn and McCready[13] recognised that the main polymeric linkage was β-(1 → 3) by the isolation of 2,4,6-tri-*O*-methyl-D-glucose from methylated glucan. Barry and Dillon[60] further confirmed this by the identification of laminaribiose from a hydrolysate of the periodate-oxidised polysaccharide. Bell and Northcote[61] later postulated a highly branched structure for glucan in which unit chains of about nine β-(1 → 3)-linked glucose residues were interconnected through (1 → 2) links.

The fine structure of glucan has been elucidated by Peat, Whelan and Edwards[62] and Peat, Turvey and Evans[63]. The first group of workers isolated glucose, gentiobiose, laminaribiose, gentiotriose, 6-*O*-β-laminaribiosylglucose, laminaritriose, 3-*O*-β-gentiobiosylglucose and gentiotetraose from the acid hydrolysis products of glucan. These products enabled them to postulate that glucan could be

–3β-Glc–6β-Glc–6β-Glc–6β-Glc–6β-Glc–3β-Glc–6β-Glc–3β-Glc–3β-Glc–3β-Glc–

No evidence was found for the presence of the (1 → 2) linkages postulated by Bell and Northcote[61]. Further confirmation of the presence of (1 → 6) linkages was obtained by tosylation of the glucan and exchange of the tosyl groups introduced with iodine. It was concluded from the iodine content that some 10–20% of the primary hydroxyl groups are involved in (1→6) linkages.

(d) Nigeran

Although this polyglucosan was recognised[52] in 1914 as a constituent of certain strains of *Aspergillus niger* its fine structure was not elucidated[37] until 1953. Two striking features of this polysaccharide were its extremely high optical rotation ($[\alpha]_D^{20} + 251°$ in 0.1 *N* NaOH) and its ability to crystallise out on cooling hot aqueous solutions of the polysaccharide. Its triacetate and trimethyl ether also showed high optical rotations of $[\alpha]_D^{17} + 157°$ (in CHCl$_3$) and $[\alpha]_D^{17} + 217.8°$ (in CHCl$_3$) respectively. This behaviour was ascribed to the presence of α-glucosidic linkages and confirmed by its infrared spectrum and the isolation of an homologous series of α-linked oligosaccharides. These included nigerose (3-*O*-α-D-glucopyranosyl-D-glucose),

maltose (4-O-α-D-glucopyranosyl-D-glucose) and two trisaccharides characterised[73] as O-α-D-glucopyranosyl-(1 → 3)-O-α-D-glucopyranosyl-(1 → 4)-D-
glucose and O-α-D-glucopyranosyl-(1 → 4)-O-α-D-glucopyranosyl-(1 → 3)-D-
glucose. The isolation of equimolar amounts of 2,3,6-tri-O-methyl-D-glucose
and 2,4,6-tri-O-methyl-D-glucose confirmed the presence of α-(1 → 3) and
α-(1 → 4) linkages. The small amount of 2,3,4,6-tetra-O-methyl-D-glucose
detected corresponded with an average chain length of 300–350 anhydro-
glucose units. Evidence that most, if not all, of the α-(1 → 4) and α-(1 → 3)
inkages were arranged alternately was obtained by the isolation of D-
glucosazone after treatment of the periodate-oxidised polysaccharide with
phenylhydrazine. The absence of a polysaccharide osazone eliminated any
possibility that long sequences of α-(1 → 3) linkages were present while
resistance of the higher oligosaccharides to α-amylase and β-amylase confirmed the absence of any significant proportion of uninterrupted sequences
of α-(1 → 4) linkages.

(e) Luteose

The poly β-(1 → 6)-glucosan luteose occurs[11] as its malonyl ester luteic acid, a
highly mucilaginous polysaccharide elaborated by *Penicillium luteum* Zukal.
Luteose can be obtained from luteic acid by leaving this to stand overnight
with N NaOH at room temperature. On neutralization, luteose ($[\alpha]_D - 33°$)
separates out and further yields can be obtained by addition of alcohol.
Luteose gave a triacetate ($[\alpha]_D^{22} - 5°$ in $CHCl_3$) and a tri-O-methyl ether
($[\alpha]_D - 32°$ in $CHCl_3$). On hydrolysis the latter yielded crystalline methyl
2,3,4-tri-O-methyl-β-glucopyranoside, further characterised by conversion to
2,3,4-tri-O-methyl-δ-gluconolactone. The isolation of a derivative of 2,3,4-
tri-O-methyl-D-glucose in 85% yield established that chains of D-glucopyranose units linked by (1 → 6)-glycosidic linkages were present. Furthermore the low optical rotations of luteose and its derivative indicated that
these were of the β-type. This supposition has since been confirmed by
infrared spectra. More recent studies[74] of a luteose preparation revealed
that any tetra-O-methyl-D-glucose present in the hydrolysate of the methyl
ether was below the level of detection. It was confirmed that the main
linkage was (1 → 6) by isolation of 2,3,4-tri-O-methyl-D-glucose (66%). The
dimethylglucoses (2,3-, 16%; 2,4-, 16%) detected were unlikely therefore
to have arisen from branch points in the luteose and probably arose from (1)
incomplete methylation, (2) the unsuspected presence of residual malonyl
groups or (3) demethylation during hydrolysis of the methyl ether.

(f) Dextran

Dextrans are a group of polyglucosans in which the main polymeric linkage is α-($1 \rightarrow 6$) but which may or may not contain additionally branch points of either the α-($1 \rightarrow 4 \rightarrow 6$) type or α-($1 \rightarrow 3 \rightarrow 6$) type. Jeanes and her colleagues[3] have distinguished three main classes of dextrans, A [containing 50–97% α-($1 \rightarrow 6$), 0–50% α-($1 \rightarrow 4$), 0–2% α-($1 \rightarrow 3$)], B [containing 86–95% α-($1 \rightarrow 6$), 0–8% α-($1 \rightarrow 4$), 3–6% α-($1 \rightarrow 3$)] and C [containing 50–85% α-($1 \rightarrow 6$), 0–36% α-($1 \rightarrow 4$) and > 6% α-($1 \rightarrow 3$)]. Some organisms produce more than one of these classes of dextran simultaneously as has been shown through separation by ethanol precipitation. The major species of organisms elaborating dextrans are the *Leuconostoc* and some *Streptococci* where enzyme synthesis stems from the substrate sucrose. Dextrans can also arise from amylodextrins and such is the case with *Acetobacter capsulatum* and *viscosum*[75].

The first systematic investigation of the structure of a dextran was carried out by Fowler, Buckland, Brauns and Hibbert[33]. These workers obtained a tri-O-methylglucosan from a *Leuconostoc mesenteroides* dextran. After methanolysis of this methyl ether the products were fractionally distilled to yield methyl-2,3-di-O-methylglucoside, methyl-2,3,4-tri-O-methyl-glucoside and methyl 2,3,4,6-tetra-O-methyl glucoside in the ratio of 1:3:1. A highly branched structure for the dextran was therefore proposed in which short chains of α-($1 \rightarrow 6$)-linked glucopyranose units were joined through α-($1 \rightarrow 4$) linkages and the ratio of ($1 \rightarrow 6$) to ($1 \rightarrow 4$) linkages was 4 to 1. A careful reinvestigation[76] in which the methylated dextran was obtained in 71% yield and the methylglycosides recovered in 97% yield confirmed these findings.

Later Peat, Schlüchterer and Stacey[34] showed that the structure of *Leuconostoc dextranicum* dextran was markedly different in that very little branching occurred and the long chains of α-($1 \rightarrow 6$)-linked D-glucose units comprised some 200–550 residues. Fairhead, Hunter and Hibbert[77] also working on a *Leuconostoc dextranicum* dextran obtained similar results. A *Betabacterium vermiforme* dextran[35] was found to have an average chain length of some 25 glucose residues. The advent of periodate oxidation allowed large numbers of dextrans to be investigated. In one such study[78], six dextrans elaborated by different strains of *Leuconostoc mesenteroides* were found to have ratios of ($1 \rightarrow 6$) linkages to linkages other than ($1 \rightarrow 6$) varying from 24:1 to 3:1.

A new chapter in the chemistry of dextrans was opened by the discovery that certain of these contained α-($1 \rightarrow 3 \rightarrow 6$) branch points. Barker, Bourne, Bruce and Stacey[79] found 2,4-dimethyl-D-glucose among the hydrolysis products of the methyl ether of a *Betacoccus arabinosaceous* dextran. The disaccharide nigerose was also detected in the hydrolysis products of the dextran itself. Abdel-Akher, Hamilton, Montgomery and Smith[80] reported the application, to a certain *Leuconostoc mesenteroides* dextran, of a new procedure for structural determination. This involved periodate oxidation followed by reduction and hydrolysis and here it resulted in the production *inter alia* of glucose, indicating that the polysaccharide possessed $(1 \rightarrow 3)$ linkages. Lohmar[81] using a similar procedure deduced the presence of glucose by isolation of sorbitol from the hydrolysate.

The evidence for the presence of α-glucosidic linkages in dextran depends on three different findings, (1) the high optical rotation of dextrans examined in N potassium hydroxide or formamide[32], (2) the exhibition of the characteristic infrared absorption peak[82] at *ca.* 840 cm^{-1} and (3) the nature of the homologous series of oligosaccharides isolated by partial acid hydrolysis of dextrans[36,83]. These comprised isomaltose (6-O-α-D-glucopyranosyl-D-glucose), nigerose, isomaltotriose, isomaltotetraose, etc. Isomaltose and isomaltotriose have also been isolated in yields of 50 and 20% respectively from the enzymic hydrolysates of dextran[84]. From a study[85] of the optical rotations of 16 degraded dextrans in water and cuprammonium solutions, a claim has been made that a substantial proportion of the units in dextrans from NRRLB–1299 and NRRLB–1399 are joined by $(1 \rightarrow 2)$ linkages.

Leuconostoc mesenteroides dextrans have acquired considerable importance during recent years following the discovery that, when suitably degraded, they can be used as a substitute for blood plasma. Dextran sulphate is also used as a blood anticoagulant. Other ethers and esters of dextran find widespread applications in industry.

3. Levans (polyfructosans)

While the polyfructosans of the higher plants are mostly of the inulin type [poly-β-$(2 \rightarrow 1)$-fructofuranoses], many bacterial species (see Table I) elaborate levans where the glycosidic linkages are mainly of the β-$(2 \rightarrow 6)$ type. Structural studies[86,87] of *Bacillus mesentericus* and *Bacillus subtilis* levans established that the only isolable monosaccharide after hydrolysis was fructose and that such residues were joined by $(2 \rightarrow 6)$-links. Studies of other levans from *Xanthomonas pruni*, *Pseudomonas syringae* and *Bacillus megatherium* tended to confirm that this was a general structural feature of levans.

In 1951, Palmer[88] demonstrated that *Bacillus subtilis* levan contained small quantities of glucose. This was confirmed in a reinvestigation of the levans of *Pseudomonas syringae* and *Bacillus subtilis* by Bell and Dedonder[89]. These workers expressed the belief that bacterial levans were derived by a chain-lengthening transfer of β-fructofuranosyl radicals from the donor molecule to an acceptor *ab initio* sucrose. Such a concept would account for the presence of a glucose moiety as a molecular component. Average chain lengths of 9–10 β-$(2 \rightarrow 6)$-linked fructofuranose units with a high degree of branching were reported for the levans. With the *Bacillus subtilis* levan this branching is believed[40,90] to be due to inter-chain linkages of the β-$(2 \rightarrow 1)$ type to give a structure for levan of:

$$G_1 \longrightarrow \longleftarrow {}_2F_6 \longleftarrow {}_2F_6 \cdots \longleftarrow {}_2F_6 \longleftarrow {}_2F_6$$
$$\uparrow$$
$$\tfrac{1}{2}F_6 \longleftarrow {}_2F_6 \quad \text{etc.}$$

4. Polymannans

Bacillus polymyxa mannan[64]. The purified mannan $[\alpha]_D$ $+82°$ was electrophoretically homogeneous but appeared to contain some 13% bound protein or peptide. Methylation with dimethyl sulphate/NaOH and later silver oxide/methyl iodide in dimethylformamide afforded a methyl ether $[\alpha]_D$ $+92°$ in chloroform and containing OCH_3, 38.2%. Formic acid hydrolysis followed by further treatment with o.1 N hydrochloric acid gave a mixture of ethers characterised as 2,3,4,6-tetra-O-methyl-D-mannose (identified by oxidation to the lactone and isolation of a crystalline phenylhydrazide), 3,4,6-tri-O-methyl-D-mannose, 2,4,6-tri-O-methyl-D-mannose and 3,4-di-O-methyl-D-mannose (ratio 2:1:1:2). D-Mannopyranose residues linked $(1 \rightarrow 2)$, $(1 \rightarrow 3)$ and involved in $(1 \rightarrow 2 \rightarrow 6)$ branch points were thus indicated. On periodate oxidation, the mannan consumed 1.31 moles periodate and liberated 0.46 moles of formic acid per anhydro-hexose unit. The formic acid presumably arose primarily from the non-reducing end groups of mannose. Reduction of the oxidised polysaccharide and hydrolysis gave *inter alia* mannose and glycerol. Mannose arose from the residues linked $(1 \rightarrow 3)$ and those involved in branch points. The detection of glycerol rather than erythritol indicated the absence of $(1 \rightarrow 4)$-linked mannose residues.

Saccharomyces rouxii mannan. Gorin and Perlin[50] have established that the main slime polysaccharide produced during the fermentation of this yeast is a mannan. The mannan $([\alpha]_D$ $+53°)$ on acetolysis gave a mixture of acetates which were deacetylated to the parent oligosaccharides. A disaccharide so isolated was shown to be 2-O-α-D-mannopyranosyl-D-mannose by methylation and isolation of 2,3,4,6-tetra-O-methyl-D-mannose and 3,4,6-tri-O-methyl-D-mannose from the hydrolysate of the methyl ether. Further evidence was obtained from the results of periodate oxidation of the 2-O-α-D-mannopyranosyl-D-mannitol obtained by reduction of the disaccharide. Acid hydrolysis of the methylated mannan gave mainly 2,3,4,6-tetra-O-methyl-D-mannose, 3,4,6-tri-O-methyl-D-mannose and 3,4-di-O-methyl-D-mannose. Small amounts of 2,4,6-tri-O-methyl-D-mannose and 3-O-methyl-D-mannose were also detected. Such products suggested that the average structural unit consisted of a main chain of D-mannopyranose units containing alternate $(1 \rightarrow 2)$ and $(1 \rightarrow 6)$ linkages to which single D-mannopyranose units were attached by (1 →2) linkages as side chains. An alternative arrangement was one where (1 →2)-disaccharide units were attached as side chains by (1 →2) linkages to a (1 →6) linked main chain. The latter structure now seems the more likely possibility since Gorin and Perlin[65] have reported the isolation of O-α-D-mannopyranosyl-(1 → 2)-O-α-D-mannopyranosyl-(1 →2)-D-mannose from the deacetylated acetolysis products. The structure of this trisaccharide was established by the methylation technique and by a novel degradation to yield 2-O-α-D-mannopyranosyl-D-mannose and 2-O-α-D-mannopyranosylglycerol, each containing one of the glycosidic linkages of the parent trisaccharide. The mannan thus appears to differ somewhat from the mannan of *Saccharomyces cerevisiae*[49, 66] which contained a much higher proportion of (1 →3) linkages. Both mannans showed the common feature of (1 →2) glycosidic linkages.

5. Polygalactans

Galactocarolose[67] is a polygalactan elaborated by *Penicillium charlesii*. Acid hydrolysis of galactocarolose[68] at pH 2.2 at 75° for 18 h gave the homologous series of D-galactose (4.5%), galactobiose (1.8%), galactotriose (1.4%), galactotetraose (0.4%) and galactopentaose (0.8%). The structure of the galactobiose was established as 5-O-D-galactofuranosyl-D-galactose by (1) its acid lability, (2) its conversion to a galactobiitol which consumed 4 moles of periodate with the concomitant release of 2 moles each of formic acid and formaldehyde and (3) by reduction of the periodate-resistant fragment of galactobiitol to 2-O-L-arabofuranosylglycerol. The configuration of the glycosidic linkage was designated α from a comparison of the calculated (—108°) and found (—129°) optical rotations of the arabofuranosylglycerol.

The structure of the galactobiose was thus in agreement with that expected from the methylation data of much earlier workers[48]. The galactocarolose was methylated and the product hydrolysed with methanolic hydrogen chloride to give a mixture of methylated galactosides. Fractional distillation of the mixture afforded a methyl-tetra-O-methyl-D-galactoside (12.4%) and a methyl-tri-O-methyl-D-galactoside (80%). The former was identified as methyl-2,3,5,6-tetra-O-methyl-D-galactofuranoside by hydrolysis and oxidation of the product obtained to yield 2,3,5,6-tetra-O-methyl-D-galacto-furanolactone isolated as its crystalline amide. The trimethyl derivative on hydrolysis gave mainly 2,3,6-tri-O-methyl-D-galactose characterised by conversion to crystalline 2,3,6-tri-O-methyl-D-galactofuranolactone. It was therefore concluded that galactocarolose was a polymer of (1 → 5)-linked D-galactofuranose units, each chain containing some 9–10 sugar residues. The suggestion that the residues were linked β-glycosidically now appears erroneous in view of the later findings of Gorin and Spencer[68].

6. Colominic acid (poly-*N*-acetylneuraminic acid)

Colominic acid[69] is an acidic aminopolysaccharide elaborated in the culture medium of *Escherichia coli* K_{235} from which it can be isolated[70] by alternate dialysis and lyophilization followed by fractional precipitation with aqueous ethanol and ammonium sulphate. Pure preparations ($[\alpha]_D^{20}$ —50.5° ± 2° in water) showed a single peak (mobility —11.1·10^{-5} cm^2/volt·sec) when subjected to electrophoretic analysis in 0.1 *M* borate buffer pH 9.2. It was degraded by acid with formation of humin and when heated in 0.1 *N* alkali gave a product with $\lambda_{max.}$ 260 mμ in the ultraviolet. It reacted both with Ehrlich's reagent ($\lambda_{max.}$ 530 mμ)and Bial's orcinol reagent ($\lambda_{max.}$ 540 mμ). Analysis suggested a formula of $(C_{12}H_{19}NO_9)_n$ and revealed that each monomer unit contained one acetyl group and one carboxylic acid function. Acidic hydrolysis of colominic acid and subsequent fractionation of the products on a Dowex-1 column gave as the major fraction a crystalline compound identified as *N*-acetylneuraminic acid. This was confirmed by analysis, and from its optical rotation ($[\alpha]_D$ —35.0°), infrared spectrum, decomposition point and chromatographic mobility in various solvents. The other major product of hydrolysis appeared to be a decomposition product of *N*-acetylneuraminic acid. It was therefore concluded that colominic acid was a polysaccharide constituted primarily, if not solely, of units of *N*-acetylneuraminic acid. Colominic acid was not antigenic in rabbits and there appeared to be no correlation between the ability of *E. coli* K_{235} to elaborate colominic acid and its virulence in mice. From a study[71] of a series of strains of *Escherichia coli* containing K antigens it was concluded that the distribution of sialic acid (group name for the neuraminic acid derivatives) was not widespread and was unrelated to the presence of bacteriocine or haemolysin.

7. Chitin

Chitin is a cell wall polysaccharide occurring in many of the higher micro-organisms. In most cases the evidence for its detection is based on X-ray powder photographs and the formation from the chitin of the characteristic chitosan sulphate spherocrystals[72] which are negatively birefringent. Such properties are compared with those of authentic crustacean chitin. Kreger[57] has claimed that chitosan (de-*N*-acetylated chitin) also occurs in *Phycomyces blakesleeanus* and therefore recommends that in the chitosan sulphate test for the detection of chitin, acid extraction should precede the conversion of chitin into chitosan to make the method unambiguous. Some of the organisms in which chitin has been detected are given in Table I. Chitin is absent[57] from *Schizosaccharomyces octosporus*, *Sch. pombe* and *Sch. versatilis*.

These appear to contain a cell wall substance which was detected in *Endomyces* and *Penicillium notatum* in emphasis of the close relationship between *Schizosaccharomyces* and the hyphal fungi. Chitin does, however, occur in *Penicillium notatum*. No detailed structural work has been done on fungal chitin but its close resemblance to crustacean chitin suggests that it is a poly-2-*N*-acetamide-2-deoxy-D-glucosan linked β-(1 →4)-glycosidically in linear chains.

8. Vi antigen (poly-2-*N*-acetamido-2-deoxy-D-galacturonic acid)

The Vi antigen is a component common[91] to *Escherichia coli*, *Salmonella typhosa* and *Paracolobacterium ballerup*. It is a strongly acidic polymer which requires hydrolysis with concentrated hydrochloric acid at 100° for 2 h to liberate the monosaccharide units. A crystalline compound isolated from such an hydrolysate analysed correctly for a monoamino-monodeoxy-hexuronic acid hydrochloride. In the Elson–Morgan test it gave 70% of the colour given by glucosamine, but did not give the colour reaction (Dische[92]) typical of normal uronic acids. It exhibited 70% of the reducing power of glucose. The Vi antigen exhibited[93] a very high optical rotation ($[\alpha]_D$ +291°) and since it was immune to attack by periodate it was suggested that it was a poly-α-(1 →3)-linked hexosaminuronic acid. Recently[94] the monosaccharide constituent has been identified as 2-amino-2-deoxy-D-galacturonic acid which occurs as its *N*-acetamido derivative in the polysaccharide.

9. Hyaluronic acid

Many bacteria, particularly gram-positive organisms, elaborate a protective capsule of hyaluronic acid. Such capsules also appear to be related to the virulence of the organism, *e.g.* those forms of group A streptococci whose capsules are removed by hyaluronidase are ten times less virulent than those with the capsules. A much more dramatic loss in virulence occurs when group C streptococci are similarly treated—loss of the hyaluronic acid capsule here results in a 100,000-fold decrease in virulence[95].

Hyaluronic acid was isolated from group A haemolytic streptococci by Kendall, Heidelberger and Dawson[96] and shown to be composed of equal numbers of *N*-acetyl glucosamine and glucuronic acid residues. A preparation[97] isolated from the same group of organisms had $[\alpha]_D$ —60.2°, N 3.3% and acetyl 11.5%. No precise structural studies have been carried out on bacterial hyaluronic acid but it probably has the same structure as human tissue hyaluronic acid *i.e.* a polymer composed of alternate *N*-acetylglucosamine and D-glucuronic acid units linked β-glycosidically through positions 3 and 4 respectively.

TABLE II

COMPLEX POLYSACCHARIDES OF GRAM-POSITIVE BACTERIA

Organism	Carbohydrate constituents of the complex polysaccharide
Staphylococcus aureus	
strain IC [98]	Pentose, glucosamine
strain CB [98]	Pentose, glucosamine
Pneumococcus	
type I [99]	Galacturonic acid, amino sugar
type II [100]	Glucuronic acid, glucose, rhamnose
type III [101]	Glucuronic acid, glucose
type IV [102]	Amino sugar, galactose
type V [103]	Glucose, glucuronic acid, pneumosamine, amino sugar X
type VI [104]	Glucose, galactose, rhamnose, ribitol
type VII [105]	Glucose, galactose, rhamnose, amino sugar
type VIII [106]	Glucose, galactose, glucuronic acid
type IX [107]	Glucose, amino sugar, uronic acid
type X [107]	Amino sugar + ?
type XI [107]	Amino sugar + ?
type XII [107]	Glucose, galactose, amino sugar
type XIII [107]	Amino sugar + ?
type XIV [108]	Glucose, galactose, glucosamine
type XV [107]	Amino sugar + ?
type XVI [107]	Amino sugar + ?
type XVII [109]	Glucose, rhamnose
Streptococcus	
haemolytic group A [110]	Glucosamine, rhamnose
group D [111]	Galactose, rhamnose, galacturonic acid
Lactobacillus bifidus[112]	Galactose, glucose, fucose, unidentified pentose
Corynebacterium diphtheriae[113]	Galactose, mannose, arabinose
Bacillus	
anthracis[114]	Galactose, glucosamine
subtilis ATCC 9945[115]	Galactose, glucosamine, galactosamine, 2,4-diamino-2,4,6-trideoxyhexose
polymyxa (S-33 var. *lactoviscosus*)[116]	Glucose, fucose
brevis 799[117]	Glucose, uronic acid
alvei 683[117]	Glucose, uronic acid
circulans 294[117]	Glucose, mannose, uronic acid
circulans 396[117]	Glucose, mannose, uronic acid
circulans 295[117]	Glucose, mannose, uronic acid, xylose
circulans 760[117]	Glucose, mannose, uronic acid
megatherium[118]	Glucose, galactose

References p. 259

10. Complex polysaccharides of gram-positive bacteria

Table II shows some of the constituents of the complex polysaccharides of gram-positive bacteria. Only the structures of certain *Pneumococcus* polysaccharides are known in more precise detail and these results can be summarised as follows:

Type II *Pneumococcus* polysaccharide contains D-glucose involved in $(1 \to 4 \to 6)$ branch points, L-rhamnose linked through the 1 and 3 positions and some D-glucuronic acid residues present as non-reducing end groups.

Type III polysaccharide is a polymer of cellobiuronic acid units ($4\text{-}O\text{-}\beta\text{-}$D-glucuronosyl-D-glucose) joined by $(1 \to 3)$ linkages. Type V polysaccharide consists at least in part of repeating units of $3\text{-}O\text{-}\beta\text{-}$D-glucuronosyl-$N$-acetyl-L-fucosamine. To some of these units glucose is attached since a trisaccharide containing all three monosaccharide units has been isolated. Type VI polysaccharide probably has the structure 4- or $2\text{-}\beta\text{-}$D-Gal$p$1–3-D-Gluc$p$1–3-L-Rham$p$1–3Ribitol 1- or 2-PO$_4$Ca$_{\frac{1}{2}}$.

Type VIII polysaccharide is a polymer of the unit D-glucuronic acid-$(\beta(1 \to 4)\text{-}$D-glucose)$_2\text{-}\alpha\text{-}(1 \to 4)\text{-}$D-galactose.

Type XIV consists of a repeating unit containing two non-reducing end groups of D-galactose, a D-galactose linked through positions 1 and 3, a D-glucose residue linked through positions 1 and 4 and two $(1 \to 4 \to 6)$-linked 2-acetamido-2-deoxy-D-glucose residues.

11. Complex polysaccharides of gram-negative bacteria

Comprehensive lists of the monosaccharide constituents of gram-negative bacteria are to be found elsewhere[119,120] and it has therefore not been felt necessary to reproduce them here. Few of the finer details of their structure are known except in the cases of *Azotobacter chroococcum* polysaccharide[121] and some capsular polysaccharides derived from *Klebsiella*[122,123]. It is noteworthy, however, that certain sugars occur in these polysaccharides which are not found abundantly elsewhere in nature. These include abequose (3,6-dideoxy-D-galactose), colitose (3,6-dideoxy-L-galactose), tyvelose (3,6-dideoxy-D-mannose), and paratose (3,6-dideoxy-D-glucose) which play such a dominant role in determining the serological specificity of the *Salmonella* polysaccharides. D-Fucosamine and a series of aldoheptoses are also encountered.

ACKNOWLEDGEMENT

The author wishes to thank Professor M. Stacey, F.R.S., for his interest in this work.

REFERENCES

[1] F. C. MCINTIRE, W. H. PETERSON AND A. J. RIKER, *J. Biol. Chem.*, 143 (1942) 491.

[2] R. E. REEVES, *J. Biol. Chem.*, 154 (1944) 49.

[3] E. W. PUTMAN, A. L. POTTER, R. HODGSON AND W. Z. HASSID, *J. Am. Chem. Soc.*, 72 (1950) 5024.

[4] F. B. SEIBERT, M. STACEY AND P. W. KENT, *Biochim. Biophys. Acta*, 3 (1949) 632.

[5] P. W. KENT, *J. Chem. Soc.*, (1951) 364.

[6] H. HIBBERT AND J. BARSHA, *Can. J. Research*, 5 (1931) 580; 10 (1934) 170.

[7] H. L. A. TARR AND H. HIBBERT, *Can. J. Research*, 4 (1931) 372.

[8] R. KAUSHAL AND T. K. WALKER, *Biochem. J.*, 48 (1951) 618.

[9] K. S. BARCLAY, E. J. BOURNE, M. STACEY AND M. WEBB, *J. Chem. Soc.*, (1954) 1501.

[10] J. H. BIRKINSHAW AND H. RAISTRICK, *Biochem. J.*, 27 (1933) 370.

[11] C. G. ANDERSON, W. N. HAWORTH, H. RAISTRICK AND M. STACEY, *Biochem. J.*, 33 (1939) 272.

[12] J. BADDILEY, J. G. BUCHANAN AND E. M. THAIN, *J. Chem. Soc.*, (1953) 1944.

[13] W. Z. HASSID, M. A. JOSLYN AND R. M. MCCREADY, *J. Am. Chem. Soc.*, 63 (1941) 295.

[14] J. FRATEUR, *La Cellule*, 53 (1950) 287.

[15] J. TOSIC AND T. K. WALKER, *J. Gen. Microbiol.*, 4 (1950) 192.

[16] E. J. HEHRE, A. S. CARLSON AND D. M. HAMILTON, *J. Biol. Chem.*, 177 (1949) 289.

[17] J. MONOD AND A. TORRIANI, *Compt. rend.*, 227 (1948) 240.

[18] E. J. HEHRE, A. S. CARLSON AND J. M. NEILL, *Science*, 106 (1947) 523.

[19] H. NASR AND F. BAKER, *Nature*, 164 (1949) 745.

[20] F. BOAS, *Biochem. Z.*, 81 (1917) 80.

[21] J. MAGER, *Biochem. J.*, 41 (1947) 603.

[22] A. LWOFF, H. IONESCO AND A. GUTMANN, *Biochim. Biophys. Acta*, 4 (1950) 270.

[23] E. J. HEHRE AND D. M. HAMILTON, *J. Biol. Chem.*, 166 (1946) 777.

[24] M. HEIDELBERGER, F. E. KENDALL AND H. W. SCHERP, *J. Exptl. Med.*, 64 (1936) 559.

[25] G. BARRY, R. GAVARD, G. MILHAUD AND J. P. AUBERT, *Compt. rend.*, 235 (1952) 1062.

[26] P. W. KENT AND M. STACEY, *Biochim. Biophys. Acta*, 3 (1949) 641.

[27] D. H. NORTHCOTE, *Biochem. J.*, 53 (1953) 348.

[28] G. FORSYTH, E. L. HIRST AND A. E. OXFORD, *J. Chem. Soc.*, (1953) 2030.

[29] D. J. MANNERS AND J. F. RYLEY, *Biochem. J.*, 52 (1952) 480.

[30] S. A. BARKER, E. J. BOURNE, G. T. BRUCE AND M. STACEY, *J. Chem. Soc.*, (1958) 4414.

[31] R. W. BAILEY, *Biochem. J.*, 72 (1959) 42.

[32] A. JEANES *et al.*, *J. Am. Chem. Soc.*, 76 (1954) 5041.

[33] F. L. FOWLER, I. K. BUCKLAND, F. BRAUNS AND H. HIBBERT, *Can. J. Research*, 15 (1937) 486.

[34] S. PEAT, E. SCHLÜCHTERER AND M. STACEY, *J. Chem. Soc.*, (1939) 581.

[35] W. D. DAKER AND M. STACEY, *J. Chem. Soc.*, (1939) 585.

[36] S. A. BARKER, E. J. BOURNE, G. T. BRUCE, W. B. NEELY AND M. STACEY, *J. Chem. Soc.*, (1954) 2395.

[37] S. A. BARKER, E. J. BOURNE AND M. STACEY, *J. Chem. Soc.*, (1953) 3084.

[38] A. FUCHS, *Nature*, 178 (1956) 921.

[39] C. GAINOR AND D. E. WEGEMER, *Appl. Microbiol.*, 2 (1954) 95.

[40] D. S. FEINGOLD AND M. GEHATIA, *J. Polymer Sci.*, 23 (1957) 783.

[41] C. F. NIVEN, K. L. SMILEY AND J. M. SHERMAN, *J. Biol. Chem.*, 140 (1941) 105.

[42] F. C. HARRISON, H. L. A. TARR AND H. HIBBERT, *Can. J. Research*, 3 (1930) 449.

[43] R. R. LYNE, S. PEAT AND M. STACEY, *J. Chem. Soc.*, (1940) 237.

[44] D. MURPHY, *Can. J. Chem.*, 30 (1952) 872.

[45] W. G. C. FORSYTH AND D. M. WEBLEY, *Biochem. J.*, 44 (1949) 455.

[46] J. P. GROSSMANN AND J. R. POSTGATE, *J. Gen. Microbiol.*, 12 (1955) 429.

[47] D. MURPHY, C. T. BISHOP AND G. A. ADAMS, *Can. J. Biochem. and Physiol.*, 34 (1956) 1271.

[48] W. N. HAWORTH, H. RAISTRICK AND M. STACEY, *Biochem. J.*, 29 (1935) 612.

[49] W. N. HAWORTH, E. L. HIRST AND F. A. ISHERWOOD, *J. Chem. Soc.*, (1937) 784.

[50] P. A. J. GORIN AND A. S. PERLIN, *Can. J. Chem.*, 34 (1956) 1796.

[51] W. N. HAWORTH, H. RAISTRICK AND M. STACEY, *Biochem. J.*, 31 (1937) 640.

[52] A. W. DOX AND R. E. NEIDIG, *J. Biol. Chem.*, 18 (1914) 167; 19 (1914) 235.

[53] P. PLACKETT AND S. H. BUTTERY, *Nature*, 812 (1958) 1236.

[54] Y. KHOUVINE, *Compt. rend.*, 195 (1932) 396.

[55] L. GLAZER AND D. H. BROWN, *Biochim. Biophys. Acta*, 23 (1957) 449.

[56] P. A. ROELOFSEN, *Biochim. Biophys. Acta*, 10 (1953) 477.

[57] D. R. KREGER, *Biochim. Biophys. Acta*, 13 (1954) 1.

[58] A. M. BRESLAU, *J. Histochem. and Cytochem.*, 3 (1955) 141.

[59] L. ZECHMEISTER AND G. TOTH, *Biochem. Z.*, 270 (1934) 309; 284 (1936) 133.

[60] V. C. BARRY AND T. DILLON, *Proc. Roy. Irish Acad., B*, 49 (1943) 177.

[61] D. J. BELL AND D. H. NORTHCOTE, *J. Chem. Soc.*, (1950) 1944.

[62] S. PEAT, W. J. WHELAN AND T. E. EDWARDS, *J. Chem. Soc.*, (1958) 3862.

[63] S. PEAT, J. E. TURVEY AND J. M. EVANS, *J. Chem. Soc.*, (1958) 3868.

[64] D. H. BALL AND G. A. ADAMS, *Can. J. Chem.*, 37 (1959) 1012.

[65] P. A. J. GORIN AND A. S. PERLIN, *Can. J. Chem.*, 35 (1957) 262.

[66] W. N. HAWORTH, R. L. HEATH AND S. PEAT, *J. Chem. Soc.*, (1941) 833.

[67] P. W. CLUTTERBUCK, W. N. HAWORTH, H. RAISTRICK, G. SMITH AND M. STACEY, *Biochem. J.*, 28 (1934) 94.

[68] P. A. J. GORIN AND J. F. T. SPENCER, *Can. J. Chem.*, 37 (1959) 499.

[69] G. T. BARRY AND W. F. GOEBEL, *Nature*, 179 (1957) 206.

[70] G. T. BARRY, *J. Exptl. Med.*, 107 (1958) 507.

[71] G. T. BARRY, *Nature*, 183 (1959) 117.

[72] H. BRUNSWIK, *Biochem. Z.*, 113 (1921) 111.

[73] S. A. BARKER, E. J. BOURNE, D. M. O'MANT AND M. STACEY, *J. Chem. Soc.*, (1957) 2448.

[74] P. F. LLOYD, G. PON AND M. STACEY, *Chem. & Ind. (London)*, (1956) 172.

[75] E. J. HEHRE AND D. M. HAMILTON, *J. Biol. Chem.*, 192 (1951) 161.

[76] I. LEVI, W. L. HAWKINS AND H. HIBBERT, *J. Am. Chem. Soc.*, 64 (1942) 1959.

[77] E. C. FAIRHEAD, M. J. HUNTER AND H. HIBBERT, *Can. J. Research*, B16 (1938) 151.

[78] A. JEANES AND C. A. WILHAM, *J. Am. Chem. Soc.*, 72 (1950) 2655.

[79] S. A. BARKER, E. J. BOURNE, G. T. BRUCE AND M. STACEY, *Chem. & Ind. (London)*, (1952) 1156.

[80] M. ABDEL-AKHER, J. K. HAMILTON, R. MONTGOMERY AND F. SMITH, *J. Am. Chem. Soc.*, 74 (1952) 4970.

[81] R. LOHMAR, *J. Am. Chem. Soc.*, 74 (1952) 4974.

[82] S. A. BARKER, E. J. BOURNE, M. STACEY AND D. H. WHIFFEN, *J. Chem. Soc.*, (1954) 171.

[83] L. W. GEORGES, I. L. MILLER AND M. L. WOLFROM, *J. Am. Chem. Soc.*, 69 (1947) 473.

[84] A. JEANES, C. A. WILHAM, R. W. JONES, H. M. TSUCHIYA AND C. E. RIST, *J. Am. Chem. Soc.*, 75 (1953) 5911.

[85] T. A. SCOTT, N. N. HELLMAN AND F. R. SANTI, *J. Am. Chem. Soc.*, 79 (1957) 1178.

[86] H. HIBBERT AND F. BRAUNS, *Can. J. Research*, 4 (1931) 596.

[87] H. HIBBERT, R. S. TIPSON AND F. BRAUNS, *Can. J. Research*, 4 (1931) 221.

[88] A. PALMER, *Biochem. J.*, 48 (1951) 389.

[89] D. J. BELL AND R. DEDONDER, *J. Chem. Soc.*, (1954) 2866.

[90] R. DEDONDER, *Bull. soc. chim. biol.*, 40 (1958) 863.

[91] M. E. WEBSTER, J. F. SAGIN, P. R. ANDERSON, S. S. BRUSE, M. E. FREEMAN AND M. LANDY, *J. Immunol.*, 73 (1954) 16.

[92] Z. DISCHE, *J. Biol. Chem.*, 167 (1947) 189.

[93] W. R. CLARK, J. MCLAUGHLIN AND M. E. WEBSTER, *J. Biol. Chem.*, 230 (1958) 81.

[94] K. HEYNS, G. KIESSLING, W. LINDENBERG, H. PAULSEN AND M. W. WEBSTER, *Chem. Ber.*, 92 (1959) 2435.

[95] J. F. WILKINSON, *Bacteriol. Reviews*, 22 (1958) 46.

[96] F. E. KENDALL, M. HEIDELBERGER AND M. H. DAWSON, *J. Biol. Chem.*, 118 (1937) 61.

[97] G. K. HIRST, *J. Exptl. Med.*, 73 (1941) 493.

[98] O. N. FELLOWES AND J. L. ROUTH, *J. Lab. Clin. Med.*, 29 (1944) 1054.

[99] M. HEIDELBERGER, F. E. KENDALL AND H. W. SCHERP, *J. Exptl. Med.*, 64 (1936) 559.

[100] K. BUTLER, P. F. LLOYD AND M. STACEY, *J. Chem. Soc.*, (1955) 1531.

[101] R. E. REEVES AND W. F. GOEBEL, *J. Biol. Chem.*, 139 (1941) 511.
[102] M. HEIDELBERGER, *Lectures in Immunochemistry*, Academic Press, New York.
[103] S. A. BARKER, M. STACEY AND J. M. WILLIAMS, *Bull. soc. chim. biol.*, 42 (1960) 1611.
[104] M. HEIDELBERGER AND P. REBERS, *J. Am. Chem. Soc.*, 81 (1959) 2415.
[105] S. A. BARKER, M. STACEY AND M. HEIDELBERGER, (1956) unpublished results.
[106] J. K. N. JONES AND M. B. PERRY, *J. Am. Chem. Soc.*, 79 (1957) 2787.
[107] R. BROWN, *J. Immunol.*, 37 (1939) 445.
[108] S. A. BARKER, M. HEIDELBERGER, M. STACEY AND D. J. TIPPER, *J. Chem. Soc.*, (1958) 3468.
[109] H. MARKOWITZ AND M. HEIDELBERGER, *J. Am. Chem. Soc.*, 76 (1954) 1313.
[110] W. C. SCHMIDT, *J. Exptl. Med.*, 95 (1952) 105.
[111] P. N. HOBSON AND M. J. MACPHERSON, *Biochem. J.*, 57 (1954) 145.
[112] R. F. NORRIS, M. SIPIN, F. ZILLIKEN, T. S. HARVEY AND P. GYORGY, *J. Bacteriol.*, 67 (1954) 159.
[113] O. K. ORLOVA, *Biokhimiya*, 19 (1954) 449.
[114] G. IVÁNOVICS, *Z. Immunitätsforsch.*, 97 (1940) 402; 98 (1940) 373.
[115] SHARON AND R. W. JEANLOZ, *Biochim. Biophys. Acta*, 31 (1959) 277.
[116] A. MISAKI *et al.*, *J. Fermentation Technol.*, 32 (1954) 147, 191, 311, 315, 341.
[117] W. G. C. FORSYTH AND D. M. WEBLEY, *Biochem. J.*, 44 (1949) 455.
[118] J. P. AUBERT, *Ann. inst. Pasteur*, 80 (1951) 644.
[119] S. A. BARKER AND M. STACEY, *Polysaccharides of Micro-organisms*, Oxford University Press, 1960.
[120] D. A. L. DAVIES in *Advances in Carbohydrate Chem.*, *Polysaccharides of Gram-Negative Bacteria*, Academic Press, New York, 1960.
[121] G. LAWSON AND M. STACEY, *J. Chem. Soc.*, (1954) 1925.
[122] G. O. ASPINALL, R. S. P. JAMIESON AND J. F. WILKINSON, *J. Chem. Soc.*, (1956) 3483.
[123] S. A. BARKER, A. B. FOSTER, I. R. SIDDIQUI AND M. STACEY, *J. Chem. Soc.*, (1958) 2358.

Chapter VII

Section e

Mucopolysaccharides (Acidic Glycosaminoglycans)

ROGER W. JEANLOZ

Departments of Biological Chemistry and Medicine,
Harvard University Medical School and Massachusetts General Hospital,
Boston, Mass. (U.S.A.)

1. Introduction

Since the word "mucopolysaccharide" was introduced by Meyer[1] in the biochemical literature, numerous substances have been classified under this name, which in turn has changed its meaning quite a few times[2]. However, recent progress in the chemistry of complex carbohydrates and of carbohydrates attached to proteins or lipids has resulted in a better understanding of the chemical structure of these compounds possessing high viscosity. Consequently two groups of substances, which in the past had been described under the name of mucopolysaccharide, namely the glycoproteins and the glycolipids, will be discussed in other chapters of this book.

The present chapter will be restricted to a discussion of the chemical properties of a group of substances called sometimes acidic mucopolysaccharides. Most of them are present in the connective tissue of animals. They can be isolated as pure polysaccharides, free from proteins, without appreciable degradation of the carbohydrate molecule. Their most characteristic chemical feature is a structure built of alternate units of amino sugar and glycuronic acid, the acidic character being reinforced in some of them by sulfate groups. In addition to the polysaccharides from connective tissue, four other substances will be considered here: chitin, which is present in many living species, and built only of D-glucosamine units; two bacterial polysaccharides, one similar to chitin, but composed of D-galactosamine, the second composed of galactosamine and glucuronic acid; and finally, keratan sulfate, which contains D-galactose in addition to D-glucosamine, and a sulfate ester group. The chemical structure of keratan sulfate seems quite different from the ones described in the same chapter, but it will be discussed here because of its unique chemical composition, and also because of its presence in animal connective tissue accompanying the other muco-polysaccharides.

Detailed reviews on the recent progress in the chemistry of the muco-polysaccharides have been published[3-7].

2. Nomenclature

Not only has the definition of mucopolysaccharide been changed frequently, but some of the substances described in this chapter have received up to three names. Unfortunately, many of these names are not in keeping with modern carbohydrate nomenclature, since the polysaccharide character of the substances had not been recognized at the time of their isolation. Consequently, in an attempt for simplification, new names have been introduced in this chapter, or alternatively, known names have been slightly modified to conform to modern nomenclature. Semi-systematic names, such as glycosaminoglycans, glycosaminoglycuronoglycans will also be used, when the chemical structure is well known. Names not presenting problems of ambiguity and well accepted, like chitin, hyaluronic acid, chondroitin sulfate and heparin, are used without modification. A detailed discussion concerning these changes has been presented elsewhere[2].

3. General methods

Since many of the substances discussed in this chapter are present in the same tissue and show similar chemical structures, it is possible to generalize the description of methods of isolation, purification, analysis of the con-stituents, and determination of the chemical structure.

(a) Isolation and purification

Starting from fresh tissues, or tissues dehydrated with acetone, a limited amount of the mucopolysaccharide can be extracted with water or with salt solution. However, a large proportion seems to be bound to protein, and solubilization requires degradation of the protein part with enzymes, or scission of the carbohydrate–protein linkage with weak alkali.

Proteins coextracted by salt or alkaline solutions can be precipitated with the usual reagents, such as phosphotungstic acid, phosphomolybdic acid, picric acid, etc., or denatured with Sevag's reagent, followed by precipi-tation of the polysaccharide with alcohol. Trichloroacetic acid, phenol or acetic acid extractions have also been used with success.

Fractionation of the glycosaminoglycuronoglycans has been based general-ly on the precipitation of the various salts Na, K, Ca, Ba, Cd, Zn, with alcohol, or on ammonium sulfate precipitation. Recently the use of complex formation with quaternary ammonium salts[8], of separation on ion exchange resins[9] and on modified cellulose[10], or of preparative electrophoresis[11] has been introduced.

(b) Determination of the constituents

The resistance to hydrolysis of each glycosaminoglycan varies greatly, depending on the nature of the component bound to the amino sugar, and on the anomery of the glycosidic linkages.

The presence of both glucuronic acid and α-linkages in heparin and heparitan sulfate results in a polysaccharide resistant to hydrolysis, and the uronic acid part is decarboxylated before the amino sugar part is completely released. Similar difficulties are encountered in the hydrolysis of chondroitin 4- and 6-sulfates (chondroitin sulfates A and C), whereas dermatan sulfate (β-heparin, chondroitin sulfate B) can be hydrolyzed under conditions mild enough to allow the isolation of iduronic acid.

The amino sugar components, D-glucosamine and D-galactosamine are generally detected by the Elson and Morgan reaction or, after N-acetylation, the Morgan and Elson reaction. Distinction between these two sugars is obtained by paper chromatography of the hydrochlorides as such[12], or after ninhydrin degradation[13]. Quantitative determination is most successfully done by separation[14] on Dowex-50, whereas final identification uses the formation of various Schiff's bases, the most convenient being obtained by condensation with 2-hydroxynaphthaldehyde[15].

Because of its facile decarboxylation, the uronic acid part has been identified in the past as glycaric acid, after oxidative splitting[16]. More recent work has taken advantage of new reagents for reducing carboxyl groups, and uronic acids have been identified as the parent hexoses[17].

Other components, such as sulfate and N-acetyl groups, galactose, amino acid contaminations, etc. have been identified by the conventional procedures.

(c) Determination of the chemical structure

The methods generally used for the elucidation of the chemical structure of polysaccharides have been applied with varying degrees of success to the glycosaminoglycuronoglycans.

Formation of derivatives like triphenylmethyl ethers and p-toluylsulfonyl esters, which has been used in simpler polysaccharides to locate free hydroxyls at C-6, has been hindered by the low solubility of the mucopolysaccharides in the solvents generally used to carry out the reaction.

Periodate oxidation has been only partly successful, because of the complexity of the components, and of the possibility of overoxidation at C-5 of the uronic part, and at C-3 of the glycosamine moiety. Recent improvements and refinements of the periodate method, like reduction of the aldehydes formed followed by mild hydrolysis, and determination of the components resistant to oxidation, have not been applied extensively to this group of substances.

Among the other classical methods of structure determination, two were used with success and are responsible for most of our present knowledge of the chemical structure of glycosaminoglycans.

The oldest method is based on the degradation of the polysaccharide into oligosaccharides using acids or enzymes. Information deriving from its application had been sought long ago, and in 1914 the disaccharide chondrosine was isolated from chondroitin sulfate. However, the difficulty in elucidating the structure of chondrosine was so great that only in 1955 could it be definitely established. The advantages of the above procedure reside in the possibility of determining the anomery of the glycosidic linkages and their location, by subsequent synthesis of the oligosaccharide. The disadvantages are the low yields of the degradation products, and also the fact that generally one type of linkage is markedly more resistant than the other one, and only one type of disaccharide is obtained. Degradation with enzymes raises the possibility of artefacts, especially if the resulting compounds are obtained in extremely low yields, whereas acid degradation removes rapidly the sulfate group, making the identification of its location impossible. However, the structure of the oligosaccharide can be established unambiguously by synthesis, still the best proof available.

Application of the second method, the methylation procedure, to glycosaminoglycans has met with success only in recent years. Preliminary experiments before 1940 had resulted in degraded polymers, from which crystalline products could be obtained only in very low yields. When Haworth's original procedure, using dimethyl sulfate and sodium hydroxide was used at low temperatures, undegraded products with a high degree of methylation were obtained. Hydrolysis of these substances afforded crystalline methylated monosaccharides in high yields. During the procedure, neither degradation of the carboxyl and acetamido groups, nor scission or migration of the sulfate groups, could be observed. In the glycosaminoglycuronoglycans investigated up to now, however, a major problem in the interpretation of the results obtained by this procedure derives from the incomplete methylation of the uronic part.

The application of the methylation procedure to amino sugar-containing carbohydrates remained limited so long as no reference compounds were available. Attempts to identify components of the hydrolyzates of methylated mucopolysaccharides using periodate oxidation were not successful. Only since the recent completion of the preparation of all the methylated derivatives of the pyranose forms of D-glucosamine and D-galactosamine as reference substances, has this method been proved very useful[18].

4. Chitin

(a) Introduction

Chitin was discovered in 1811 by Braconnot[19] in the alkali-resistant fraction of fungi. Its name, derived from the Greek Χιτών (tunic), was proposed by Odier[20], who isolated it from the elytra of the cockchafer. Occurring in invertebrates, fungi, and green algae, it is one of the most abundant amino sugar polysaccharides. Because its physical and chemical properties are very similar to those of cellulose, chitin has been called an "animal cellulose". The similarity between the two polymers extends even into their biological functions, since both play a role of support and defense. An extensive review of the chemistry of chitin has recently been published[21].

(b) Occurrence, detection and isolation

Chitin is the major organic component of the skeleton of annelids, arthropods, molluscs, coelenterates and nematods. It is not only a part of the covering, but it may also be found in gut linings, tracheae, and in the internal shell of the squid. In addition to chitin, the crustacean shell contains a large proportion of proteins and up to 75 % of calcium carbonate. A weak bonding has been detected between chitin and soluble protein in the soft cuticle of arthropods, whereas this bonding is strong in the sclerotized cuticle.

The cell wall of all fungi, with the exception of two families in the *phycomycetes* and two in the *saccharomycetes*, contains chitin. In some of the higher fungi, its concentration may reach 45 % of the dry constituents. Since chitin is closely associated with other components of the cell wall, it is rarely isolated in a high degree of purity. On the basis of physico-chemical and chemical determinations, however, there is little doubt that fungal and animal chitins are identical. Chitin has also been detected in green algae, but there is still some doubt concerning its presence in yeasts.

The most frequently used method of detection is based on the insolubility of chitin in a concentrated solution of alkali at 160°. Partial deacetylation occurs during this treatment, resulting in the formation of chitosan. This degradation product reacts with iodine–potassium iodide to give a brown color, which becomes violet on addition of sulfuric acid. When chitosan is treated directly with sulfuric acid, spherocrystals of chitosan sulfate are formed. These crystals are characteristically stained with fuchsin and picric acid[22]. X-ray diffraction diagrams have also been used for the identification of chitin, but purification of the samples for this purpose might be tedious. The accuracy of the quantitative determination of chitin has been limited by the difficulty of controlling the purity of the chitin investigated.

Since chitin is closely connected with other materials in animal or fungal tissues, its isolation usually entails a certain amount of degradation. The most used source for laboratory investigation is the shell of crustaceans (crab or lobster). Extraction with dilute hydrochloric acid removes the inorganic constituents, whereas dilute sodium hydroxide solubilizes the proteins[23]. Further purification may involve bleaching with permanganate and precipitation from solution in concentrated mineral acids, but important degradation probably occurs during these treatments.

(c) Properties

Chitin is a white, amorphous solid, insoluble in water, dilute acids, dilute and concentrated alkali, and organic solvents. It readily dissolves in concentrated hydrochloric, sulfuric, nitric, and phosphoric acids, in anhydrous formic acid, with difficulty in liquid ammonia, but not in Schweizer's reagent. Hot, concentrated solutions of neutral salts, like lithium and calcium thiocyanate, dissolve chitin, which can then be reprecipitated by dilution with alcohol or acetone, without apparent degradation.

In hydrochloric acid solution, chitin shows an initial optical rotation of $[\alpha]_D - 14°$, slowly changing to $+ 56°$ as a result of hydrolysis. This change in rotation may be taken as evidence for the presence of β-D-linkages.

Viscosity measurements on partly degraded chitin in nitric acid solutions gave values (η spec.) of $14.3 \cdot 10^{-3}$ and $13.1 \cdot 10^{-3}$ for crab and fungal chitin respectively, and $13.0–17.0 \cdot 10^{-3}$ for purified wood cellulose.

The crystalline nature of the polysaccharide has been well established by X-ray investigation. The biological analogy between chitin and cellulose led Meyer and Mark to the conclusion that the glucosamine units in chitin are linked in a similar fashion as the glucose units in cellulose, and they proposed a rhombic unit cell containing 4 chitobiose residues. In this unit the chains are directed in opposite senses, and the rings follow one another in a digonal screw sequence[24]. Two different crystalline cells have been observed, one in the chitins isolated from arthropods and fungi, the other one in chitins isolated from annelides. They have received the names of α- and β-chitin respectively.

(d) Composition and chemical structure

(i) Degradation

Complete hydrolysis of chitin with mineral acids yields solely 2-amino-

2-deoxy-D-glucose (D-glucosamine) and acetic acid. The isolation of D-glucosamine hydrochloride from lobster shell had been already accomplished in 1876 by Ledderhose[25], but it was not until 1939 that the configuration of this important amino sugar was unequivocally proved by synthesis. In a later investigation, hydrolysis under milder conditions afforded 2-acetamido-2-deoxy-D-glucose (N-acetylglucosamine).

Oligosaccharides have been obtained by degradation of chitin. Thus, the disaccharide di-N-acetyl-hexa-O-acetylchitobiose* (I) and the trisaccharide (II) were isolated directly after acetolysis or after partial hydrolysis, followed

by acetylation[26]. Attempts to obtain higher homologues using acetolysis did not succeed, because of artefact formation during deacetylation. The difficulties encountered in the controlled partial hydrolysis of chitin, due to its insolubility in weak acids, have been overcome by using chitosan, the water-soluble deacetylated derivative. After N-acetylation and fractionation on a column of carbon and Celite, the first seven chitin oligosaccharides were isolated[27].

Degradation of chitin by an enzymic preparation obtained from the in-

---

* In the nomenclature system proposed by Foster and Webber[21].

testine of the snail afforded up to 80 % of *N*-acetylglucosamine. Other chitinases have been isolated from emulsin and from *Streptomyces griseus*, the latter enzyme giving tri- and tetrasaccharides.

The results of the various acidic and enzymic degradations are conclusive evidence that chitin is a homogeneous polymer composed of 2-acetamido-2-deoxy-D-glucose residues attached by β-glycosidic linkages.

(ii) Structure of the oligosaccharides and of chitin

Six of the eight acetyl groups of di-*N*-acetyl-hexa-*O*-acetylchitobiose (I) are easily saponified, showing that the two remaining acetyl residues in III are linked to the amino groups. Oxidation of III with iodine in presence of alkali affords a diacetylaldobionic acid (IV), which on hydrolysis gives glucosamine and glucosaminic acid. Consequently, the disaccharide III contains a free aldehyde group, and C-1 and C-2 of the reducing moiety are not involved in the glycosidic linkage. Treatments of IV with acetic anhydride and sodium acetate gave the unsaturated acid Va, with the double bond located between C-2 and C-3. Since 2-amino-2-deoxy-D-gluconic acid, treated under the same conditions, gives a product with double bonds located between C-2 and C-3, and C-4 and C-5, carbon 4 was assumed to be the site of the linkage[26].

Periodate oxidation of di-*N*-acetylchitobiose, tri-*N*-acetylchitotriose, chitosan, and chitin supports the proposed glycosidic linkage at C-4 in the chitin molecule[28]. Additional evidence for the structure deduced from the

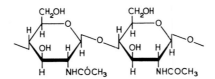

Fig. 1. Repeating unit of chitin.

above described experiments, and represented in Fig. 1, was obtained in the study of the oligosaccharides resulting from degradation. They showed a negative Morgan and Elson reaction, which is characteristic for 4-substituted *N*-acetylglucosamines[27].

(iii) Derivatives

Since chitin does not swell in most media used for esterification, the preparation of esters requires energetic conditions, resulting in extensive degradation. Thus, acetate, nitrate and sulfate esters have been prepared, the latter ones for a possible use as synthetic blood anticoagulant.

The etherification of chitin presents the same difficulties. Repeated methylation could not introduce more than 50 % of the theoretical amount of methoxyl group, but at the same time an extensive degradation occurred. Under these conditions it was not possible to use this procedure for structural investigation[29].

Treatment of chitin with alkali at high temperature afforded a mixture of deacetylated, degraded products with varying degrees of N-acetylation, called chitosan[30]. N- and O-sulfation of this product gave a substance showing 50 % of the anticoagulant activity of heparin. No activity, however, was found with N-sulfation alone, proving the inability of the sulfoamino group to confer by itself anticoagulant properties[31].

5. Galactosaminoglycan of *Aspergillus parasiticus*

The presence of galactosamine-containing substances was demonstrated in the mycelia of six strains of fungi[32]. In some of them, the proportion of galactosamine was found to be as high as that of glucosamine. From the growth medium of one of these fungi, *Aspergillus parasiticus*, was isolated a viscous galactosaminoglycan possessing $[\alpha]_D + 51.5°$ in phosphate buffer, pH 5.6, and a relative viscosity of 9.4. It contained only one component, D-galactosamine, which was identified after hydrolysis by paper chromatography, and formation of the crystalline N-carbobenzyloxy derivative. Approximately two thirds of the amino groups were free, the remainder being linked to acetyl groups. N-acetylation of the free amino groups gave a product almost completely N-acetylated, insoluble in water and dilute alkali, but soluble in 10 % sodium hydroxide at 100°. This property allowed the separation of the galactosaminoglycan from chitin. No further information on the chemical structure of this galactosamine-containing polysaccharide has been reported.

6. Hyaluronic acid

(a) Introduction

Hyaluronic acid was isolated by Meyer and Palmer in 1934, for the first time in a pure state, from bovine vitreous humor[33]. Its name had been derived from "hyaloid (vitreous) + uronic acid". This substance is found in the ground substance of many connective tissues, where it seems to play an important physiological role. In tissues or fluids, this polysaccharide exists free or very loosely associated with proteins, giving highly viscous solutions. The resistance of tissues to infection depends probably in part on this property. Hyaluronic acid binds water in intercellular spaces, serving as a lubricant in joints. Because of its high degree of hydration with marked interaction between molecules, it impedes the passage of interstitial water, thus increasing the resistance to compression.

(b) Occurrence, detection and isolation

Hyaluronic acid is found in varying amounts, up to 5 % of the dry weight, in different animal tissues, the highest concentrations being in umbilical cord, vitreous humor, joint fluids, and skin. It has also been reported in cornea, bone, heart valve, tumor fluids, in the cock's comb, in the chick oviduct, and in groups A and C hemolytic streptococci. In mesenchymal tissue, hyaluronic acid seems to be produced at the site by young fibroblasts and mast cells.

Differentiation of hyaluronic acid from the other glycosaminoglycuronoglycans is difficult. This has been responsible in the past for the description of non-existent entities, such as mucoitin sulfate and hyaluronic acid sulfate.

One of the earliest methods of detecting hyaluronic acid was the formation of a so-called "mucin clot" in presence of proteins, by addition of acetic acid to fluids or tissue extracts[34]. Detection by measurements of the decrease of viscosity, after addition of hyaluronidase, is not reliable, because the pure enzyme is not available, and the mixture of enzymes used also degrades the chondroitin sulfates. Definite identification by chemical means requires separation on a microscale, using selective adsorption on a column, or fractionation by electrophoresis, determination of the physical characteristics, and analysis of the components.

The determination in tissues by histochemical methods has given rise to many controversial statements in the past, since hyaluronic acid is generally associated with glycoproteins. Thus the latter substances have been responsible for the positive periodate Schiff reaction ascribed to hyaluronic acid. At the present time, the best histochemical method is based on the detection of the carboxyl group by ferric ion fixation or Alcian Blue[35], but unfortunately it is not specific enough, and will detect many accompanying components.

The methods of isolation vary with different materials, but consist in general of a solubilization, followed by removal of the protein contaminations and then fractionation of the crude mixture. Vitreous humor, and synovial and tumor fluids, in which the concentration is small, are treated with acetone or acetic acid to precipitate a mixture of protein and hyaluronic acid. Tissues, such as umbilical cords, can be extracted directly with saline solution, and the solubilized hyaluronic acid is precipitated by subsequent addition of ammonium sulfate and pyridine. With this treatment, part of the hyaluronic acid is left in the tissue, but contamination with chondroitin sulfate is avoided. Extraction of the whole of the hyaluronic acid requires a pretreatment with proteolytic enzymes, or an extraction with trichloroacetic acid or phenol. The product obtained is, however, contaminated with other glycosaminoglycuronoglycans.

From the crude solution of hyaluronic acid, the protein contaminations are removed by Sevag's treatment with chloroform and amyl alcohol, or by adsorption on Lloyd's reagent, kaolin, etc. Hyaluronic acid is then isolated by precipitation with acetone or alcohol, or by lyophilization of the solution.

The products obtained from fluids are generally free from other acidic polysaccharides. Those obtained from tissues contain sulfated polysaccharides and can be purified through precipitation with pyridine and ammonium sulfate[36], or by fractionation with cetylpyridinium chloride[8].

(c) Properties

Hyaluronic acid, a white amorphous solid, is soluble in water, insoluble in organic solvents, and shows an optical rotation of $-70°$ to $-80°$ in water. The most striking property of hyaluronic acid is the high viscosity of its solution, much greater than that of sulfated mucopolysaccharides. The viscosity varies with the molecular weight of the material, but is also greatly influenced by the pH and ionic strength.

Decrease of the viscosity is observed after treatment with acid, base or enzyme, and is probably due to the hydrolysis of the glycosidic bonds. A similar decrease, which has not been satisfactorily explained as yet, occurs also after treatment with many reducing agents, such as cysteine, pyrogallol, ascorbic acid, or heavy metal ions, or after irradiation with ultraviolet light or beams of electrons.

The molecular weight of hyaluronic acid has been determined by osmotic pressure, sedimentation–diffusion and light scattering methods. Values between $5 \cdot 10^4$ and $8 \cdot 10^6$ have been found, depending on the source, on the technique of preparation and on the methods of determination. Since the substance is polydisperse, the values obtained by light scattering are always higher. Hyaluronic acid obtained from vitreous body shows a molecular weight markedly smaller than those observed for the hyaluronic acids isolated from synovial fluid, umbilical cord, skin, or rooster comb. The dimensions, shape, volume and hydration of the molecule also depend greatly on the methods used for their study and on the way of preparing the sample. For a hyaluronic acid of low molecular weight, the observed length of the molecule varied from 1600 to 3400 Å. For a high molecular sample, with a randomly-kinked coil, the value of the length[37] was observed to vary from 2400 to 6400 Å. Sodium hyaluronate shows some degree of crystallinity when stretched as a film in a mixture of ethanol and water, thus allowing the determination of X-ray diffraction data[38].

The hyaluronic acid molecule is negatively charged, migrating in the electric field with a speed of 9 to $14 \cdot 10^{-5}$ cm^2/sec·volt. The polyelectrolyte character is clearly shown in the viscous behavior and in the fact that the viscosity–concentration relationship follows the Fuoss equation. In fluids and tissues, the formation of a complex of hyaluronic acid with a definite protein is still uncertain, but the physical properties of hyaluronic acid seem to be independent of such specific combination.

(d) Composition and chemical structure

(i) Degradation

Complete hydrolysis of hyaluronic acid with mineral acids produces D-glucosamine, acetic acid, and carbon dioxide, the last named indicating the presence of a uronic acid. The latter compound was identified as D-glucuronic acid by oxidation with nitric acid, which led to the formation of D-glucaric acid. D-Glucuronic acid was subsequently isolated after enzymic degradation. The carboxyl group of the uronic moiety is free, as shown by salt formation, titration, and the positive hydroxamic test after ester formation.

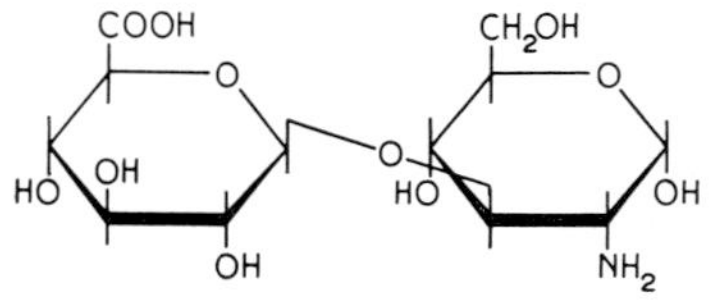

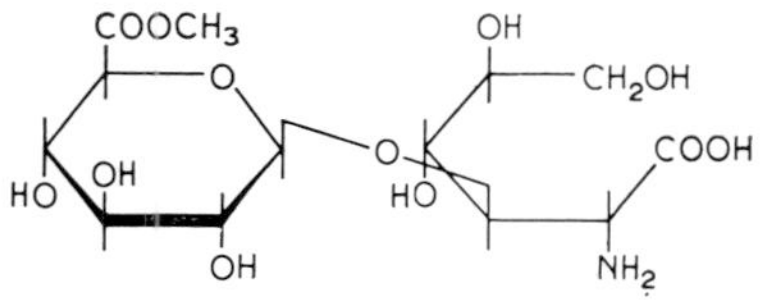

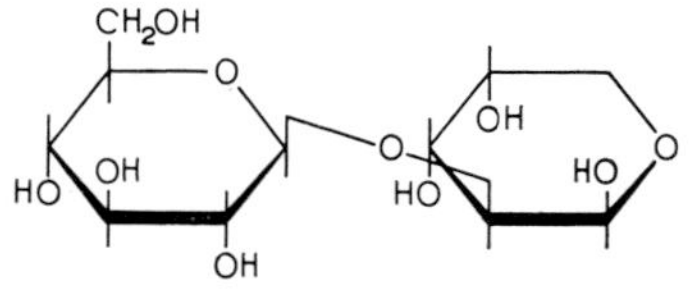

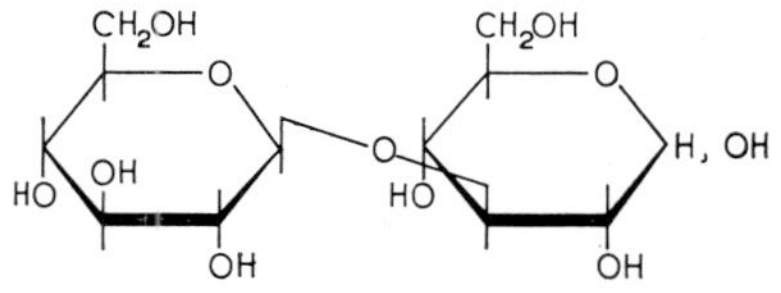

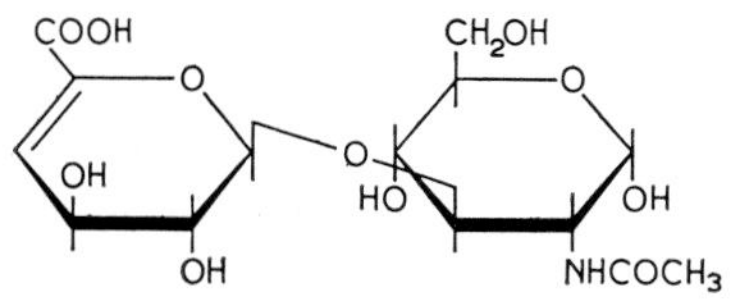

Action of dilute sulfuric acid for a short period of time afforded a crystalline disaccharide (Vb), in a 20 to 30 % yield. It contained equal amounts of D-glucosamine and D-glucuronic acid, and a free amino group. Esterification of the carboxyl group, followed by oxidation with mercuric oxide, gave the free acid VI. The uronic moiety of this product was reduced to a glucose residue with sodium borohydride, then the glucosaminic part was degraded with ninhydrin, affording finally 2-O-β-D-glucopyranosyl-D-arabinose (VII), identified through its crystalline heptaacetyl derivative. The same disaccharide VII was obtained by a Wohl degradation of laminaribiose (VIII), thus establishing the β-anomery and pyranose structure of the glucuronosyl residue, and its linkage with position 3 of the hexosaminyl moiety[39].

Degradation with testis hyaluronidase produced the disaccharide Vb in a very low yield, and a tetrasaccharide resulted as main product of the reaction (yield 90 %). When bacterial hyaluronidase acted upon the polysaccharide, the final product of hydrolysis was an unsaturated disaccharide IX, the structure of which was established by degradation. From the location of the double bond at positions 4 and 5 of the uronic moiety, it was inferred that the glucosaminyl residue was linked[40] at position 4.

Oxidation of hyaluronic acid with periodate has shown the consumption of less than 0.5 mole of oxidant per disaccharide unit, an amount difficult to explain in view of the established structure.

(ii) Methylation studies

Repeated action of dimethyl sulfate and sodium hydroxide in the cold, followed by treatment with diazomethane, afforded the methyl ester of a highly methylated hyaluronic acid[41]. Degradation by methanolysis gave a 60 % yield of a crystalline methyl ester methyl glycoside (X). Methylation

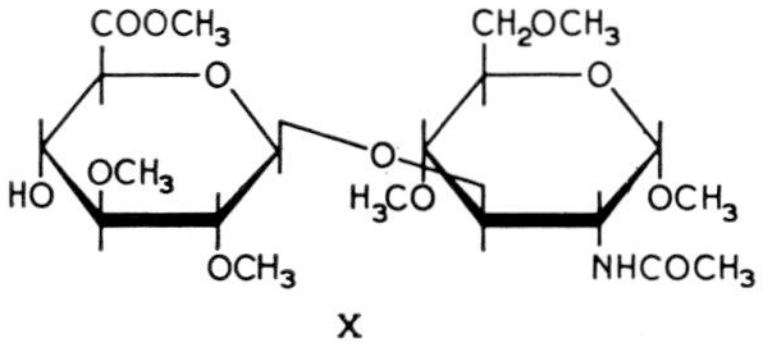

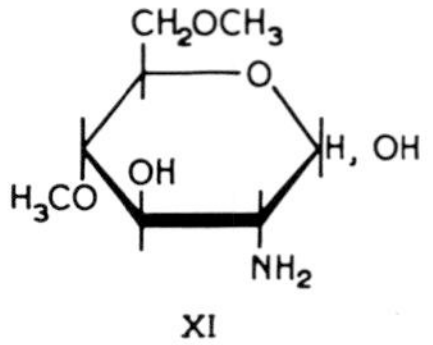

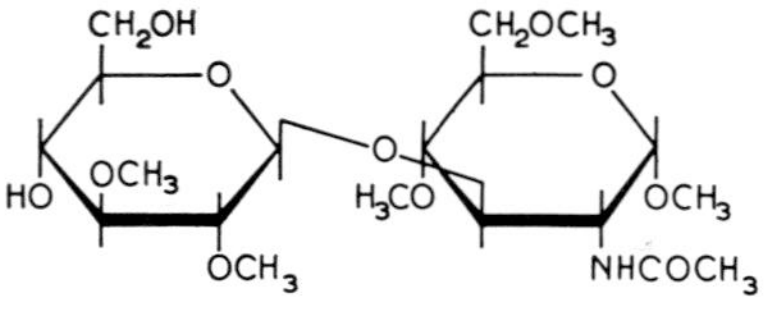

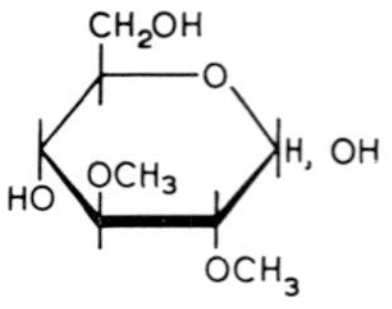

of the remaining free hydroxyl of X, followed by hydrolysis, gave 2-amino-2-deoxy-4,6-di-O-methyl-D-glucose (XI), showing the glucosaminyl moiety to be located at the reducing end of the disaccharide X. Hydrolysis of X gave the same dimethylglucosamine XI in a 70–75 % yield, thus showing the glucuronosyl moiety to be linked at position 3 of the hexosaminyl residue. In addition, this residue was shown to possess a pyranose ring. Reduction of X with sodium borohydride gave the crystalline glucosyl erivative XII, which afforded, after hydrolysis, 2,3-di-O-methyl-D-glucose

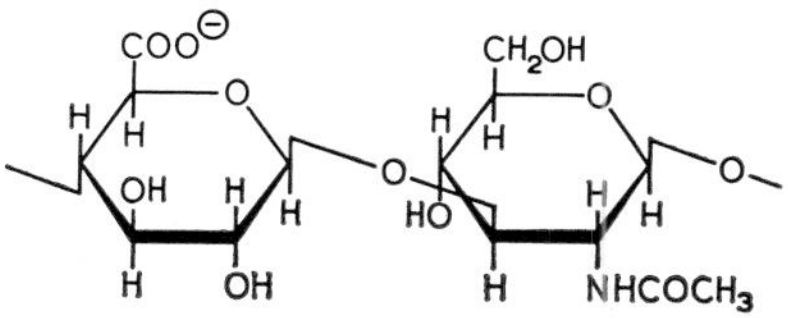

Fig. 2. Repeating unit of hyaluronic acid.

XIII. This same crystalline compound XIII was also obtained by reduction of methylated hyaluronic acid, followed by hydrolysis. The isolation of XIII proves the location of the hexosaminyl residue to be at position 4 of the uronic acid. The isolation of the crystalline ester X in so high a yield shows clearly the regular alternate sequence of the repeating unit shown in Fig. 2 as basic structure of the hyaluronic acid molecule. No trimethyl-glucosamine from the methylated polysaccharide, or trimethylglucose from its reduced derivative, could be identified, proving the absence of branching[42].

The isolation of 2,3,6-tri-O-methyl-α-D-glucopyranose from a reduced and permethylated tetrasaccharide obtained by enzymatic degradation of hyaluronic acid is further evidence for the location of the hexosaminyl residue[42a].

(iii) Derivatives

In addition to the various methylated and reduced derivatives already mentioned, the methyl ester of hyaluronic acid and the partially acetylated, tritylated, tosylated and sulfated derivatives have been described, the last named possessing anticoagulant properties.

7. Teichan (Teichuronic acid)

(a) Introduction

The cell wall of the vegetative cells of *Bacillus subtilis* strain 6346 contains a high molecular polysaccharide possessing N-acetylgalactosamine and glucuronic acid units[43], in addition to the muramic-glycopeptide, a protein, and teichoic acid. This polysaccharide has been named teichuronic acid; however since it has been shown to be a pure glycan, we would propose the name of teichan.

(b) Isolation and properties

Teichoic acid was removed from the cell wall by preliminary trichloroacetic acid treatment, and successive extractions with the same solvent gave a solution, from which teichan was precipitated with cetylpyridinium bromide. The product was purified by ethanol precipitation, and from 1.2 g of dry cell wall material, 81 mg was obtained.

This material, a white powder, gave a viscous solution in water. In electrophoresis at pH 6.5, it moved more rapidly than hyaluronic acid, but less than chondroitin sulfate, and the optical rotation in water was $[\alpha]_D + 38°$ to $+ 40°$. The homogeneity of teichan was shown by column fractionation on diethylaminoethylcellulose.

(c) Composition and chemical structure

After hydrolysis and paper chromatography, the amino sugar component of teichan was identified as galactosamine, and the uronic component as glucuronic acid.

Partial hydrolysis afforded very small yields of disaccharides. They reacted with the Elson and Morgan reagent, and the absorbance maxima suggested the presence of a 3-O-glucuronosyl-N-acetylgalactosamine unit.

Teichan was shown to be very labile in presence of hot alkali, which would indicate some difference in its chemical structure from those of hyaluronic acid and chondroitin. The results of the periodate oxidation of teichan were similar to those of hyaluronic acid, whereas infrared spectra studies confirmed the presence of α-glycosidic linkages, already suggested by the positive optical rotation.

The chemical structure of teichan seems to be very similar to the structure of chondroitin, but with α-glycosidic linkages. The identification of the position of the glucuronosyl residue needs further confirmation, whereas the position of the galactosaminidic linkage is still unknown.

8. Chondroitin 4-sulfate

(a) Introduction

Chondroitin 4-sulfate[44], one of the major constituents of cartilage, was isolated in a relatively pure form as early as 1884. Five years later, a pure preparation was obtained[45], and the product received the name of "chondroit acid" (later chondroitin sulfuric acid) from cartilage (Greek $Xov\delta\rho os$); the designation "chondroitin sulfate A" was subsequently introduced, to differentiate it from a similar product, also isolated from cartilage[46]. Since the difference seems to reside solely in the position of the sulfate group, the term chondroitin 4-sulfate will be used instead.

Chondroitin 4-sulfate is easily differentiated from the sulfated poly-saccharides of the heparin type by its negative optical rotation, and from dermatan sulfate (also called "chondroitin sulfate B" or β-heparin) by the identification of L-iduronic acid in the latter. However, it is difficult to distinguish it from chondroitin 6-sulfate ("chondroitin sulfate C"), since the differences in optical rotation, solubility, and susceptibility to enzymic degradation between the two substances are minimal or non-existent. It is probable that studies made in the past with products isolated from in-completely characterized sources have dealt with mixtures of both chon-droitin sulfates.

The viscosity and the water retention of the chondroitin sulfates give them, in connective tissues, a role quite similar to that of hyaluronic acid. In addition, they possess a high ion-binding capacity due to the strongly dissociated sulfate groups.

(b) Occurrence, detection and isolation

Chondroitin 4-sulfate represents 40 % of the dry cartilage of pig nasal septa. It has also been isolated from numerous other cartilages, from skin, cornea, sclera, bones, umbilical cords, urine and chondrosarcoma, and is abundant in granulation tissues. Detection and identification of chondroitin 4-sulfate with any degree of certainty requires isolation, since no convenient method of determination of glucuronic acid in tissue has been devised, and galactos-amine is present in many different substances.

Identification by histochemical methods will not differentiate between chondroitin 4- and 6-sulfate, and dermatan sulfate. It is based on the use of dyes, such as toluidine blue, which change color in presence of the sulfated polysaccharides (metachromasia)[47], or on the use of radioactive sulfur.

Separation from hyaluronic acid and from more sulfated glycosamino-glycuronoglycans has been successfully achieved by precipitation with alcohol, or with cetylpyridinium chloride solution in presence of salt, by electrophoresis, or by chromatography on modified cellulose ion-exchanger. A clear cut separation from chondroitin 6-sulfate, however, still remains to be achieved.

Pure chondroitin 4-sulfate is obtained when extracted from nasal septa or trachea cartilage. Complete extraction was obtained in the past by treating the cartilage with a 2 % solution of sodium or potassium hydroxide in the cold. In order to avoid degradation, milder conditions have been applied, using salt extraction (calcium chloride or potassium chloride), but this resulted in low yields of the final product. A satisfactory procedure consists in treating the dry, finely granulated cartilage with 30 % potassium chloride containing 1 % of potassium carbonate[48]. The protein impurities are removed by precipitation with picric acid or phosphotungstic acid, by denaturation with amyl alcohol and chloroform, or by adsorption on kaolin; it is also possible to precipitate the polysaccharide as a complex with cobalthexamine, the proteins remaining in the solution. Traces of glycoprotein contamination may remain in the product, and a final purification can be obtained by slow precipitation of the calcium salt in presence of acetic acid and alcohol, giving a crystalline-like product.

Careful extraction of cartilage with water, salt solutions, or phenol, affords complexes of chondroitin sulfate with proteins.

(c) Properties

Chondroitin 4-sulfate is soluble in water, but insoluble in organic solvents. The neutral salt shows an optical rotation $[\alpha]_D -28°$ to $-33°$ in water. The viscosity of the solutions of chondroitin sulfate is lower than that of hyaluronic acid, but follows the Fuoss equation, and is also dependent on the pH and the ionic strength.

Determination of molecular weight by physical methods has given a large range of values, depending on the mode of isolation. Careful treatment leaves part of the chondroitin sulfate in a high molecular complex with proteins, whereas too strong a treatment causes degradation of the polysaccharide chain itself. Values of 40,000 to 50,000 obtained by osmotic pressure measurements are most commonly accepted.

Chondroitin 4-sulfate, possessing a strongly negatively charged molecule, migrates in the electrical field at a speed slightly greater than that of hyaluronic acid ($16 \cdot 10^{-5} cm^2/sec \cdot volt$). It can thus be easily separated, especially with paper electrophoresis. The pK value of the carboxyl group of chondroitin 4-sulfate is close to that of free glucuronic acid, 3.1. Examination by X-ray diffraction has shown the fractions seemingly possessing a crystalline shape to be amorphous, whereas fractions seemingly amorphous gave a crystalline pattern.

(d) Composition and chemical structure

(i) Degradation

Prolonged hydrolysis of chondroitin 4-sulfate with concentrated mineral acids affords, in equal molecular amount, acetic acid, sulfuric acid, and D-galactosamine. Most of the D-glucuronic acid component is destroyed, but it has been identified in the methylated polysaccharide.

A disaccharide, chondrosine (XIV) was obtained as the crystalline ethyl ester as early as 1914, by using milder conditions[49]. However, its correct structure was only established 40 years later. The results of the iodine oxidation, the positive Elson and Morgan reaction, the periodate oxidation, and the inability to obtain a glycoside derivative starting from the hydro-chloride, whereas the *N*-acetyl derivative forms readily a glycoside, showed the galactosamine moiety to be located at the reducing end of chondrosine (XIV).

Reduction of both aldehyde and carboxyl groups gave a glucosyl-galactosaminitol XV, which could be cleaved with β-glucosidase, and after

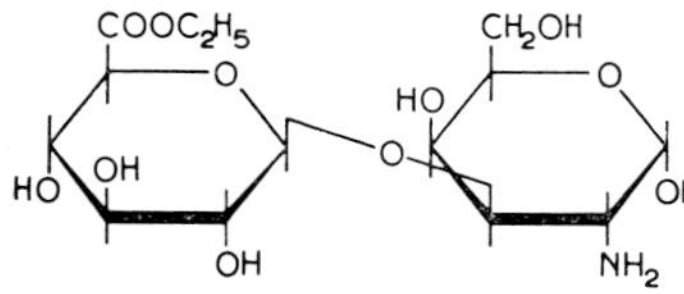

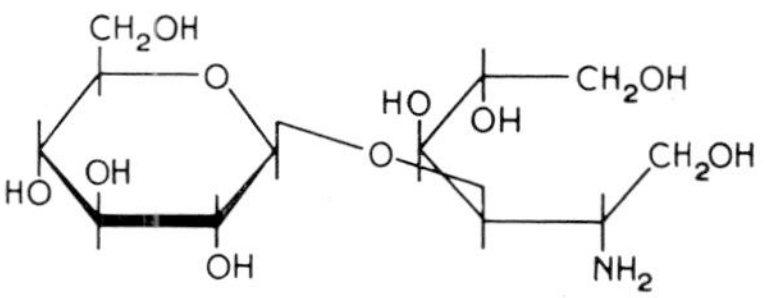

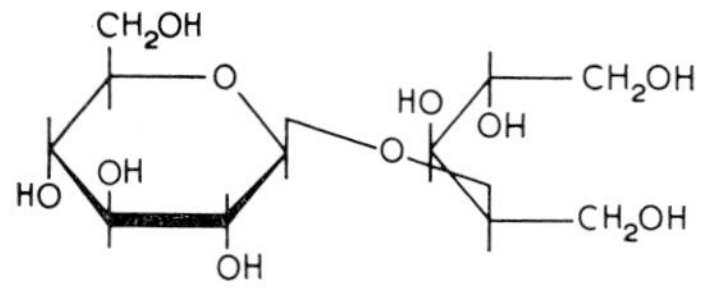

hydrolysis afforded D-glucose as the pentaacetate derivative. Degradation of chondrosine with ninhydrin, followed by reduction of the aldehyde and carboxyl groups gave a glucopyranosyl-lyxitol XVI, isolated as the crystalline octaacetate. Periodate oxidation of XVI consumed 4 moles of periodate, with the formation of 2 moles of formic acid and 1 mole of formaldehyde. These results are consistent solely with a β-(1 → 3)-glucuronidic linkage in the original chondrosine[50].

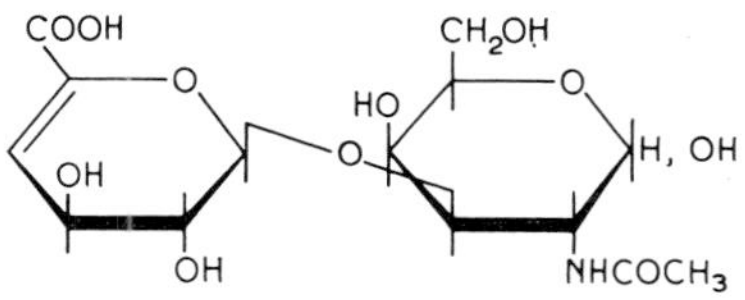

Desulfated chondroitin sulfate is degraded by bacterial hyaluronidases and affords an unsaturated disaccharide XVII. Action of induced enzymes from flavobacteria splits the sulfate group and gives the same unsaturated disaccharide XVII, nearly identical with the disaccharide IX, isolated from hyaluronic acid.

Thus, the results of degradation studies have established the β-(1 → 3)-glucuronidic linkage, and suggested a linkage at C-4 of the glucuronic moiety.

(ii) Methylation

The development of a desulfation procedure, resulting in a complete removal of the sulfate groups with an extremely small degradation of the glycosidic bonds[51], allowed full use of the methylation procedure to establish the structure of chondroitin 4-sulfate. Repeated methylation of chondroitin sulfate and of its desulfated derivative XVIII, with dimethyl sulfate and sodium hydroxide in the cold, resulted in the almost fully methylated

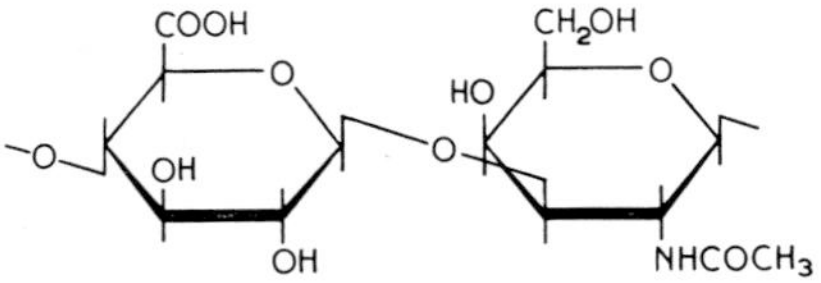

XVIII

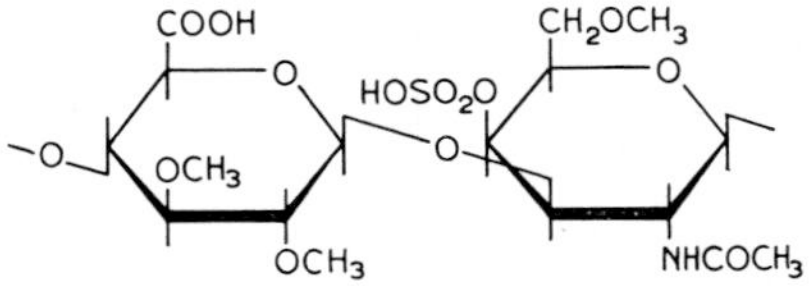

XIX

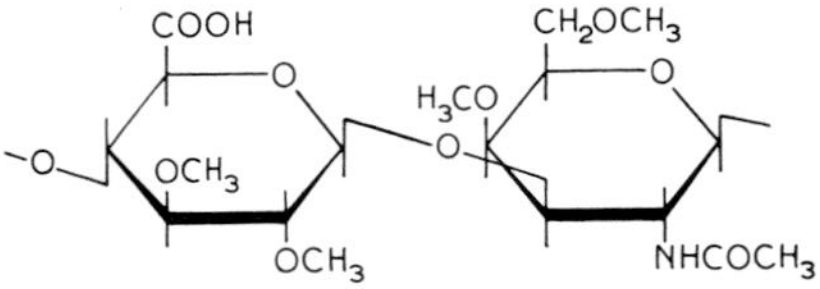

XX

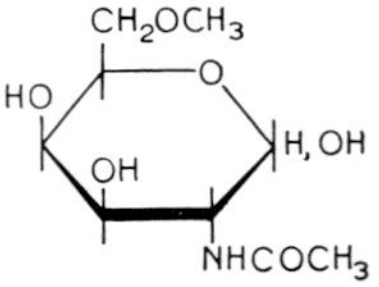

XXI

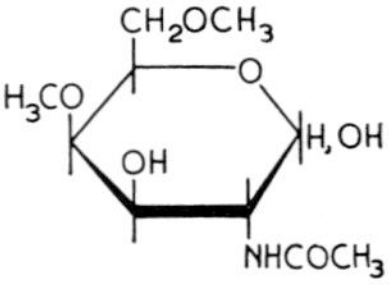

XXII

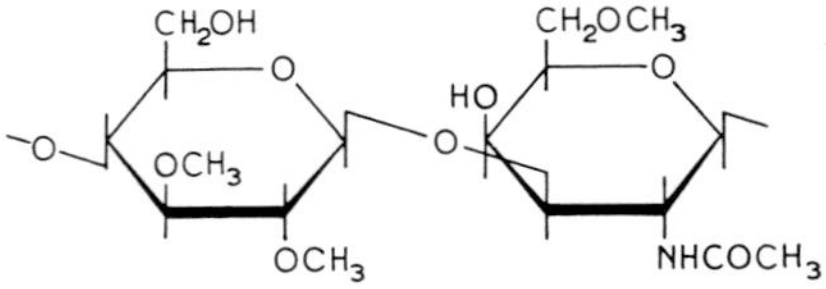

XXIII

polysaccharides XIX and XX. Hydrolysis of desulfated and reduced XIX, followed by N-acetylation of the hexosamine part gave crystalline 2-acetamido-2-deoxy-6-O-methyl-α-D-galactose (XXI), in a 85 % yield, further characterized as the crystalline methyl-2-acetamido-2-deoxy-6-O-methyl-α-D-galactopyranoside and its crystalline 3,4-O-isopropylidene derivative. The same treatment of XX resulted in the isolation of crystalline 2-acetamido-2-deoxy-4,6-di-O-methyl-α-D-galactopyranose (XXII) in a 65 % yield, further characterized as the crystalline methyl-α-D-glycoside. These isolations established conclusively the position of the glucuronosyl residue at C-3 of the galactosamine moiety, a fact already indicated by the study of the structure of chondrosine. Since no 4-O-methyl derivative could be observed, and since it is very unlikely that a sulfate group would migrate from the primary alcoholic group to the secondary group at C-4 during methylation, the isolation of XXI was conclusive evidence for the location of the sulfate group at position 4 of the galactosamine moiety. The absence, in the hydrolyzate of XIX, of any significant amount of a dimethylhexosamine, as shown by paper chromatography, proved that a branched structure with hexosaminyl residues as end group was unlikely. The possibility of the galactosamine moiety having a furanose structure was eliminated by the failure to detect formaldehyde after periodate oxidation of desulfated chondroitin sulfate XVIII.

The methylated chondroitin 4-sulfate (XIX) was subsequently desulfated, and reduced with sodium borohydride, about three quarters of the glucuronic residues being transformed into glucose residues (XXIII). Hydrolysis, followed by adsorption of the basic component, gave a mixture of methylated glucoses, from which 2,3-di-O-methyl-D-glucose (XIII) could be isolated in a 50 to 60 % yield. After reduction, it was characterized as the crystalline tetra-p-azobenzoate of the glycitol. The isolated monomethylglucoses would derive from the residues which had not been fully methylated in the original

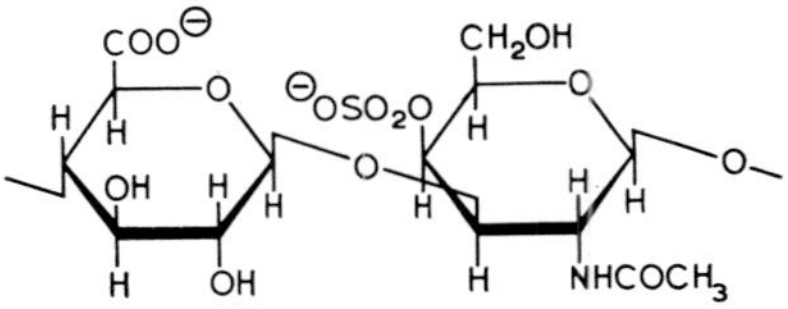

Fig. 3. Repeating unit of chondroitin 4-sulfate.

chondroitin 4-sulfate, and the amount of trimethylglucose detected by chromatography was estimated not to be greater than the amount expected from an unbranched molecule[52].

The above described isolations are conclusive evidence for the location of the galactosaminyl residue at C-4 of the glucuronic moiety, since the pyranose form of the glucuronosyl residue is ascertained by the structure of chondrosine. The anomery at C-1 of the galactosamine moiety is shown to be β on the basis of the negative rotation, thus establishing the structure of chondroitin 4-sulfate as represented in Fig. 3.

(iii) Derivatives

In addition to the desulfated, reduced and methylated derivatives already mentioned, the preparation of sulfated, and of N-deacetylated, then sulfated chondroitin 4-sulfates, has been described, and the anticoagulant properties of these derivatives studied.

9. Chondroitin 6-sulfate

(a) Introduction

A chondroitin sulfate possessing properties slightly different from those of chondroitin 4-sulfate has been isolated from human umbilical cord, tendon, cartilage, heart valve, skin, nucleus pulposus, saliva, and from a chordoma[46]. The material obtained from the latter two sources is probably a pure polysaccharide, whereas material obtained from the other sources seems not to be free of chondroitin 4-sulfate. A polysaccharide sulfate obtained from

shark cartilage is identical in many respects to the product obtained from
the above described sources, but additional information on the chemical
structure of both substances is needed to establish their identity.

(b) Properties and chemical structure

Chondroitin 6-sulfate possesses properties very similar to those of chondroitin
4-sulfate. The optical rotation is slightly lower, $[\alpha]_D -12°$ to $-18°$ for the
neutral calcium salt; but molecular size and shape, viscosity, and electrophoretic mobility are practically identical.

Prolonged hydrolysis of chondroitin 6-sulfate affords galactosamine,
whereas a shorter time of degradation results in a disaccharide identical to
chondrosine. Degradation by enzymes results in the same unsaturated
disaccharide XVII observed in the degradation of chondroitin 4-sulfate.

The first and still only clue for a difference between the chemical structure
of chondroitin 4-sulfate and chondroitin 6-sulfate was supplied by studies
of the infrared spectra[53]. An adsorption band corresponding to an axial
sulfate group was observed in the 840 to 850 wave number region for
chondroitin 4-sulfate, whereas this band shifted to the 815 to 825 wave
number region for the 6-isomer, corresponding to an equatorial position.
Since the only hydroxyl group, in equatorial position and available for

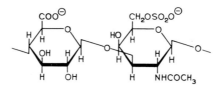

Fig. 4. Repeating unit of chondroitin 6-sulfate.

esterification in the galactosaminyl residue, is located at position 6, the
evidence obtained from the infrared spectra suggests that the sulfate ester
is at this location. The chemical structure of chondroitin 6-sulfate could,
thus, tentatively be established as described in Fig. 4.

Chondroitin sulfates possessing more than one sulfate residue per disaccharide unit have been recently isolated from the cartilage of shark, squid
and crab[53a].

10. Chondroitin

A product possessing a constitution similar to those of chondroitin 4- and
6-sulfate, but with a very small content of sulfate, was isolated from cornea
and named chondroitin[9]. It is degraded by testicular and bacterial hyal-

uronidases, and with the latter enzymes give an unsaturated disaccharide, probably identical to the one (XVII) previously described. Its chemical structure seems very similar to the structures of the two chondroitin sulfates, less the sulfate group, but this hypothesis needs further confirmation.

11. Dermatan sulfate

(a) Introduction

A polysaccharide, isolated at first from pig skin in impure state[54], and thought to be identical to the chondroitin sulfate of cartilage, was found later to be chemically different, and was called "chondroitin sulfate B". Further work established its presence in tendon, heart valves and aorta[55]. The identity of this substance with a well characterized product possessing anticoagulant properties named β-heparin[56], which had been isolated from the residual liquors of the preparation of heparin from beef lungs, was established. Since this polysaccharide is biologically and chemically different from the chondroitin sulfates, and from heparin, the name dermatan sulfate will be used in the present chapter[2].

(b) Occurrence, detection and isolation

Dermatan sulfate is found in variable amounts in tissues and in fluids. In connective tissue, it is associated with the other glycosaminoglycurono-glycans. The amount of dermatan sulfate in the organism seems to increase with age, the ratio to hyaluronic acid being 0.2 or less in the skin of the pig embryo, and increasing to 1.25 in the skin of the adult pig. In Hurler's syndrome, a systemic disease of connective tissue in humans, dermatan sulfate is stored in large amounts intracellularly, and is excreted in the urine.

In addition to the sources previously mentioned, the spleen, brain and ligamentum nuchae contain relatively large amounts of dermatan sulfate, which represents 50% of the total acidic polysaccharides in the last named tissue.

Differentiation of dermatan sulfate from hyaluronic acid and from the chondroitin sulfates is readily made on the basis of the color reaction given by the different uronic acid components. The ratio of intensities of the colors obtained in the carbazole and in the orcinol reactions is approximately 0.5 for L-iduronic acid, the component of dermatan sulfate, whereas it is 1.4 to 1.8 for D-glucuronic acid, the component of the other acidic polysaccharides.

Separation of dermatan sulfate from chondroitin 4-sulfate has not been achieved as yet by electrophoresis, or by partition on column. Alcohol fractionation of the calcium salt, however, or of the zinc or lead salt, gives good results. Since chondroitin 4-sulfate is degraded by hyaluronidases, it can thus be removed from its mixture with dermatan sulfate.

The most convenient starting material for obtaining large amounts of dermatan sulfate is the residual liquor of the technical preparation of heparin. Treatment with alcohol gives a precipitate, which is fractionated through the barium salt with acetic acid, then through the zinc salt with methanol. From 1 kg of crude precipitate, 20 g of dermatan sulfate was thus obtained. Further purification has also been carried out through the cobalt salt.

(c) Properties

Dermatan sulfate has the appearance and the solubility properties of the chondroitin sulfates. The neutral salt shows an optical rotation $[\alpha]_D -60°$ in water, but values up to $-76°$ have been reported. The solubility of dermatan sulfate in a mixture of alcohol and water is lower than those of the chondroitin sulfates. Viscosity and electrophoretic mobility are in an identical range, but the molecular weight of the samples examined showed values about half of those of the chondroitin sulfates. It is quite certain that there is a great similarity between the shape of the molecule of dermatan sulfate and the shape of the molecule of chondroitin sulfate, both being unbranched linear polymers.

(d) Composition and chemical structure

(i) Degradation

Hydrolysis of dermatan sulfate with strong mineral acid afforded equal molecular amounts of acetic acid, sulfuric acid and D-galactosamine. In contrast to the molecule of chondroitin sulfate, the molecule of dermatan sulfate is far more susceptible to hydrolysis, and treatment with dilute acid did not afford a disaccharide, but an undegraded uronic acid. Paper chromatographic analysis indicated that it was similar to iduronic acid[57], which explains the low intensity of the color shown by dermatan sulfate in the carbazole reaction.

Final identification of the uronic component was carried out by desulfation of dermatan sulfate with methanolic hydrochloric acid, followed by reduction

XXIV   XXV

of the carboxyl group to give an idose-galactosamine polymer (XXIV). Hydrolysis of this product with dilute sulfuric acid gave 1,6-anhydro-β-L-idopyranose (XXV), characterized by the crystalline 2,3,4-triacetate, identical to the compound synthesized in five steps from D-glucose[17]. A small amount of D-glucose was also isolated, indicating the presence of D-glucuronic acid in the original material. It is not clear as yet whether the D-glucuronic acid component is part of the molecule of dermatan sulfate, or of a contaminating chondroitin sulfate.

Action on dermatan sulfate of a mixture of induced enzymes extracted from flavobacteria gave an unsaturated disaccharide, which was shown by infrared studies to be probably identical to the disaccharide XVII isolated from chondroitin 4-sulfate[58]. These results confirm the (1 → 3)-iduronidic linkage already shown by methylation studies (see below), they establish the α-anomery of this linkage, and indicate the probability of a (1 → 4)-galactosaminidic linkage.

(ii) Methylation

Methylation of dermatan sulfate and of its desulfated derivative XXVI, with dimethyl sulfate and sodium hydroxide, resulted in completely methylated polysaccharides (XXVII and XXVIII respectively). Since it

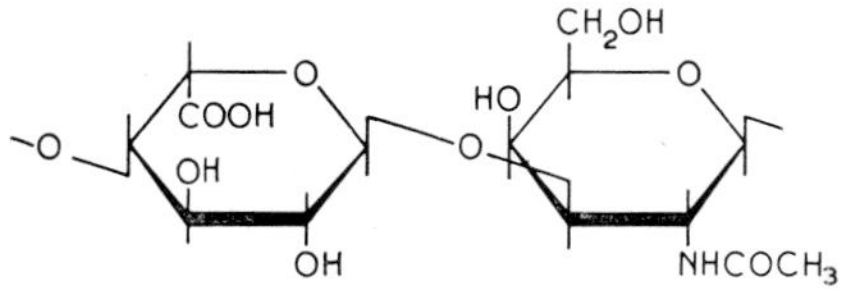

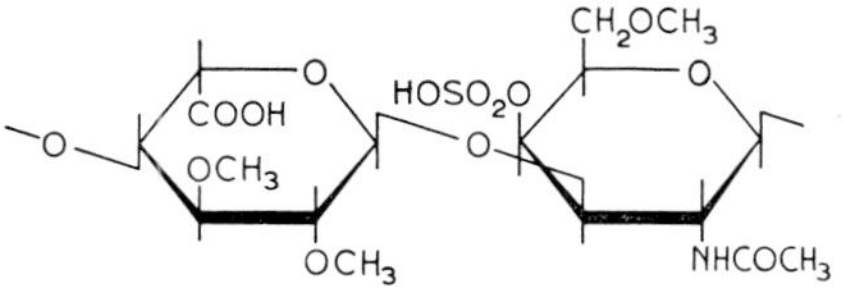

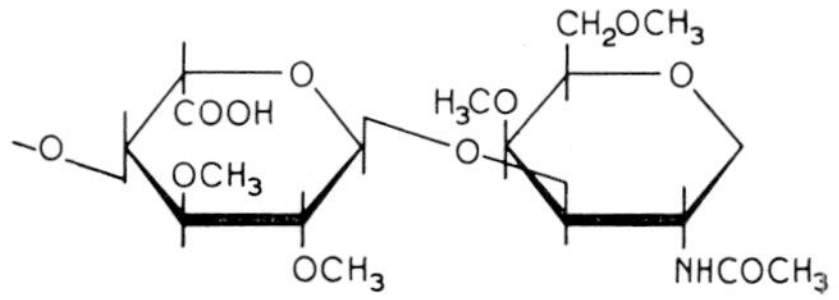

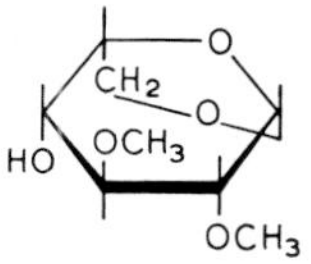

is the D-glucuronic acid moiety of hyaluronic acid and chondroitin 4-sulfate which resists complete methylation, it becomes clear that the special location of the carboxyl group can have a profound influence on the reactivity of the polysaccharide.

After acid hydrolysis of reduced XXVII, the amino sugar fraction was separated, and 6-O-methyl-D-galactosamine was isolated as the crystalline

N-acetyl derivative (XXI) in a 90% yield, and further characterized as methyl-2-acetamido-2-deoxy-3,4-*O*-isopropylidene-6-*O*-methyl-α-D-galacto-pyranoside. The same treatment of XXVIII afforded 4,6-di-*O*-methyl-D-galactosamine, also isolated as crystalline *N*-acetyl derivative (XXII) in a 76% yield, and characterized as the methyl-α-D-glycoside.

These results clearly establish the location of the sulfate group on the hydroxyl at C-4 of the galactosamine moiety, and the location of the L-iduronosyl residue at C-3 of the same moiety. No 4-*O*-methyl derivative could be observed, suggesting that the sulfate groups were located solely at C-4 of the galactosamine residues. A branched structure is not likely, since no dimethylgalactosamine or trimethylgalactosamine could be detected in the hydrolyzates of XXVII or XXVIII respectively. A furanose ring structure of the hexosamine moiety was considered very unlikely[59], since no formaldehyde was produced by periodate oxidation of XXIV.

Reduction of methylated desulfated dermatan sulfate with sodium boro-hydride transformed the L-iduronic acid moiety into an L-idose moiety. Hydrolysis, followed by adsorption of the hexosamine fraction, gave a neutral fraction consisting of sirupy 1,6-anhydro-2,3-di-*O*-methyl-β-L-ido-pyranose (XXIX), identical with a synthetic sample, and of a mixture of 2,3-di-*O*-methyl, 2-*O*-methyl and 3-*O*-methyl-D-glucose. The yield of XXIX was low, because of the volatility of the substance, which was further characterized as a crystalline mono-*p*-azobenzoate. No other methylidoses were observed[60].

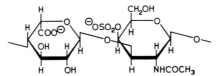

Fig. 5. Repeating unit of dermatan sulfate.

These results are conclusive evidence for the location of the galactosaminyl residue at C-4 of the L-iduronic acid moiety. The anomery of the galactos-aminidic linkage can be assumed to be β, and that of the L-iduronidic to be α, since the molecule of dermatan sulfate possesses a strongly negative optical rotation. The structure of dermatan sulfate is represented in Fig. 5.

No derivatives of dermatan sulfate, with the exception of those reported in the study of the structure, have been reported.

12. Heparan sulfate

(a) Introduction

In 1948, Jorpes and Gardell isolated, as by-product in the preparation of heparin from liver and lung, a polysaccharide composed of D-glucuronic acid and D-glucosamine units. It had a positive rotation, similar to that of heparin; but, in contrast, the content of sulfate groups was low, and it was called "heparin monosulfate"[61]. A product of similar composition and properties was subsequently isolated from the liver of a patient with amyloidosis, and was named "heparitin sulfate"[62]. Since there is some structural similarity between these products and heparin, but with a lower degree of sulfation, we would like to propose the generic name of "heparan" for the desulfated polysaccharide, reserving the word heparin for the highly sulfated, biologically active, substance.

(b) Properties, detection and isolation

Values of optical rotations from $[\alpha]_D +38°$ to $+ 78°$, and various ratios of sulfate to hexosamine content have been reported; these ratios, however, are all in the vicinity of 1. Various contents of sulfamate and N-acetyl groups have also been observed, and it has become evident that one is dealing more with a family of substances, possessing varying degrees of N- and O-sulfation, than with a chemical entity. Since our knowledge of the chemical structure of the polysaccharide chain is still scant, it has not been possible to ascertain definitely the chemical identity between the various low sulfated heparans.

The electrophoretic mobility in acetate buffer, pH 5.0, and in veronal buffer, pH 8.6, was observed to be -15.8, and $-18.6 \cdot 10^{-5}$ cm^2/sec·volt respectively. The molecular weight is small, since the substance dialyzed slowly through Visking membranes; values between 1240 and 2075 have been observed for especially low molecular weight, highly polydisperse samples, isolated from patients with Hurler's syndrome[63].

Different values for anticoagulant activity have been reported, but these discrepancies may be explained by contamination with higher sulfated homologues. The similarity between these low sulfated heparans and biologically active heparin resides in the same positive rotation, the same D-glucosamine and D-glucuronic acid moieties, the same resistance to hyaluronidase, and the same susceptibility to an enzyme extracted from heparin-adapted flavobacteria.

In addition to the sources already mentioned, heparan sulfate has been isolated from hen oviduct, and also from the urine and tissues of patients suffering from Hurler's syndrome. Final identification of heparan sulfate requires its isolation and analysis.

The most convenient method of preparation of heparan sulfate uses a side-fraction in the preparation of commercial heparin. Fractionation with cetylpyridinium chloride, in presence of sodium chloride, afforded substances possessing a positive optical rotation and varying amounts of N-acetyl, N-sulfate, and O-sulfate groups. A similar separation was obtained, using Dowex 1-Cl resin and sodium chloride. Finally, a substance with the optical rotation [α] +60°, 0.91 N-acetyl groups, 0.16 N-sulfate groups and 0.54 O-sulfate groups was isolated, in a 37% yield, from the crude "heparin monosulfate"[64].

(c) Chemical structure

Hydrolysis of heparan sulfate gave crystalline D-glucosamine hydrochloride as the sole amino sugar constituent. Glucuronic acid could be detected by paper chromatography after hydrolysis, the scission of the glycosaminidic linkage being facilitated by the presence of the neighboring N-acetyl group. This behavior contrasts with that of heparin, in which the sulfoamino group is very susceptible to acid hydrolysis and the glucosaminidic linkage is protected by the formation of a neighboring free amino group. Consequently the conditions required for hydrolysis of heparin are so strong that the uronic acid is decarboxylated, and cannot be identified as such.

In heparan sulfate the amount of uronic acid estimated by the carbazole method was much higher than the one found by the decarboxylation method, an observation also made in the case of heparin. Although it has been suggested that this high value was due to the presence of sulfate groups, it is still possible that it depends on the presence of another uronic acid, besides glucuronic acid.

Controlled hydrolysis of heparan sulfate afforded oligosaccharides, which could be separated on charcoal. Most of these degradation products contained a large proportion of uronic groups at the reducing end. On the basis of the reaction of these fragments with the Morgan and Elson, and with the Elson and Morgan reagents, it has been proposed that they contain chiefly (1 →6)-uronosyl-hexosamine linkages. Heparan sulfate would differ in this way from heparin, which would contain mostly (1 →4)-uronosyl-hexosamine linkages[65].

Degradation of heparan sulfate with a crude enzyme extracted from flavobacteria has indicated that the O-sulfate group is attached to the same hexosamine as the one containing the N-sulfate group. From the enzymic hydrolyzate, disaccharides possessing glucosamine or N-acetylglucosamine units at the reducing end, and also unsaturated disaccharides have been isolated[66].

The results of both types of degradation, with mineral acid and with enzymes, would favor a branched type of structure.

13. Heparin

(a) Introduction

Heparin was isolated, in 1916, by McLean from liver as a component having properties to prevent blood coagulation[67]. Its name was derived from the tissue in which it was found in greatest abundance, the liver (Greek ἤπαρ)[68]. Because heparin is biologically very active, it has been the most investigated glycosaminoglycuronoglycan; its chemical structure is, however, one of the least known. The early advances in the study of heparin have been described by Jorpes[69], whereas two reviews describe the more recent work[70, 71].

As already mentioned in the preceding section, there is a marked similarity between the chemical constitutions and chemical properties of heparan sulfate and of heparin. Thus, it has been proposed to place in the same class of compounds the "dextrorotatory sulfated polysaccharides composed of D-glucosamine and D-glucuronic acid residues", such as the "heparin monosulfate", the "heparitin sulfates" with various degrees of sulfation, and the heparins with various degrees of sulfation[71].

(b) Occurrence, detection and isolation

Heparin has been found in many tissues, the larger amounts in liver, muscle and lung, lesser amounts in heart, kidneys, thymus, spleen and blood. It has also been reported in rat skin, but seems absent from the skin of other species. The content of "purified heparin" in beef muscle reaches 0.6 g per kg of tissue[72].

Heparin combines readily with basic dyes; with toluidine blue, the reaction is metachromatic and results in a deep purple color. Using this procedure, heparin has been detected mainly in the mast cells, which are located in connective tissues, especially alongside the capillaries and in the walls of blood vessels. It seems also to be present in basophilic leucocytes, in the stomach, and in the intestinal wall. In the cell itself, heparin seems to be localized in the granules and absent from the cytoplasm. A substance called "mactin", which is probably identical to heparin, has been prepared from mollusca[73].

Identification of heparin requires its isolation and purification, using the methods described in the preceeding chapters, such as fractionation with cetylpyridinium chloride, or column chromatography on ion exchange materials. Final identification and estimation of the degree of purity are based on the biological activity.

The process of extraction of heparin has been developed industrially, and is covered by many patents. Usually, minced beef liver (or beef lungs) is autolyzed at room temperature in presence of water and xylol. The material is extracted with a solution of sodium hydroxide and ammonium sulfate at 50° to 55°. The proteins are then denatured by heating at 70° to 80°, the solution is filtered off, and the pH is adjusted to 2.5, precipitating a complex of protein and heparin. The fat contaminants are removed with alcohol, and after dissolution of the precipitate at pH 8.0, the proteins are digested with trypsin. Following the removal of the enzyme, the crude heparin is precipitated with acetone[74]. For further purification, adsorption on Lloyd's reagent, acetone fractionation, treatment with cadmium chloride and ammonium oxalate, and precipitation with benzidine have been used, and the barium salt of heparin is then obtained in crystalline form. Purification has also been attempted by fractionation of the brucine salts. Other methods of extraction have used milder conditions, such as potassium thiocyanate and phenol solutions.

(c) Properties

Heparin in the acid state, and its amorphous sodium and potassium salts are very soluble in water, whereas its crystalline barium acid salt and its amorphous lead salt have a low solubility. In addition to the barium salt, other salts of heparin have a crystalline appearance, for example those formed with piperidine, n-pentylamine, and isopentylamine. Values of the optical rotation of the barium salt have been reported from +45° to +70°.

The homogeneity of heparin has been studied by electrophoresis and counter-current distribution. Electrophoretic migration values of 8 to $24 \cdot 10^{-5} cm^2/sec \cdot volt$ have been reported, depending on the degree of sulfation and the conditions of the experiment. The molecular weight of various preparations lies between 15,000 and 20,000, consequently higher than those observed for heparan sulfate. Heparin has the lowest intrinsic viscosity of all the glycosaminoglycuronoglycans.

(d) Composition and chemical structure

(i) Composition

Extensive analysis of different preparations of crystalline barium heparinate shows various proportions of sulfate groups, reaching 3 sulfate residues per disaccharide unit for the most active material. The absence of acetyl groups was first observed by Masamune, Suzuki and Kondoh[75], and later confirmed by other workers. Crystalline D-glucosamine hydrochloride was isolated from the acid hydrolyzate of heparin[76], and a paper chromatographic investigation was unable to show the presence of another amino sugar[71]. Since the strong conditions, required to hydrolyze heparin, result in decarboxylation, it has not been possible to isolate D-glucuronic acid. Hydrolysis with simultaneous bromine oxidation, however, gave D-glucaric acid, thus proving the presence of D-glucuronic acid in the polysaccharide[16]. Confirmation of this finding has recently been obtained by reduction of N-desulfated, N-acetylated heparin with sodium borohydride and isolation of D-glucose after hydrolysis, and also by direct isolation of D-glucuronic acid after partial degradation, followed by acetylation and hydrolysis. The yield in the latter product however is small, and the fact that the carbazole reaction for uronic acid is much greater than expected for D-glucuronic acid, has suggested the presence of an additional component.

(ii) The sulfate groups

The absence of acetyl groups and the rapid loss of biological activity in presence of dilute acid, was evidence for the presence of a new type of linkage in amino sugar containing polysaccharides. Studies of the acid hydrolyzate showed that free amino groups were released at the same rate as free sulfuric acid, establishing the presence of a sulfoamino group in the original heparin[77]. The same conclusion was reached after a comparative study of hydrolysis of heparin and glucosamine-N-sulfate, and after the preparation of a nitroso derivative of heparin with nitrous acid[78].

The other sulfate groups are most probably located, as O-esters, in the glucosamine moiety, but no definite evidence has been put forward up to now.

(iii) Degradation

Weak acid hydrolysis of heparin resulted at first in a rapid cleavage of the sulfoamino group, giving N-desulfated heparin. Subsequent hydrolysis of this product is controlled by the presence of the positive charges on the amino groups in acid solution. Fractionation of the hydrolyzate on charcoal gave a mixture of amorphous oligosaccharides. The majority of them contained the uronic acid at the reducing end, the remaining having as reducing end the glucosamine unit linked[65] at position 4 and/or 6.

Since the presence of O-sulfate and free amino groups, in the molecule of heparin during acid hydrolysis, presents difficulties in the interpretation of the course of the reaction, heparin was first N-desulfated, then N-acetylated, and hydrolyzed. An amorphous disaccharide still containing a sulfate group was isolated, and periodate oxidation studies of this product, as well as of its amorphous N-acetyl derivative, suggested the structure of 4-O-α-(D-glucosaminyl 4-sulfate)-D-glucuronic acid[79]. The evidence for this tentative structure is strongly supported by the isolation of a disaccharide from a desulfated and N-acetylated heparin. This compound was shown, by the formation of a flavazole derivative, to possess the structure of 4-O-(2-acetamido-2-deoxy-α-D-glucopyranosyl)-D-glucuronic acid[79a].

References p. 295

In a recent investigation, heparin was N-desulfated, N-acetylated and partially O-desulfated, according to the method of Kantor and Schubert[51], giving a product containing nitrogen and sulfur atoms, and acetyl and methoxyl groups, in the ratio 2:1:2:2. This substance was subsequently partially hydrolyzed, and studies of the isolated disaccharide by color reactions, before and after N-acetylation, suggested as structure 6-O-D-glucuronosyl-D-glucosamine. In addition to this disaccharide, another one containing the uronic acid at the reducing end was isolated[80].

In a study carried out by another group of investigators, acid hydrolysis of a partially desulfated, acetylated, reduced and partially de-O-acetylated heparin afforded the crystalline hydrochloride of a disaccharide in a 21% yield; study of the colors produced by this compound before and after borohydride reduction, in the Elson and Morgan, and Morgan and Elson tests, showed the disaccharide to be O-α-D-glucopyranosyl-$(1 \rightarrow 4)$-2-amino-2-deoxy-α-D-glucopyranose hydrochloride[80a].

The reaction of nitrous acid on glucosamine containing polysaccharides was first studied on chitosan, which afforded 2,5-anhydro-O-mannose. The same result was obtained in the degradation of the methyl-2-amino-2-deoxy-α- or β-D-glucopyranoside. When applied to N-desulfated heparin, the rate of this reaction resembled more that of the α-anomer than that of the β-anomer, thus establishing on a firmer basis the presence of the α-linkages, suggested by the positive optical rotation[70].

Heparin was found to be degraded by bacterial enzymes from flavobacteria, but no study of the degradation products has been reported up to now.

Studies of the periodate oxidation of heparin and of its product of degradation have also been used as a basis for proposing various chemical structures. The lack of precision of this method, and the erroneous conclusion derived from similar studies on other glycosaminoglycuronoglycans, render the structural allocation uncertain. The liberation of ammonia by periodate oxidation of an N-desulfated heparin suggests, however, the absence of linkage at position 3 of the glucosamine residue[81].

(iv) Methylation

Methylation of a quaternary ammonium salt of heparin with methyl iodide and silver oxide at low temperature in an organic solvent gave a monomethyl derivative extensively degraded. From the hydrolyzate of this product, the crystalline hydrochloride of 3-O-methyl-D-glucosamine (**XXX**) was isolated, showing the absence of linkage at position 3 in the glucosamine unit of heparin[81].

(v) Conclusion

The present data are still too inconclusive to allow the drawing of a definite chemical structure for heparin. The remaining problems to be elucidated are: the presence besides D-glucosamine and D-glucuronic acid of a third component; the degree of branching; the proportions of linkages at positions 4 and 6 in the D-glucosamine unit and the positions of the O-sulfate esters.

In view of the observations made with other glycosaminoglycuronoglycans and of the various results obtained in the study of the structure of heparin, it seems necessary to ascertain that the various samples investigated are identical.

14. Keratan sulfate

(a) Introduction

In 1953, a polysaccharide composed of D-galactose and D-glucosamine units, and sulfate groups in a molar ratio 1:1:1 was isolated in a pure state from cornea, and was named "keratosulfate"[82]. It was subsequently found also in the costal cartilage of two cases of Marfan syndrome[83]. Studies in other laboratories described the preparation of a similar product from nucleus pulposus[84], and from the cartilage of bovine nasal septa. These products showed, however, the presence of small amounts of galactosamine, and of larger amounts of fucose, sialic acid, and amino acids. It has been since recognized that the polysaccharide isolated from cornea contains also methylpentoses, and that in addition it is cleaved by blood group substance-degrading enzymes, but not by hyaluronidases and chondrosulfatases, and that it cross-reacts with anti blood-group sera after desulfation[85]. It is the writer's opinion that the chemical structure of keratan sulfate resembles more that of glycoproteins isolated from plasma and secretions, with additional sulfate groups, than that of the polysaccharides of connective tissue described on the preceding pages.

A keratan sulfate containing a proportion of sulfate groups higher than 1 has been isolated from the cartilage of elasmobranchs[53a].

(b) Isolation, properties and chemical structure

The minced tissue, cornea, nucleus pulposus or cartilage, was first treated with proteolytic enzymes, pepsin, trypsin, or papain. Further removal of the protein, after pepsin treatment, was effected according to Sevag's procedure, or by adsorption on Lloyd's reagent. The polysaccharide mixture was then fractionated by alcohol precipitation, or by alcohol elution of the barium salt on a cellulose column, or by passage through Dowex-1 or Sephadex columns.

Hydrolysis of keratan sulfate gave crystalline D-glucosamine hydro-

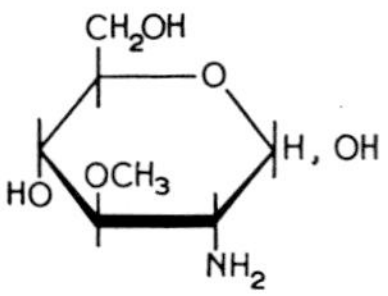

chloride and D-galactose, the latter substance being characterized as the
crystalline α-methylphenylhydrazone. The other constituents were identified by color reactions or paper chromatography.

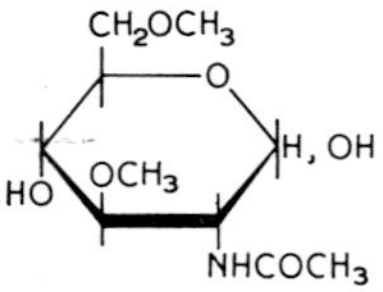

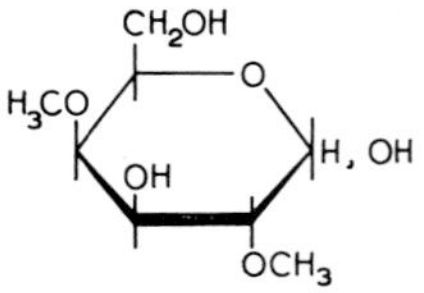

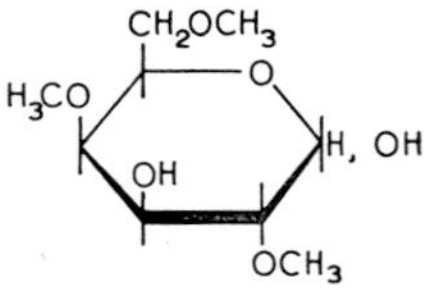

Keratan sulfate and its desulfated derivative were methylated with
dimethyl sulfate and sodium hydroxide. Hydrolysis of the methylated
keratan sulfate afforded 6% of monomethylglucosamines, from which
3-O-methyl-D-glucosamine (XXX) was isolated as the crystalline N-acetyl
derivative, in a 0.8% yield. From the desulfated and methylated derivative,
5% of dimethylglucosamines were isolated, from which a small amount of
3,6-di-O-methyl-D-glucosamine could be obtained as the crystalline N-acetyl
derivative (XXXI). The same dimethylglucosamine was also found in the
hydrolyzate of methylated keratan sulfate. From the hydrolyzates of both
methylated keratan sulfate and its desulfated derivative, small amounts of
dimethylgalactose (4 and 3% respectively), containing mostly 2,4-di-O-
methyl-D-galactose (XXXII); of trimethylgalactose (9%), containing
mostly 2,4,6-tri-O-methyl-D-galactose (XXXIII); and a trace of 2,3,4,6-
tetra-O-methyl-D-galactose were isolated. These results have suggested the
presence, in keratan sulfate, of a repeating unit[86] possessing the structure
described in Fig. 6.

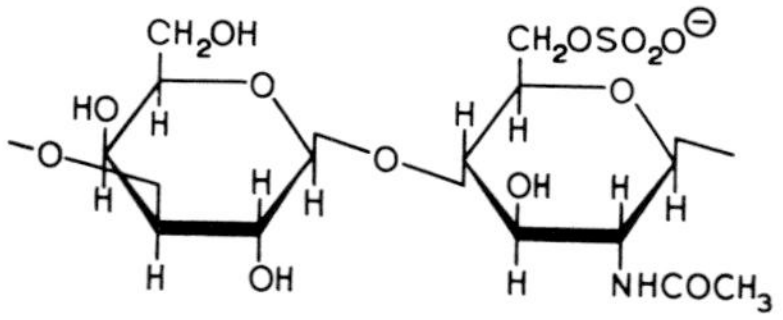

Fig. 6. Repeating unit in keratosulfate.

It is interesting that this structure, less the sulfate group, has been reported
in oligosaccharides and glycoproteins[87]. However, the very small yield of
crystalline methylated derivatives isolated, points to the complexity of the
molecule of keratan sulfate, which may possess a branched structure, as
has been proposed for other glycoproteins.

MUCOPOLYSACCHARIDES 295

REFERENCES

[1] K. MEYER, Cold Spring Harbor Symposia Quant. Biol., 6 (1938) 91.
[2] R. W. JEANLOZ, Arthritis and Rheumatism, 3 (1960) 233.
[3] R. W. JEANLOZ, Proc. 3rd Int. Congress Biochem., Academic Press, New York, 1956, p. 65.
[4] G. E. W. WOLSTENHOME AND M. O'CONNOR (Eds.), Ciba Foundation Symp., Chemistry and Biology of Mucopolysaccharides, Churchill, London, 1958.
[5] H. GIBIAN, Mucopolysaccharide und Mucopolysaccharidasen, Franz Deuticke, Wien, 1959.
[6] R. W. JEANLOZ, Bull. soc. chim. biol., 42 (1960) 303.
[7] F. CLARK AND J. K. GRANT (Eds.), The Biochemistry of Mucopolysaccharides of Connective Tissue, Biochem. Soc. Symposium, University Press, Cambridge, 1961.
[8] J. E. SCOTT, Chem. & Ind. (London), (1955) 168.
[9] E. A. DAVIDSON AND K. MEYER, J. Biol. Chem., 211 (1954) 605.
[10] N. R. RINGERTZ AND P. REICHARD, Acta Chem. Scand., 13 (1959) 1467.
[11] S. GARDELL, A. H. GORDON AND S. ÅQVIST, Acta Chem. Scand., 4 (1950) 907.
[12] F. G. FISCHER AND H. J. NEBEL, Z. physiol. Chem., Hoppe-Seyler's, 302 (1955) 10.
[13] P. J. STOFFYN AND R. W. JEANLOZ, Arch. Biochem. Biophys., 52 (1954) 373.
[14] S. GARDELL, Acta Chem. Scand., 7 (1953) 207.
[15] Z. E. JOLLES AND W. T. J. MORGAN, Biochem. J., 34 (1940) 1183.
[16] M. L. WOLFROM AND F. A. H. RICE, J. Am. Chem. Soc., 68 (1946) 532.
[17] P. J. STOFFYN AND R. W. JEANLOZ, J. Biol. Chem., 235 (1960) 2507.
[18] R. (W.) JEANLOZ, Advances in Carbohydrate Chem., 13 (1958) 189.
[19] H. BRACONNOT, Ann. chim. (Paris), 79 (1811) 265.
[20] A. ODIER, Mém. soc. histoire nat. Paris, 1 (1823) 29.
[21] A. FOSTER AND J. M. WEBBER, Advances in Carbohydrate Chem., 15 (1960) 371.
[22] A. G. RICHARDS, The Integuments of Arthropods, University of Minnesota Press, Minneapolis, Minn., 1951.
[23] R. H. HACKMAN, Australian J. Biol. Sci., 7 (1954) 168.
[24] K. H. MEYER AND G. W. PANKOW, Helv. Chim. Acta, 18 (1935) 589.
[25] G. LEDDERHOSE, Ber., 9 (1876) 1200.
[26] M. BERGMANN, L. ZERVAS AND E. SILBERKWEIT, Ber., 64 (1931) 2436.
[27] S. A. BARKER, A. B. FOSTER, M. STACEY AND J. M. WEBBER, J. Chem. Soc., (1958) 2218.
[28] R. (W.) JEANLOZ AND E. FORCHIELLI, Helv. Chim. Acta, 33 (1950) 1690.
[29] P. SCHORIGIN AND N. N. MAKAROWA-SEMLJANSKAJA, Ber., 68 (1935) 969.
[30] E. LÖWY, Biochem. Z., 23 (1909) 47.
[31] D. T. WARNER AND L. L. COLEMAN, J. Org. Chem., 23 (1958) 1133.
[32] J. J. DISTLER AND S. ROSEMAN, J. Biol. Chem., 235 (1960) 2538.
[33] K. MEYER AND J. W. PALMER, J. Biol. Chem., 107 (1934) 629.
[34] C. T. MÖRNER, Z. physiol. Chem., Hoppe-Seyler's, 18 (1894) 233.
[35] L. LISON, Stain Technol., 29 (1954) 131.
[36] Z. HADIDIAN AND N. W. PIRIE, Biochem. J., 42 (1948) 260.
[37] E. A. BALAZS, Federation Proc., 17 (1958) 1086.
[38] F. A. BETTELHEIM, J. Phys. Chem., 63 (1959) 2069.
[39] B. WEISSMANN AND K. MEYER, J. Am. Chem. Soc., 76 (1954) 1753.
[40] A. LINKER, K. MEYER AND P. HOFFMAN, J. Biol. Chem., 219 (1956) 13.
[41] R. W. JEANLOZ, J. Biol. Chem., 197 (1952) 141.
[42] R. W. JEANLOZ AND P. J. STOFFYN, Federation Proc., 21 (1962) 81.
[42a] S. HIRANO AND P. HOFFMAN, J. Org. Chem., 27 (1962) 395.
[43] E. JANCZURA, H. R. PERKINS AND H. R. ROGERS, Biochem. J., 80 (1961) 82.
[44] C. F. W. KRUKENBERG, Z. Biol., 20 (1884) 307.
[45] C. T. MÖRNER, Skand. Arch. Physiol., 1 (1889) 210.
[46] K. MEYER AND M. M. RAPPORT, Science, 113 (1951) 596.
[47] M. SCHUBERT AND D. HAMERMAN, J. Histochem. and Cytochem., 4 (1956) 159.
[48] J. EINBINDER AND M. SCHUBERT, J. Biol. Chem., 185 (1950) 725.
[49] J. HEBTING, Biochem. Z., 63 (1914) 353.

[50] E. A. DAVIDSON AND K. MEYER, *J. Am. Chem. Soc.*, 77 (1955) 4796.

[51] T. G. KANTOR AND M. SCHUBERT, *J. Am. Chem. Soc.*, 79 (1957) 152.

[52] R. W. JEANLOZ AND P. J. STOFFYN, *Abstr. Communs. 5th Intern. Congr. Biochem., Moscow*, 1961, Pergamon, London, 1962, p. 5.

[53] S. F. D. ORR, *Biochim. et Biophys. Acta*, 14 (1954) 173.

[53a] T. FURUHASHI, *J. Biochem. (Japan)*, 50 (1961) 546; M. B. MATHEWS, J. DUH AND P. PERSON, *Nature*, 193 (1962) 378.

[54] K. MEYER AND E. CHAFFEE, *J. Biol. Chem.*, 138 (1941) 491.

[55] K. MEYER, E. (A.) DAVIDSON, A. LINKER AND P. HOFFMAN, *Biochim. et Biophys. Acta*, 21 (1956) 506.

[56] R. MARBET AND A. WINTERSTEIN, *Helv. Chim. Acta*, 34 (1951) 2311.

[57] P. HOFFMAN, A. LINKER AND K. MEYER, *Science*, 124 (1956) 1252.

[58] P. HOFFMAN, A. LINKER, V. LIPPMAN AND K. MEYER, *J. Biol. Chem.*, 235 (1960) 3066.

[59] R. W. JEANLOZ AND P. J. STOFFYN, *Federation Proc.*, 17 (1958) 249.

[60] P. J. STOFFYN AND R. W. JEANLOZ, *Federation Proc.*, 21 (1962) 81.

[61] J. E. JORPES AND S. GARDELL, *J. Biol. Chem.*, 176 (1948) 267.

[62] A. LINKER, P. HOFFMAN, P. SAMPSON AND K. MEYER, *Biochim. et Biophys. Acta*, 29 (1958) 443.

[63] D. H. BROWN, *Proc. Natl. Acad. Sci. U.S.*, 43 (1957) 783.

[64] J. A. CIFONELLI AND A. DORFMAN, *J. Biol. Chem.*, 235 (1960) 3283.

[65] J. A. CIFONELLI AND A. DORFMAN, *Biochem. Biophys. Research Communs.*, 4 (1961) 328.

[66] A. LINKER AND P. SAMPSON, *Biochim. et Biophys. Acta*, 43 (1960) 365.

[67] J. McLEAN, *Am. J. Physiol.*, 41 (1916) 250.

[68] W. H. HOWELL AND E. HOLT, *Am. J. Physiol.*, 47 (1918) 328.

[69] J. E. JORPES, *Heparin*, 2nd ed., Oxford University Press, London, 1946.

[70] A. B. FOSTER AND A. J. HUGGARD, *Advances in Carbohydrate Chem.*, 10 (1955) 336.

[71] R. W. JEANLOZ, *Federation Proc.*, 17 (1958) 1082.

[72] A. F. CHARLES AND D. A. SCOTT, *J. Biol. Chem.*, 102 (1933) 431.

[73] S. L. BURSON JR., M. J. FAHRENBACH, L. H. FROMMHAGEN, B. A. RICCARDI, R. A. BROWN, J. A. BROCKMAN, H. V. LEWRY AND E. L. R. STOKSTAD, *J. Am. Chem. Soc.*, 78 (1956) 5874.

[74] A. F. CHARLES AND D. A. SCOTT, *J. Biol. Chem.*, 102 (1933) 425.

[75] H. MASAMUNE, M. SUZUKI AND Y. KONDOH, *J. Biochem. (Tokyo)*, 31 (1940) 343.

[76] (J.) E. JORPES AND S. BERGSTRÖM, *Z. physiol. Chem., Hoppe-Seyler's*, 244 (1936) 253.

[77] J. E. JORPES, H. BOSTRÖM AND V. MUTT, *J. Biol. Chem.*, 183 (1950) 607.

[78] K. H. MEYER AND D. E. SCHWARTZ, *Helv. Chim. Acta*, 33 (1950) 1651.

[79] M. L. WOLFROM, R. MONTGOMERY, J. V. KARABINOS AND P. RATHGEB, *J. Am. Chem. Soc.*, 72 (1950) 5796.

[79a] P. HOFFMAN, *Federation Proc.*, 21 (1962) 170.

[80] I. DANISHEFSKY, H. B. EIBER AND E. LANGHOLTZ, *Biochem. Biophys. Research Communs.*, 3 (1960) 571.

[80a] M. L. WOLFROM, J. R. VERCELOTTI AND D. HORTON, *J. Org. Chem.*, 27 (1962) 706.

[81] G. NOMINÉ, R. BUCOURT AND D. BERTIN, *Bull. soc. chim. France*, (1961) 561.

[82] K. MEYER, A. LINKER, E. A. DAVIDSON AND B. WEISSMANN, *J. Biol. Chem.*, 205 (1953) 611.

[83] K. MEYER, P. HOFFMAN AND A. LINKER, *Science*, 128 (1958) 896.

[84] S. GARDELL, *Acta Chem. Scand.*, 11 (1957) 668.

[85] O. ROSEN, P. HOFFMAN AND K. MEYER, *Federation Proc.*, 19 (1960) 147.

[86] S. HIRANO, P. HOFFMAN AND K. MEYER, *J. Org. Chem.*, 26 (1961) 5064.

[87] E. H. EYLAR AND R. W. JEANLOZ, *J. Biol. Chem.*, 237 (1962) 622.

Chapter VIII

Cyclitols

S. J. ANGYAL

School of Chemistry, University of New South Wales,
Kensington, N.S.W. (Australia)

The cyclitols (polyhydroxy-derivatives of cyclohexane) are usually discussed in conjunction with the carbohydrates although chemically or biochemically their relationship is rather tenuous. The main connecting link between the cyclitols and sugars is the presence of several hydroxyl groups, and consequently there is a similarity in such physical properties as solubility and a sweet taste. Chemically, since the cyclitols are devoid of reducing groups, they resemble the acyclic polyols rather than the sugars.

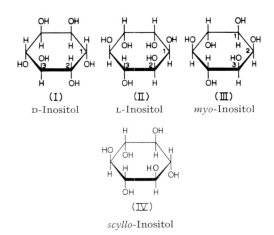

(I) D-Inositol   (II) L-Inositol   (III) *myo*-Inositol

(IV) *scyllo*-Inositol

1. The inositols

Owing to their wide distribution in Nature, the inositols (cyclohexanehexols) are the most important cyclitols[1,2]. Theory predicts the existence of nine inositols which are in the same relation to each other as, for example, the sixteen aldohexoses. All the nine are now known but only those which occur in Nature[3] are discussed here. In contrast to the aldohexoses, which are all

optically active, there exists only one pair of enantiomorphous inositols
(I and II), all the others being symmetrical *meso*-forms. Hence the name
meso-inositol for the isomer III, which has been used for over a hundred
years ever since Scherer[4] isolated this compound from muscle in 1850, is an
inappropriate one and the term *myo*-inositol is now preferred[5].

(a) Occurrence

myo-Inositol (*meso*-inositol, *i*-inositol) (III), often termed simply inositol,
is a compound ubiquitous in Nature. It appears to occur in all living
organisms: in the free state, as a phosphate, or as a constituent of phospho-
lipids. In plants it is commonly found as phytic acid, the hexaphosphate
ester; compared to the sugar phosphates, this compound has a remarkably
high phosphate content and is probably used by plants as a phosphate
reservoir. *myo*-Inositol is commercially produced from phytic acid: corn-
steep liquor is a good source of phytin, the calcium-magnesium salt of
phytic acid, which is hydrolyzed by acids to *myo*-inositol and phosphoric acid.

Inositol phosphatides, or phosphoinositides, are found in plants, animals,
and micro-organisms and comprise 2 to 9% of the total phosphatides of
animal tissues. On hydrolysis they yield *myo*-inositol, *myo*-inositol phosphate,
glycerol, fatty acids and, in many cases, various sugars. In the few cases
which have been investigated the phosphate group appears to be attached
to carbon 3 of *myo*-inositol[6]. A more detailed discussion of the phosphoinositides appears in another chapter.

The active inositols (I and II) are found in small amounts only but their
methyl ethers are widespread in Nature. A fourth isomer, *scyllo*-inositol
or scyllitol (IV), has been found in such diverse sources as the cocos palm,
shark and dogfish, and in mammalian urine.

In plants—but apparently not in animals—methyl ethers of inositols
are of common occurrence. The following methyl ethers of *myo*-inositol have
been isolated from natural sources[2]: (+)-bornesitol, the 1-methyl ether
(numbered as in formula III); (—)-bornesitol, the 3-methyl ether; sequoyitol,
the 5-methyl ether; (+)-ononitol, the 6-methyl ether; dambonitol, the 1,3-
dimethyl ether; and liriodendritol, the 3,6-dimethyl ether.

(—)-Quebrachitol, 2-*O*-methyl-L-inositol, occurs in many plants and can
be readily recovered from the latex of *Hevea brasiliensis*, the common
Malayan rubber tree. (+)-Pinitol, 3-*O*-methyl-D-inositol, is a common
constituent of many plants, particularly conifers, and can be readily isolated
from the heartwood of the sugar pine, *Pinus lambertiana*. The enantiomorph,
(—)-pinitol, has also been found in Nature. All these methyl ethers are
demethylated to the parent inositols by boiling hydriodic acid.

Two *C*-methyl-inositols have been found: mytilitol, *C*-methyl-*scyllo*-

inositol, in a musseld an (—)-laminitol, 4-C-methyl-*myo*-inositol, in algae. These compounds can, of course, not be demethylated to inositols.

(b) Constitution and synthesis

The structure of the inositols was readily established by conversion to benzene derivatives and by showing the presence of six esterifiable hydroxyl groups[1]. The determination of the configuration was a much more difficult task and was not carried out, in the case of *myo*-inositol, till 1942. Since every hydroxyl group is secondary and no other reactive group is present, it was found difficult to open the ring specifically in one position, or to prepare partially substituted derivatives. Two reactions helped to overcome this difficulty: enzymic dehydrogenation and acetonide formation (see below). Each of these led, through several steps and through the opening of the cyclohexane ring, to DL-idaric acid[7,8]. Formation of the acetonide (V) had

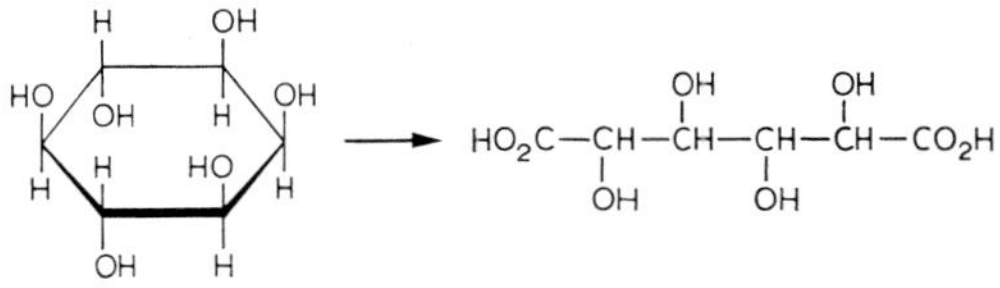

DL-Idaric acid

already indicated the presence of a pair of *cis*-hydroxyl groups; isolation of idaric acid then established the configuration of *myo*-inositol.

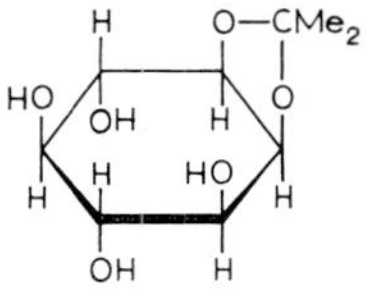

(V)

myo-Inositol and the optically active inositols are readily available from natural sources; *scyllo*-inositol, however, is best synthesized by the reduction of *scyllo*-inosose (see below). The synthesis of *myo*-inositol has been achieved in several different ways and can be used to incorporate ^{14}C into the molecule. Thus, the hydrogenation of hexahydroxybenzene gives a mixture of inositols and related compounds from which *myo*-inositol can be isolated by column chromatography[9]. 6-Nitro-6-deoxy-D-glucose (VI) cyclizes in alkaline solution to a mixture of deoxynitro-inositols; the main component of this mixture has the *scyllo*-configuration (VII) and its reduction gives the corresponding amino-compound[10]. Treatment of the latter with nitrous acid causes deamination with inversion, giving *myo*-inositol.

(VI)   (VII)

(c) Chemical properties

The inositols are very stable compounds. They will withstand the action of alkalis and acids, even of boiling hydriodic acid, of reducing agents, and of heat up to about 250°. They are all crystalline solids with melting points over 200°. Concentrated nitric acid will attack them only at an elevated temperature. Hexa-esters are readily formed.

An interesting specific reaction of inositols is their dehydrogenation which can be achieved either chemically—by air and a platinum catalyst[11]—or enzymically by *Acetobacter suboxydans*[12]; the latter method is more convenient and gives better yields. By either method, only axial hydroxyl groups are dehydrogenated: thus *myo*-inositol is only attacked at C-2, the optically active inositols at C-1 and C-6, and *scyllo*-inositol is not attacked at all. *myo*-Inositol gives *scyllo*-inosose (VIII) which can be converted to

(VIII)

scyllo-inositol by reduction. All the inososes are very sensitive to oxidation (they reduce Fehling's solution in the cold) and to alkali (which causes aromatisation).

Another useful reaction is the condensation of inositols with acetone to give isopropylidene derivatives[13]. Normally a pair of hydroxyl groups will only react when vicinal and *cis*, hence *myo*-inositol gives a monoisopropylidene derivative (V), the active inositols give diisopropylidene compounds, and *scyllo*-inositol does not react. This is the best method for producing partially substituted derivatives of inositols, useful as intermediates for the synthesis of methyl ethers, phosphates, etc.

(d) Analysis

The only characteristic—but unfortunately not very sensitive—colour reaction of the inositols is the classical Scherer test[1]. This test depends on the oxidation of the cyclitol with nitric acid, and the formation of coloured alkaline-earth salts of the resulting hydroxyquinones. In recent years it has been largely supplanted by paper chromatography which also has the advantage that it identifies individual inositols. The best quantitative method for the estimation of *myo*-inositol is a microbiological one with *Saccharomyces cerevisiae* or *carlsbergensis* as test organism[2]. A chemical method of analysis for all inositols is based on their oxidation by periodate. Other polyols interfere but they can be removed by vigorous treatment with hot acids or alkalis, followed by ion-exchange purification[2].

2. The quercitols

The quercitols (cyclohexanepentols) are less important than the inositols. All the stereoisomers predicted by theory are now known but only two of them were found in Nature[1]: (+)-*proto*-quercitol (IX) originally named "quercitol", in the acorn and several other sources, and (—)-*vibo*-quercitol (X) first named "*levo*-rotatory quercitol" and later "viburnitol", in several plants. Other quercitols have been made by catalytic hydrogenation of inososes in acid solution.

In physical and chemical properties, and in their reactions, the quercitols

(IX)   (X)
proto-Quercitol   *vibo*-Quercitol

resemble the inositols. They are more readily attacked, however, by nitric acid, and the reaction leads to the opening of the ring at the CH_2 group, in contrast to that of the inositols. The quercitols do not give the Scherer test but they give the iodoform reaction. Quercitols are not known to have any biological activity.

3. The inosamines

The inosamines are in the same relation to the inositols as the amino-sugars are to the sugars, *i.e.*, they contain one or more amino-groups in place of hydroxyl groups. No inosamine has yet been found in Nature in the free state but they have been revealed as constituents of several antibiotics[2].

Streptamine (1,3-diamino-1,3-deoxy-*scyllo*-inositol) (XI) forms part of the streptomycin molecule and can be readily obtained from the latter by hydrolysis. It has been synthesized by two different routes.

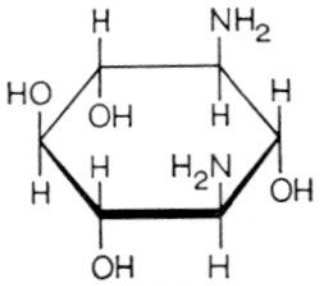

XI
Streptamine

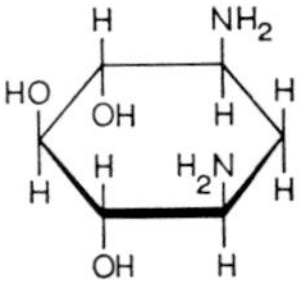

XII
Deoxystreptamine

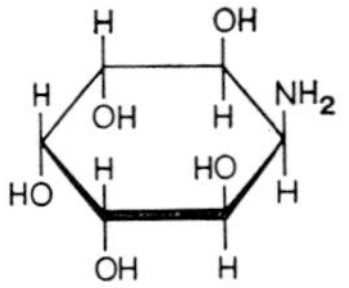

XIII
neo-Inosamine

Closely related to streptamine is deoxystreptamine (XII) produced on hydrolysis of the neomycins and the kanamycins. This quercitol derivative has not yet been synthesized and its configuration requires confirmation.

The hydrolysis of hygromycin A produces *neo*-inosamine, which has also been synthesized from the inositol of corresponding configuration.

4. Quinic acid and shikimic acid

Two cyclitolcarboxylic acids occur in Nature: quinic and shikimic acid. Structurally they are closely related to each other, shikimic acid being a dehydroquinic acid; their interconversion has been achieved by chemical means. The difficult proof of their constitution was obtained by Fischer and Dangschat through several degradative sequences[1].

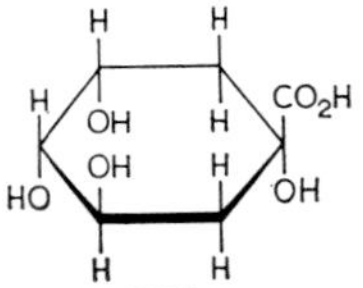

XIV
Quinic acid

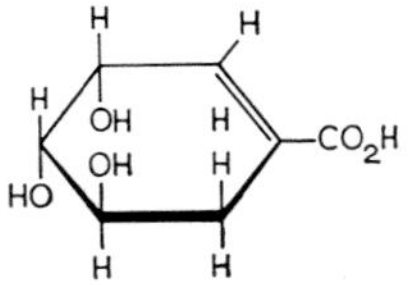

XV
Shikimic acid

(—)-Quinic acid (XIV) is found in cinchona bark, meadow hay, and other plants[3], and combined with caffeic acid as chlorogenic acid in coffee and other plants. Its total synthesis has been accomplished.

Shikimic acid (XV) was first found in star anise (*Illicium religiosum*) and later in many other plants. In recent times it has been experimentally established as a biogenetic key link in the elaboration of aromatic amino-acids and lignin *in vivo*, and it appears to be involved in other biosynthetic reactions[14]. The total synthesis of shikimic acid has only recently been accomplished[15].

REFERENCES

[1] H. G. FLETCHER JR., *Advances in Carbohydrate Chem.*, 3 (1948) 45.
[2] S. J. ANGYAL AND L. ANDERSON, *Advances in Carbohydrate Chem.*, 14 (1959) 135.
[3] G. DANGSCHAT in W. RUHLAND (Ed.), *Encyclopedia of Plant Physiology*, Vol. 6, Springer, Berlin, 1957, p. 363.
[4] J. SCHERER, *Ann.*, 81 (1852) 375.
[5] H. G. FLETCHER JR., L. ANDERSON AND H. A. LARDY, *J. Org. Chem.*, 16 (1951) 1238.
[6] F. L. PIZER AND C. E. BALLOU, *J. Am. Chem. Soc.*, 81 (1959) 915.
[7] G. DANGSCHAT, *Naturwissenschaften*, 30 (1942) 146.
[8] T. POSTERNAK, *Helv. Chim. Acta*, 25 (1942) 746.
[9] S. J. ANGYAL AND D. J. McHUGH, *J. Chem. Soc.*, (1957) 3682.
[10] J. M. GROSHEINTZ AND H. O. L. FISCHER, *J. Am. Chem. Soc.*, 70 (1948) 1479.
[11] K. HEYNS AND H. PAULSEN, *Angew. Chem.*, 69 (1957) 600.
[12] L. ANDERSON, R. TAKEDA, S. J. ANGYAL AND D. J. McHUGH, *Arch. Biochem. Biophys.*, 78 (1958) 518.
[13] S. J. ANGYAL AND C. G. MACDONALD, *J. Chem. Soc.*, (1952) 686.
[14] E. WENKERT, *Experientia*, 15 (1959) 165.
[15] R. McCRINDLE, K. H. OVERTON AND R. A. RAPHAEL, *J. Chem. Soc.*, (1960) 1560.

SUBJECT INDEX

β-Glucosan, 54
Glucose, 12, 22, 23
— oxidase, 67, 68
— 2-phosphate, removal of phosphate by
  phenylhydrazine, 129
— 3-phosphate, formation of meta-
  saccharinic acid by alkali, 127
— —, removal of phosphate by phenylhydrazine, 129
— 6-phosphate, sources, preparation, 135
α-Glucose 1-phosphate, hydrolysis, 122,
  123
D-Glucose 1,6-diphosphate, 48
— 4,6-cyclic phosphate, preparation, 135
— 2-phosphate, preparation, 135
— 3-phosphate, preparation, 135
— 4-phosphate, preparation, 135
— 5-phosphate, preparation, 135
α-D-Glucose 1-phosphate, preparation,
  28, 118, 135
β-D-Glucose 1-phosphate, preparation,
  28, 118, 135
L-Glucose 1-phosphate, preparation, 135
Glucosidases, 27
β-Glucosyl transfer, 175, 176
α-D-Glucosyl phosphate-6-phosphate (D-
  glucose 1,6-diphosphate), 48
— α-L-ribuloside, formation by sucrose
  phosphorylase, 179
— β-D-xyluloside, formation by sucrose
  phosphorylase, 179
β-D-Glucosyl D-xyloside formation by
  maltose phosphorylase, 179
Glucuronic acid, UDP — in formation of
  glucosiduronic acids, 74
D-Glucuronic acid, 79
—, constituent of plant products, 74
—, formation of glucosiduronic acids, 74
—, furanose and pyranose forms, 151
—, preparation from menthol glucosiduronate in urine, 75
α-D-Glucuronic acid 1-phosphate, preparation, 137
—, — from glucose 1-phosphate, 76
β-D-Glucuronic acid 1-phosphate, preparation, 137
—, — from acetobromoglucuronic acid
  methylester and silver phosphate, 76
D-Glucuronolactone, formation by catalytic oxidation of 1,2-O-isopropylidene-
  α-D-glucofuranose, 76
Glucuronosides, synthesis, 74
3-O-β-D-Glucuronosyl-N-acetyl-L-fucos-
  amine, 258
6-O-D-Glucuronosyl-D-glucosamine, 292
4-O-β-D-Glucuronosyl-D-glucose (cellobiuronic acid), 258
Glucuronoxyloglycans, 187

Glutinous starches, 212
Glycamines, definition, 96
Glycaric acid, 264
Glyceraldehyde 3-phosphate, formation of
  lactic acid by alkali, 127
D-Glyceraldehyde 3-phosphate, preparation, 131
D-Glycero-D-galactoheptose in Chromobacterium violaceum, 15
D-Glycero-L-mannoheptose in Shigella
  sonnei, 15
L-Glycero-D-mannoheptose in E. coli B, 15
Glycerophosphate, methyl and choline
  ester, alkaline hydrolysis, 128
—, migration of phosphate group during
  acid hydrolysis, 125
1,2-Glycerophosphate, cyclic, preparation,
  131
α-Glycerophosphate, estimation by oxidation with periodate, 129
β-Glycerophosphate, hydrolysis, 122
—, preparation, 131
L(—)α-Glycerophosphate, sources, preparation, 131
Glycofuranosides, preparation by Fischer
  reaction, 147
Glycogen, 186, 217–219
—, anomalous linkages, 219
—, branching, 218
—, degradation with β-amylase, formation of limit dextrin, 218
—, extraction from tissues, 217
—, molecular weight, 218
—, reaction with iodine, 218
Glycolaldehyde phosphate, acid hydrolysis, 126
—, preparation, 130
—, removal of phosphate by phenylhydrazine, 129
Glycolic acid, formation from ketoses, 2
Glycosaminoglycans, acidic (see also mucopolysaccharides), 262
Glycosaminoglycuronoglycans, definition,
  263
4-O-α-(D-Glucosaminyl-4-sulfate)-D-
  glucuronic acid, 291
Glycoproteins, amino sugars of polysaccharides in —, 19
Glycosans, 27, 54
Glycoside(s), 26–30, 146–153
— acetates, deacetylation, 150
—, glycosyl residue, aglycone, definition, 6
—, literature, 152
—, natural, 28–30
—, synthesis of α- and β-anomers, 146–150
— —, cation-exchange resins as catalysts,
  147
— —, Fischer reaction, 146, 147

COMPREHENSIVE BIOCHEMISTRY

SECTION I (VOLUMES 1–4)

Physico-Chemical and Organic Aspects of Biochemistry